The World Natural History
THE EARTH

The World Natural History

Editor: Richard Carrington

Associate Editors:

Dr. L. Harrison Matthews, FRS

Professor J. Z. Young, FRS

The Earth

CARL O. DUNBAR

*Professor of Paleontology and Stratigraphy
and Director of Peabody Museum of Natural
History, Emeritus, Yale University*

THE WORLD PUBLISHING COMPANY
CLEVELAND AND NEW YORK

Published by The World Publishing Company
2231 West 110th Street, Cleveland, Ohio 44102

Library of Congress Catalog Card Number: 66–25428

Second Printing 1967

Contents

	Preface	xi
1	THE ROAD TO UNDERSTANDING	1
2	THE SCALE OF TIME	13
3	THE UNIVERSE AROUND US	30
4	THE PLANET EARTH: 1 THE LITHOSPHERE	48
5	THE PLANET EARTH: 2 THE HYDROSPHERE	68
6	THE PLANET EARTH: 3 THE ATMOSPHERE	102
7	ORIGIN OF THE SOLAR SYSTEM	113
8	FORMATIVE STAGES OF THE EARTH	126
9	EARTH'S EVER-CHANGING FACE	138
10	CLIMATES OF THE PAST	158
11	THE DRIVING FORCE WITHIN	177
12	LIFE'S RECORD IN THE ROCKS	217
	Bibliography	237
	Index	245

List of Plates

[*between pages* 114 *and* 115]

1 A manuscript in stone
2 Diagrams to illustrate atomic structure
3 Photosphere of the sun with two groups of sun spots
4 Spectroheliogram of a portion of the sun
5 Photograph of the chromosphere, solar flares, and halo at time of total solar eclipse
6 The solar corona seen at the moment of total solar eclipse
7 Photograph of the moon at first quarter showing lunar craters and maria
8 Fold mountains on the floor of the maria
9 Meteor Crater from the air
10 The Weston meteorite
11 Photograph of an area of about thirty square miles of the surface of Mare Imbrium from an altitude of 11·2 miles by US satellite *Ranger VII*
12 Photograph from an altitude of 3·7 miles only 2·5 seconds before the crash landing of *Ranger VII*
13 Brook's comet
14 The Great Nebula in Andromeda
15 Spiral galaxy in Ursa Major
16 Spiral galaxy in Coma Berenices
17 Plateau basalt exposed in the river bluff at Vantage, Utah
18 Deformed gneiss in the Aiguille Range Series at Vallon de Van, France
19 Deep-sea oozes
20 Diagram to represent Laplace's hypothesis of the origin of the solar system
21 Diagram to explain how the 'resisting medium' would reduce the ellipticity of a young planet according to Chamberlin
22 Peneplaned summit of the Laramie Range near Buford, Wyoming
23 Canyon of North Platte River
24 Block diagram of the Sierra Nevada region
25 Block diagram showing structure and relief in the Rocky Mountains at the beginning of Oligocene time
26 Modern relief in the area shown in plate 25
27 Map showing the modern relief in the Central and Southern Rocky Mountains
28 Paleogeographic map of North America in mid-Cretaceous time
29 Immigrants into western North America from Europe by way of the Arctic Sea

30 Ordovician lava flows exposed in a sea cliff near Coal River on the west coast of Newfoundland

31 Late Cretaceous dinosaurs in western United States

32 Ancient sand dunes in the Coconino sandstone of mid-Permian age near Flagstaff, Arizona

33 Laminated anhydrite from the Castile formation in the Delaware Basin of west Texas

34 The Pleistocene ice sheets

35 Above, glacially smoothed and striated floor on the Milford chlorite schist near New Haven, Connecticut. Below, a glacial boulder found on the surface shown above

36 A modern scene in eastern Greenland near the source of the Dangaard–Jensen glacier

37 Valley glaciers on Andree Island on the east coast of Greenland

38 Varved clay in the Connecticut Valley, USA

39 Glacially polished floor beneath the Dwyka tillite near Kimberley, South Africa

40 Glacial boulder from the Gowganda tillite in the Huronian 'system' at Cobalt, Ontario

41 Mount Lefroy in the Canadian Rockies

42 A slice of metamorphic rock showing deformation by solid flow

43 Pliocene fossils (snails and clams) from Castell Aquato, Italy

44 Third lower molar of the American Mastodon, *Mammut Americanum*, from Peru, Indiana

45 A block of petrified wood from the fossil forest of the Yellowstone

46 Silicified snail shells and a clam shell of Middle Ordovician age

47 At the left a chunk of Devonian sandstone with natural moulds of brachiopod shells. At the right an artificial cast of the same

48 Natural mould of a pinnule of the large fern, *Neuropteris decipiens*

49 Natural mould lined with a film of carbon showing part of a leaf of the fern, *Alethopteris aquilina*, from the Coal Measures at Saarbrücken, Germany

50 A small pterosaur, *Rhamphorhynchus phyllurus*

51 Natural mould of the oldest known bird, from the Upper Jurassic limestone at Solenhofen, Bavaria

52 Footprints of a small dinosaur which had crossed a mud flat, pitted by raindrops of a passing shower

53 A fossil stonefly, *Lemmatophora typica*, from a bed of Lower Permian limestone near Abilene, Kansas

54 Walcott's fossil locality in the Burgess shale of Middle Cambrian age on the slope of Mt Wapta

Acknowledgements

The author wishes to thank the following for permission to reproduce photographs used in this volume:

Chester R. Longwell, Plate 1; Mr Wilson and Palomar Observatories, Plates 3–6, 15, 16; Yerkes Observatory, University of Chicago, Plates 7, 8, 13, 14; Spence Air Photos, Plate 9; California Institute of Technology Jet Propulsion Laboratory and the National Aeronautics and Space Administration, Plates 11, 12; Yale Peabody Museum, Plates 10, 44, 48–53; Richard Armstrong, Plates 17, 18; Kümmerly and Frey, Berne, Switzerland, for illustrations from *Arctic Riviera* by E. Hofer, Plates 36, 37; A. M. Duggan-Cronin and the Board and Directors of the Alexander McGregor Memorial Museum, Kimberley, Plate 39; Matt Walton, Plate 42.

Preface

TO UNDERSTAND the earth as an abode for life requires excursions into highly diversified fields of science. We are entirely dependent on the warmth and energy that comes to us from the sun. At the same time the earth is constantly bombarded by lethal rays of ultraviolet light from the same source and by cosmic rays that come from outer space; and from these we are protected by the recently discovered layers of the upper atmosphere. Of all the planets in the solar system the earth is unique in possessing abundant water and an atmosphere rich in free oxygen, both of which are essential for life. The origin of life itself could only have occurred when the earth was young and its atmosphere differed greatly from the present. We are deeply concerned, therefore, with many phases of astronomy, including the origin of the solar system and the evolution of the oceans and the atmosphere. Geochemistry and modern space probes have shed critical light on these problems. The creatures that now inhabit the earth are the result of millions of years of organic evolution, and the immensity of time is, therefore, critical to our understanding. This in turn involves an understanding of some aspects of atomic physics. Many features of the earth have been conditioned by geochemical laws. Finally, the course of evolution has been vitally affected by the ever-changing physical environment, by changes in the relief of the lands, by the spread and retreats of vast inland seas, by the planetary circulation of the atmosphere, and by ocean currents, all of which have conspired to produce endless climatic changes. Every phase of geology contributes, of course, to our understanding of the earth. One of the great enigmas has been the source of the driving force that has caused mountains to rise, has produced volcanic activity, and has renewed the continents after they have been worn low by erosion. Newly discovered evidences of convection currents deep within the earth have at last indicated a probable explanation. Meanwhile the newly developed study of paleomagnetism indicates that the continents have moved about like the great tabular icebergs in the polar seas. An attempt has been made to outline these new ideas which are still the subject of intensive study and of considerable controversy.

Each of these scientific disciplines has an enormous specialized literature much of which is highly technical. Moreover, the literature has grown at an exponential rate during the scientific renaissance of the last half century so that it is increasingly difficult even for a trained scientist to keep abreast of advances except in his own special field. It is obviously impossible in a single volume to do justice to this vast literature or to cite more than a few of the important works that have been consulted in this synthesis. It would also be futile to attempt to write for the specialists in each of these fields, for, except in his own domain, none of us is a specialist. It is hoped that our treatment will be acceptable to the specialists in many fields, but our purpose has been to present a broad view of the earth for the intelligent reading public. For this reason we have tried in so far as consistent with clarity to minimize the use of technical jargon, and to cite references to works written for the reading public rather than to technical journals that are available only in the great libraries.

It goes without saying that we are indebted to the many scientists whose ideas we have attempted to synthesize. Many of the text figures are adapted from the works of others, all of which are acknowledged in the legends. Our thanks go especially to Dr R. F. Flint for information incorporated in plate 27, and for permission to reproduce figure 60; to Dr Bruce C. Heezen for permission to adapt several figures from his published works; to Dr Harry H. Hess for permission to reproduce figure 30; to Dr K. O. Emery for permission to reproduce figures 32 and 33; to Dr J. Tuzo Wilson to use figures 69 and 75; to Dr Arthur D. Raff for permission to adapt figures 73 and 74 from his work; and to Dr Van Hilton to reproduce figures 85 and 86. The text figures have been drafted by the author. Special thanks go to Yerkes Observatory and to the Mount Wilson and Palomar Observatories for the fine photographs of astronomical objects, and to the California Institute of Technology Jet Propulsion Laboratory and the National Aeronautics and Space Administration for the exciting photographs of the moon taken by the *Ranger VII* satellite. My best thanks go also to Dr Richard Armstrong for the coloured prints reproduced in plates 22 and 23, to Chester R. Longwell for plate 1, and to Kümmerly and Frey of Berne, Switzerland, for the fine pictures reproduced as plates 36 and 37, and to Miss F. M. Barbour, administrative officer of the Alexander Memorial Museum, for the beautiful photograph of the Dwyka tillite reproduced as plate 39. I am greatly indebted also to John Wiley and Sons for permission to reproduce several pictures from *Historical Geology* by Dunbar, and several paleogeographical maps from Charles Schuchert's Atlas. I am happy also to acknowledge special obligation to my colleague Dr Karl Turekian for help in the original treatment of the use of atomic isotopes in the dating of rocks. And finally I thank my sister, Mrs R. H. Beamer, for critical reading of the manuscript and Miss Lillian Perdue and Miss Lois Faubel for their patience and care in preparation of the typescript.

Dunedin, Florida, 15 *March* 1965

Chapter 1

The Road to Understanding

Cease to be ruled by dogmas and authorities; look at the world.
ROGER BACON

Early Myths and Legends

KNOWLEDGE of the earth came late in human history. Primitive man had little basis for understanding a phenomenon so vast. His explorations on land were limited to distances he could travel afoot, and at sea he could not venture far from shore. No individual – and no tribe or nation – had ever seen more than a tiny segment of the earth's surface until the fifteenth century AD. Common experience indicated that the earth was flat, except for local hills and mountains that rose above the general level. Loose objects were observed to fall vertically downward, but the reason was entirely unknown and common sense seemed to indicate that if one ventured 'over the edge' he would fall away into space. Furthermore the earth seemed obviously to be the centre of the universe, for it was the solid platform about which sun and moon and stars could be seen to move.

In spite of limited horizons, insatiable curiosity impelled man often to think beyond the observable and to wonder about the origin and the history of his world. Lacking any means to come to grips with such problems, he invented myths and legends to satisfy his thirst for understanding. In the absence of widespread communication, diverse myths thus grew up locally among primitive peoples.

Since the oceans stretched away into the mysterious unknown, most of the early myths concerned the origin of the lands rather than the earth as a whole. Most of them were imaginative and fanciful and now seem fantastic. One such legend, for example, explained that a turtle once dived into the ocean and came up with a lump of mud on its back that became the land. The Polynesians held a comparable belief, but in their legend the god Tangora once fished the

I

earth out of the ocean and when his line broke it settled back into the water leaving only the highest spots exposed to form their island homes. The ancient Egyptians believed that in some obscure manner the lands had evolved out of the chaos of a universal ocean.

Some 4000 years BC the ancient Hebrews developed a legend that accounted for the creation of the entire universe out of primeval chaos. This is the legend recorded in the *Book of Genesis*, which was destined to exert a profound influence on the thought of the western world. According to this well-known belief our universe and every living thing was created within a period of six days. Out of darkness and chaos God first separated the earth from the heavens. On the second day he gathered the waters together and separated the oceans from the lands. On the third he created all the plants. On the fourth he placed the sun and moon in the heavens to light the earth; and on the fifth day he created all the animals except man. Man became the crowning achievement of creation on the sixth day and was given 'dominion over every living thing'. In this view the earth was clearly the centre of the universe.

The Beginning of Understanding

A few centuries before the birth of Christ some of the Greek philosophers began to doubt that the earth was flat. In the sixth century BC, for example, Pythagoras observed that during the changes of the moon the boundary between its sunlit and dark sides is always curved as it would be if the moon is a sphere, and he inferred that if the moon is round, the earth is probably similar in shape. Two centuries later Aristotle confirmed this belief when he observed that during lunar eclipses the shadow cast by the earth is always circular as it could be only if the earth is round. Finally, in the third century BC, Eratosthenes added proof of its shape and by a simple experiment measured its approximate size. He had been born at Syene on the Nile, near the site of the modern Aswan Dam. There, at noon on the day of the summer solstice (21 June), the sun is directly overhead so that it can be seen from the bottom of a well. Years later when he became head of the great library at Alexandria (which is five hundred miles north of Syene) he found that at noon on 21 June the sun is appreciably south of the zenith. By erecting a vertical pole and comparing its height with the length of its shadow he found that the sun stood 7° to the south (figure 1). To explain this strange fact he concluded that although the floor of the Nile Valley appears flat, it must be an arch, subtending 7° of latitude. He then calculated that if 7° amounts to 500 miles, 1° is approximately 71 miles and the full circumference of the earth is 360 times as great or about 25,000 miles.

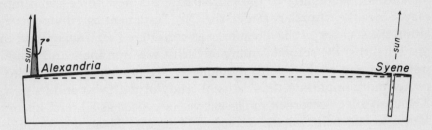

Figure 1. Eratosthenes measures the size of the earth

It may be noted that his calculation involved a basic but unproved assumption, namely, that the sun is so far away that its rays are parallel at opposite ends of his baseline. As we now know, this assumption was valid and his estimate was not wide of the mark considering the crude instruments with which he worked. Indeed, it was not improved upon for almost two thousand years!

The Lapse into the Dark Ages

In the third century BC Greek culture began a great decline and these brilliant insights about the earth were soon forgotten. Fifteen long centuries followed in which interest in natural philosophy languished as thought throughout the Mediterranean region was channelled in other directions. Because of the dearth of intellectual achievements, these years have sometimes been characterized as the Dark Ages.

The causes of the decline of Greek culture were undoubtedly complex, but a major factor was certainly the turmoil of civil strife and wars of conquest. Even as Greece attained her Golden Age, jealousies among her city-states were sowing seeds of dissension. In 431 BC the Spartans and their allies launched an attack on the Athenians. Thus began the Peloponnesian Wars that raged intermittently across the nation for the next thirty years. During the next several centuries wars of conquest swept over Greece as first one and then another of her neighbouring nations strove to dominate the Mediterranean

3

world. In 355 BC Alexander the Great overran Greece and incorporated it in his Macedonian Empire. In AD 98 Emperor Trajan overran Greece and Persia and incorporated them in the Roman Empire. Meanwhile the barbarian hordes from the north and north-east added to the turmoil and unrest.

With the beginning of the Christian era a new force came into play. Since the Church regarded the Old Testament as a divine revelation the account of the Creation was considered sacrosanct; and in the belief that the second coming of Christ was imminent and would signal the end of the world, thoughts of the hereafter seemed altogether more important than rational study of the earth and its past. The chronology recorded in *Genesis* was accepted as a literal history of the world, belief in the universal Deluge of Noah was unquestioned, and in time it came to be believed that Creation had occurred only about 4000 BC and that little change had occurred since the beginning. As the Church became dominant in the far-flung Roman Empire any diversions from the accepted theological dogmas were severely repressed, and thinkers who disagreed were persecuted as heretics. In our more enlightened age it is difficult to comprehend the long and bitter struggle to break this intellectual bondage.

The Renaissance

The Age of Enlightenment began in Italy during the fourteenth century when some of the aristocratic families, notably the Medici in Florence, revived an interest in the arts and letters. To this end they imported manuscripts of the ancient Greeks and had them translated into Latin. They also built libraries to which scholars were lured and in which they were given support. The revival in learning spread rapidly to other cities and Italy soon became a mecca for scholars from all parts of Europe.

It was from this source that Columbus rediscovered the idea that the world is round. It is a significant commentary on the intellectual climate of the time, however, that he was generally regarded as a crank; and when in 1492 he sailed westward hoping to reach the Orient, he staked his life and a queen's jewels on the gamble that the earth is not flat, and on several occasions was faced with the threat of mutiny by his crews who feared that they would sail 'over the edge' and be lost. Although he discovered a new world, Columbus failed to reach the Orient. Thirty years later, however, Magellan's flagship,

Victoria, completed her journey from Portugal around the tip of South America, westward across the wide Pacific and the Indian oceans, around the Cape of Good Hope, and home again. Magellan was killed by the natives when he went ashore in the Philippines and did not live to enjoy the triumph of being the first to circumnavigate the globe and to prove, once and for all, that the earth is round. The year was 1522.

But to determine the earth's place in the universe was more difficult and more dangerous. During several centuries before the beginning of the Christian era the Greek philosophers had developed a concept of the organization of the universe that is generally attributed to Ptolemy because it is best known from his great work, *The Almagest*. According to the Ptolemaic system the earth was the fixed centre of the universe about which the celestial bodies revolved in concentric orbits, in the order indicated in figure 2. Each was conceived to be attached to a sphere that revolved about the earth, all

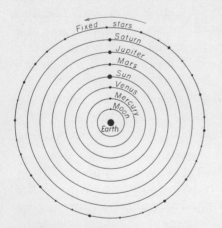

Figure 2. Organization of the universe according to Ptolemy

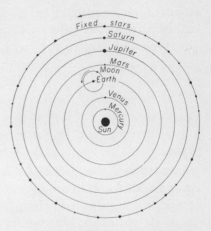

Figure 3. Organization of the universe according to Copernicus

the fixed stars being set, like jewels, in the eighth sphere. This concept of the universe was widely accepted until near the middle of the sixteenth century.

The modern concept began with the Polish astronomer, Nicolai Copernicus [1]. He had spent several years studying and teaching in Italy before returning to his native Poland to become physician to his uncle, the Bishop of Ermeland. By this time the Church had become a sort of superstate exercising strong control over the small principalities of Europe and its institutions were at once the centre of learning and a strong political force. Copernicus had therefore gone to Italy to study canon law, and upon his uncle's death he was made Canon of the Cathedral at Frauenburg. But while in Italy he had developed a consuming interest in astronomy, and after returning to Poland he spent most of the rest of his life developing a new concept of the universe which is known as the Copernican system. In this view the sun is the centre about which the earth and the other planets revolve in circular orbits, in the order indicated in figure 3, the earth meanwhile rotating daily upon its own axis.

At this time astronomy was of great interest to both Church and state because the calendar was based upon the movements of sun and moon; and since the length of the year was not precisely determined the calendar tended to get out of line so that holy days such as Easter and Christmas did not fall at exactly the same time with respect to the seasons. For this reason a major revision of the calendar had been made by Julius Caesar, based on the assumption that the year included exactly $365\frac{1}{4}$ days. But since this figure was not quite accurate the calendar was again in need of revision by the sixteenth century.

The widespread belief in astrology added to the interest in astronomy, and for this reason princes and kings commonly supported astronomers in return for their horoscopes on impending events.

Copernicus' theory was set forth in a great monograph, *De Revolutionibus Orbium Celestium*, but because it was so at variance with the accepted dogma of the time he hesitated to publish it for fear he would be persecuted for heresy. As a safeguard he prepared a dedication of the work to the reigning pope, Paul III, emphasizing its usefulness as a contribution to the revision of the calendar. Even then he withheld the manuscript until the last year of his life, and the first published copy reached him as he lay on his deathbed in 1543.

Half a century later, on 17 February 1600, the distinguished Italian philosopher, Giordano Bruno, was burned at the stake in the Campo dei Fiori at Rome, after he had languished for seven years in prison. His crime was heresy – he had been teaching the Copernican theory.

Even so, within a few years another intellectual giant entered the fray. Galilei Galileo was professor of mathematics at Padua in 1609 when he built his first telescope. At once he could see changes of phase on the planet Venus, similar to those on the moon, and could observe four of the satellites of Jupiter revolving about the planet like members of a miniature solar system. These facts strongly confirmed his belief in the Copernican theory. His vigorous support of the theory soon aroused the antagonism of the Church, and in 1616 he was brought before the Inquisition in Rome which declared this doctrine to be contrary to Holy Scripture and proscribed the publication of any work holding that the earth was not the centre of the universe. Galileo was forced to recant, but secretly held his view. He then attempted to avoid the charge of heresy when in 1632 he published a comparison of the Copernican theory with the older Ptolmaic theory, cast in the form of a dialogue between fictitious characters, and in which he expressed no personal choice. This work was published in Italian instead of Latin and immediately excited great interest because now, for the first time, the educated public could understand the problem. But the Church was quick to see that the arguments presented strongly favoured the Copernican theory, and so, in 1633, Galileo was again brought before the Inquisition where, in mortal fear of the torture chamber, he recanted. He was then sentenced to prison in the Florentine embassy and was later transferred to Siena and finally returned to his home in Florence where he remained under house arrest until his death.

The next great advance was made by the Danish astronomer, Tycho Brahe. He had spent the years 1559 to 1562 at the University of Copenhagen where he had already become deeply interested in astronomy. Apparently in the hope of weaning him away from this interest, his family then sent him to Leipzig to study law and fit himself for political office. His interest in the stars would not be denied, however, and he neglected the law and devoted himself increasingly to astronomical studies in various German universities until he was recalled to Denmark in 1568 by Frederick II, who supported him with extensive grants and enabled him to build on the island of Hveen the most important astronomical observatory of the time. This was before the invention of the telescope, but Tycho Brahe developed numerous instruments with which he could measure the positions and movements of the planets across the sky with greater accuracy than previous workers had done. Here he spent many years making a star catalogue and accumulating a great mass of information about the movement of the planets across the sky. Upon the death of Frederick II he lost the support of the young king, Christian IV, and for this and personal reasons he left Denmark and migrated to Prague where he spent his last years supported by the German emperor, Rudólph II. While here he developed a new theory of the movement of the planets which differed from that of Copernicus in one important respect, but it did not gain a following because it was soon superseded by a better modification of the Copernican system.

During his last years at Prague Tycho Brahe engaged as his chief assistant young Johannes Kepler, who had left his home in Germany because of religious persecution. Tycho's observations had shown that the movement of a planet with respect to the stars is not uniform. Copernicus had been aware of this fact and, assuming that the orbit of each planet was circular, he postulated that each moved in small cycles upon its orbit (as the moon does about the earth's orbit). When Kepler inherited Tycho Brahe's position and all his measurements, he developed the concept that the planetary orbits are not circular but elliptical. This led to three simple but fundamental generalizations that have since become known as Kepler's laws. The first two were published in 1609 and the third in 1619 [90, 91]. They may be stated as follows:

Law I. Each planet moves in an elliptic orbit about the sun which occupies one focus of the ellipse.

Law II. An imaginary line connecting a planet with the sun sweeps over equal areas in equal units of time (figure 4). (In other words, a planet does not travel at uniform velocity but moves faster when near the sun and more slowly when farther away.)

Law III. The square of the time required for a planet to revolve once about the sun is proportional to the cube of its average distance from the sun (i.e., the angular velocity varies inversely with distance from the sun).

Thus Kepler simplified the Copernican system by avoiding the epicycles. He had no reason for the elliptical orbits of the planets, but his work set the stage for the next major advance – the discovery of universal gravitation.

This fell to the lot of Sir Isaac Newton, the son of an English farmer, who was born in the year 1642, and, after attending Cambridge University, became Lucasian Professor of Mathematics at Cambridge. Early in his career he had become convinced of the validity of one of Galileo's ideas, namely that it is as natural for an object to be in motion as at rest, and that once a force has set it in

8

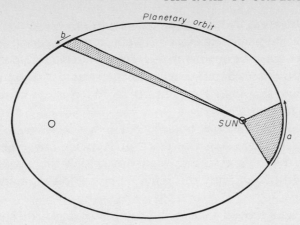

Figure 4. Diagram to illustrate Kepler's second law. Moving in an elliptic orbit a planet travels the distance *a* when nearest the sun and the distance *b* in an equal unit of time when far away. The shaded sectors are equal in area. In this diagram the ellipticity of the orbit is exaggerated; the planetary orbits are actually more nearly circular

motion it will continue to move indefinitely and in a straight line, unless and until acted upon by some other force. Thus, one day as he watched an apple fall from a tree he conceived that the earth must be exerting some mysterious force pulling objects toward itself. Perhaps then this force reaches even to the moon, preventing it from sailing off in a straight line into space. If so, the moon, like the apple, is really falling toward the earth but is held away from it by the centrifugal force imparted to it at some time in the past (figure 5). If this

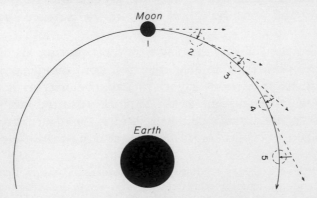

Figure 5. Diagram to illustrate that the moon is constantly falling toward the earth. If it were not for the pull of the earth the moon at station 1 would move in a straight line indicated by the dashed arrow. At station 2 it would likewise move in a straight line as indicated, etc. Since the earth's attraction is constantly exerted the moon's path is continually curved toward the earth

9

much be granted, then perhaps the sun exerts a similar force drawing each of the planets into an orbit about itself. And if this be true, then there must be a universal force of attraction pervading the physical universe whereby each object exerts a pull on every other object. This reasoning led Newton to the concept of the force of universal gravitation.

He could test this idea by seeing if it would account for the behaviour of the planets as expressed in Kepler's laws. This required an elegant mathematical treatment for which there was as yet no known method, so with the gift of genius, Newton invented the calculus.

Galileo had proved that at the earth's surface objects fall at the same velocity regardless of their size, and Newton therefore felt sure that the force of gravity must be related to the mass* rather than to some other attribute of the falling objects. By mathematical analysis he found that the force of attraction acts as though it were operating from the centre of gravity of a body, and varies directly with the mass and inversely as the square of the distance from its centre. In his *Principia*, published in 1687, he stated the Law of Universal Gravitation as follows: 'Any two bodies, large or small, throughout the physical universe, attract each other with a force that varies with the product of their masses and inversely with the distance between them.' This may be expressed as a mathematical formula, $F = kMm/r^2$, in which F is the mutual force of attraction, k is a constant (the constant of universal gravitation), M is the mass of one body and m of the other, and r is the distance between their centres.

Newton showed that this law would account for all the observed phenomena expressed in Kepler's laws. For example, a planet moving in an elliptical orbit (figure 4) gains velocity as it approaches perihelion (nearest point to the sun) because the sun's attraction increases as the distance decreases, and as the planet recedes toward the opposite pole of its orbit it loses velocity because the distance is

* The mass of an object is a measure of the amount of matter it contains, and is commonly judged by its weight, but mass and weight are not synonymous. The weight depends on the gravitative pull and varies with the distance from the centre of the attracting body. For example a man who weighs 150 pounds at sea level on the earth would weigh only 25 pounds on the moon where the moon's attraction is only one-sixth as great as that of the earth. Yet the mass, the actual amount of matter in the man's body, is constant regardless of his position.

greater. Newton also found that the calculated rate of change in velocity would account for Kepler's second law.

At the time, Newton could think of no way to demonstrate and measure the force of attraction between small objects. If present, it was too feeble to overcome the friction of a supporting surface. This goal was achieved almost a century later by a fellow-countryman, the distinguished chemist, Henry Cavendish, when he built the first torsion balance (figure 6). This device consisted of two lead balls

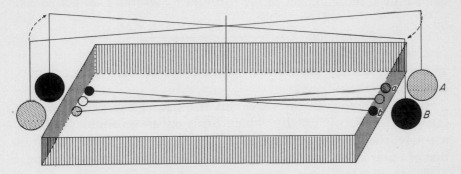

Figure 6. Diagram to illustrate the torsion balance of Cavendish

each two inches in diameter placed at opposite ends of a slender rod six feet long suspended at its centre by a very slender wire. Thus the balls hung in balance and were free to move in a horizontal plane without friction. This pendulum was then enclosed in a glass case to protect it from currents in the air and from changes in temperature. Next, he suspended two larger lead balls, each twelve inches in diameter, from the ends of a slightly longer rod so that they could be rotated closely about the ends of the pendulum. When these large balls were brought into position A with their centres about nine inches from the little balls, the pendulum rotated into position a, and when moved to position B, the pendulum swung into position b. Thus he proved that a force of attraction exists between small objects just as Newton had showed that it does between celestial bodies.

With improved models of the torsion balance it soon became possible to measure this force quantitatively. Thus it was found that the force of attraction between two objects each weighing one gram when placed one centimetre apart is 0·000,000,0666 dynes (a dyne being a measure of force about equal to that exerted by the weight of a hungry mosquito). This is the constant of universal gravitation, the k in Newton's formula. With this knowledge it was possible to determine the mass of the earth by substituting numerical values for the symbols in Newton's formula. Consider, for example, an object at the earth's surface weighing one metric ton ($=1,000,000$ grams). The force exerted by a weight of one gram equals 980 dynes. The force exerted by the weight of our object is therefore a million times as great or 980,000,000 dynes. The distance from the centre of the earth is approximately 4,000 miles or 6,400,000,000 centimetres. Substituting these figures in the formula $F = kMm/r^2$ we get

$$980,000,000 = \frac{0 \cdot 000,000,0666 \times M \times 1,000,000}{640,000,000^2}$$

and, solving for M, the mass of the earth, we get 6,000,000,000,000,000,000,000,000 metric tons.

And now, knowing the mass and the size of the earth, we can calculate its specific gravity, which turns out to be about 5·5. That is to say, the average specific gravity of the earth is about 5·5 times that of water and about twice that of surface rocks such as granite.

Thus, after millennia of ignorance and superstition, it required less than three centuries of enlightenment for man to discover the size and shape of the earth, its mass and average specific gravity, and its position in the universe as a minor planet revolving about the sun; and to understand the reason for its orbital motion.

This breakthrough was followed by advances in astronomy and physics and chemistry that have reached an amazing crescendo in our time. We can now probe the nature of the sun and even of remote stars, and understand the organization of the vast universe about us; we have explored the surface of our planet even to its frigid poles; we can map the ocean floor and even probe the deep interior of the earth whence come the elemental forces that raise mountains and shape the continents; and we can date the ancient rocks and know the history of life on earth during hundreds of millions of years. All this is truly a monumental tribute to human intellect. Ultimate causes, and the limits of time and space, probably lie for ever beyond human comprehension, but there is still much to learn about this amazing world of ours.

Chapter 2

The Scale of Time

The poor world is almost six thousand years old.
SHAKESPEARE, *As You Like It*

SHAKESPEARE reflected the thinking of his time when, about the year 1600, he wrote *As You Like It*. Based on the chronology related in the Old Testament, this idea was widely held during the Middle Ages and was given added authority by British scholars and churchmen about the middle of the seventeenth century. In 1642 John Lightfoot, a distinguished Greek scholar and Vice-Chancellor of Cambridge University, calculated that the moment of creation had been nine o'clock on the morning of 17 September, and in a later chapter of his study, published in 1644, he gave the year as 3928 BC [106]. In 1650 Archbishop Ussher, Primate of Ireland, wrote [158]: In the beginning God created Heaven and Earth, which beginning of time, according to our Chronologie, fell upon the entrance of night preceding the twenty-third day of Octob. in the year of the Julian Calendar, 710 (i.e. 4004 BC). On this authority William Lloyd, Bishop of Worcester, inserted the date 4004 BC as a marginal commentary in the Great Edition of the English Bible in 1701 [121], and this date was repeated in several later editions of the Authorized version of the Bible.

Thus it became deeply entrenched in religious dogma. The result was far-reaching. When, for example, the distinguished French scholar, Comte de Buffon, in 1749, advanced the theory that the six days of creation may have been six long epochs of time and that the earth's surface has been shaped and reshaped by processes now going on, he was forced by the Church to recant and to declare that he accepted the Old Testament as a complete and literal history of the world. Under this concept supernatural explanations were ascribed to many of the earth's features. The Deluge recounted in

13

Genesis was accepted without question, and the glacial drift so widely spread over Europe was thought to be proof of a universal flood. River valleys were interpreted as clefts in the earth produced by earthquakes, and mountains were believed to have arisen with tumultuous violence.

Shortly before Buffon's death these concepts were challenged by James Hutton, one of the *élite* at the great cultural centre in Edinburgh, Scotland. In his *Theory of the Earth*, communicated to the Royal Society of Edinburgh in 1785, he argued that erosion by wind and water is gradually wearing down the 'everlasting hills' and transporting the debris in the form of mud and sand to the sea where it is spread out, layer upon layer, to form beds of stratified rock; and from time to time such deposits are uplifted by forces within the earth to restore the lands and build new mountains [81]. 'Thus', he declared, 'the present is the key to the past'; and he concluded that 'time is to Nature endless and as nothing'. His oft-quoted statement, 'I see no vestige of a beginning and no prospect of an end', was not meant to deny that there had been a beginning but merely that so many changes have occurred that no evidence of the beginning remains.

Hutton's basic philosophy, which came to be known as Uniformitarianism, was vigorously opposed at the time, but it proved eventually to be an open sesame to progress, for it led to the conviction that the history of the world could be worked out on a rational basis.

It is a far cry from the medieval concept of a world fully formed only six thousand years ago to the time scale we now recognize that stretches back more than three thousand million years. It will be the purpose of this chapter to show the basis of the modern concept and to explain how it was achieved.

The Geologic Calendar

The history of the earth, as epitomized in figure 7, is based primarily on the study of the sedimentary rocks which, as Hutton recognized, were spread out layer upon layer as time passed. These layers form 'a manuscript in stone' more than one hundred miles thick in which Nature has recorded much of the history of the past (plate 1). The entombed fossils, for instance, reveal that life on earth was progressively changing, and record the dominant groups of animals and plants as they succeeded one another from age to age; they form the documentary evidence of organic evolution. They also distinguish areas that were land from those that were covered by the sea, and thus permit us to restore the ancient geography of departed ages. Even the local climate is commonly indicated. Thus large deposits of salt and gypsum speak of local aridity and coal beds record humid swampy lowlands. Great reptiles, palms, and alligators, denote warmth as clearly as ancient tillites record times and places of glacial climate. Ripples on the surface of sandstone layers record the direction of currents of wind and water and may indicate whether the water was standing or flowing. These are only a few of the most obvious symbols in which the earth has written its own epitaph. More sophisticated criteria are also known and are now widely used.

But the stratigraphic record is like a manuscript that has been composed in many places and now lies scattered and torn. No single region contains a complete record of the past, and if it did the older part would be deeply buried beyond our reach. The stratified rocks were laid down in basins that lasted for a time and were filled; meanwhile deposition had begun in other basins that were forming elsewhere. We deal, therefore, with fragments of a record that, like pieces of a jigsaw puzzle, must be fitted together in proper order before a picture emerges. Recorded human history presents the same problem. The manuscripts and books preserved in widely scattered libraries generally deal with local fragments of history—the story of a single dynasty or the history of a single nation or culture. A synthesis of human history becomes possible only when these local details are dated and placed in proper sequence in time.

In geology the first step was to build up a relative time scale. This began during the eighteenth century in southern England, the Paris Basin, and parts of Germany and Italy where thick sequences of stratified rocks lie gently tilted and their eroded edges are exposed like the butts of overlapping shingles. By 1750 it began to be realized that these layers extend underground where they lie in sequence one above another. With this concept a simple but fundamental principle emerged – since each bed had been spread out as a layer of sediment, each must be younger than the one on which it rests. This is the first principle in stratigraphy, the law of superposition. It postulates that in any succession of beds (if not greatly deformed) the oldest is at the bottom and the youngest at the top.

A second step was the discovery of a means of recognizing beds of equivalent age in different regions so that a composite, world-wide

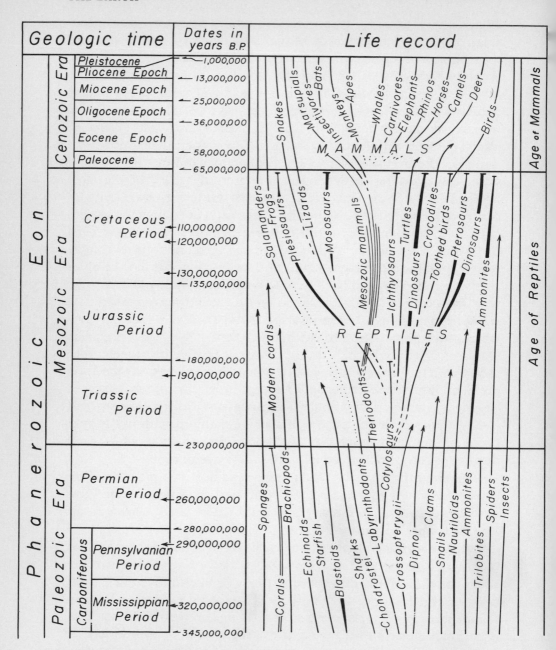

Figure 7. The geologic calendar. The first three columns show the major units of geologic time. Column four includes some of the best established absolute dates, based on radioactive isotopes. Dates closely located in the geologic time scale are shown in larger type and the darts indicate their position in column

three; dates located approximately on indirect evidence are shown in smaller type. Most of the dates are based on the work of Kulp [99], Faul [50], and Holmes [78]. In the life record a dart at the end of a line indicates that group is still living; a cross bar indicates extinction sequence could be recognized. This discovery was made by William Smith in the year 1799. As a surveyor concerned with the building of a great system of canals in southern England, he had had occasion to cross and recross a large region where the rocks dip gently under the London Basin and where their sequence was clearly evident. Here alternate formations of limestone and shale crop out in linear belts that are easily traced across the landscape; and because stone was used in construction, Smith became familiar with the lithologic peculiarities of each of these formations. Indeed, he gave each a name and many of these are still in use. Purely as a hobby, Smith had collected fossils as he worked, carefully labelling each lot as to locality. Sometime during the year 1799 it dawned on him that each of the formations yielded a unique assemblage of fossils by which it could be identified. Each assemblage of fossils constitutes a fauna and Smith had discovered the second great principle in stratigraphy—the law of faunal succession.

Smith had no idea why successive faunas were different. The explanation came sixty years later when, in 1859, Darwin published his *Origin of Species* and set forth the doctrine of organic evolution. Then it became evident that since life has been progressively changing throughout time, only rocks laid down within a limited time span could contain identical or closely similar faunas and, conversely, rocks containing identical or closely similar faunas, even in widely separated regions, must be approximately equivalent in age. This provided a means of correlation, i.e. of determining the time relations of deposits in different parts of the world as suggested by figure 8.

Smith's idea was quickly adopted by other geologists and put to the test. In each region studied, a local succession of rock units was found to yield a corresponding sequence of faunas, and soon the same faunal sequences could be recognized in other areas, even as far away as eastern Europe and North America. Thus, by matching equivalent horizons in many different regions an idealized or composite columnar section was built up that represents virtually all of the last six hundred million years of time.

The use of fossils thus proved so successful that within less than half a century the geologic column was established in approximately its present form as represented in figure 7.

But another problem had to be solved simultaneously. For purposes of description and synthesis this vast rock complex had to be

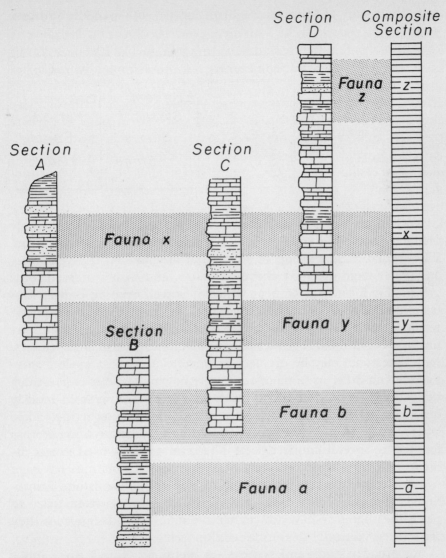

Figure 8. Diagram to illustrate the use of fossils in building up a composite geologic column. Section *B* proves that faunal zone *b* is younger than *a*; section *C* shows that zone *y* is younger than *b*; sections *A* and *C* both confirm that faunal zone *x* is younger than *y*; and finally section *D* shows that faunal zone *z* is younger than *x*. Thus a single composite section can be constructed showing all these faunal zones in their natural sequence

subdivided into units both large and small. The scheme of classification that was gradually evolved, and is now widely used, is represented in figure 9. It involves three categories of units, each including a hierarchy of subdivisions of progressively descending magnitude [137].

Figure 9. Diagram to show three hierarchies of units used in description of the geologic record

Rock units			Lithochrons	Geochrons
Group	Formation	Stratum	Erathem System Series Stage	Era Period Epoch Age

Rock units are distinguished solely on the basis of lithologic characteristics. The smallest unit is the individual layer, or stratum. The formation is a group of strata that are alike or closely similar and differ from the next above or below, and each is named for a geographic locality at or near which it is well exposed or was first described (e.g. St Louis limestone or London clay). The basic criterion is that a formation is a group of strata formed under essentially uniform conditions. A sequence of beds of the same major rock type (e.g. limestone) may be divided, however, into two or more formations which differ in some distinctive lithologic features (e.g. a thick bedded versus a thin bedded limestone, or a pure versus a muddy limestone, or a pure limestone versus one having interbedded shale layers, etc.). The thickness of a formation may be anything from a few feet to several hundred feet. The term group is used in a technical sense for a unit consisting of two or more formations having a common rock character (e.g. a succession of red sandstone formations). The rock units may vary appreciably in age from place to place and therefore have no correlative time units. In figure 9 they are written vertically to emphasize this fact.

For broader study and synthesis a hierarchy of rock units independent of lithology, but representing a distinct time span, are needed. These are the rock-time units or lithochrons (Gr. *lithos*, rock + *chron*, time). For these we recognize a parallel hierarchy of time units or geochrons (Gr. *ge*, earth + *chron*, time).

The two vast eons of time are distinguished by the fossil record. During the Cryptozoic eon (Gr. *kryptos*, hidden + *zoon*, life) life was either absent or was too primitive to leave a useful fossil record; but during Phanerozoic time (Gr. *phaneros*, plain or evident + *zoon*, life)

life was well developed and in the Phanerozoic rocks fossils are generally plentiful. The Phanerozoic eon is divided into three great eras on the basis of the dominant major groups of living organisms. The Paleozoic era was characterized chiefly by invertebrate animals and primitive plants; the Mesozoic era by the dominance of reptiles; and the Cenozoic era by the dominance of mammals and birds. The rock unit representing an era is an erathem (e.g. the Paleozoic erathem) [67]. Since the Cryptozoic eon left a negligible fossil record, it has not been feasible to subdivide it into eras.

An era is subdivided into periods of time and the corresponding erathem into systems of rocks. These are generally named after geographic regions where they were first recognized, for example, the Devonian Period and the Devonian System (after Devonshire, England). A few, named early in the history of geology, do not bear geographic names (e.g. Cretaceous for chalk) (L. *creta*, chalk). Each period of time is a few tens of millions of years long, and each system of rocks is several thousands of feet thick.

Epochs of time and series of rocks are smaller units, and these in turn are divided into ages of time and stages of rock.

For more than 150 years the geologists of the world have been collaborating in working out the faunal sequence and building up a composite geological column that now represents virtually all of the last 600,000,000 years of the earth's history, and with this standard it is possible to place any local discovery in its proper place in the geological time scale.

This, however, is only a relative time scale. The possibility of transforming it into an absolute time scale in which events could be dated in years was achieved after the turn of the present century and the discovery of radioactivity.

The Absolute Time Scale

The accidental discovery of radioactivity by Becquerel in 1895 was followed by intensive study of the structure of the atom that is still proceeding at an accelerating rate. Before attempting to explain how rocks are dated, it will be helpful to summarize the present understanding of atomic structure and the phenomenon of radioactivity [38].

The atom, of any element, consists of a small nucleus surrounded by a swarm of electrons each revolving about it at very high velocity.

The nucleus consists of two kinds of building blocks, protons and neutrons. Each proton carries a positive electromagnetic charge but a neutron is without charge.

Protons, neutrons, and electrons are the three basic building blocks of matter and are identical in all the elements, which differ only in their number and arrangement. The atoms of an element have a constant and unique number of each of these components. The mass of a proton is the same in all the elements and is considered unity in the scale of mass. A neutron has almost the same mass as a proton, but the mass of an electron is negligible.

Atoms of the lightest element, hydrogen, consist of one proton and one electron (plate 2). The next lightest is helium with two protons, two neutrons, and two electrons, and from this there is progressive complexity up through the heavier elements. Common carbon, for example, has six protons, six neutrons, and a small swarm of electrons, and common uranium has 92 protons, 146 neutrons, and a vast swarm of electrons. The number of protons determines the atomic number of an element and its place in the periodic table, but the atomic weight is the sum of its protons plus its neutrons.

Many of the elements have been found, however, to occur in two or more varieties distinguished by the number of neutrons, the number of protons being constant. Carbon, for example, invariably has six protons but one variety has six neutrons, another seven, and a third eight neutrons. The atomic weights of these three varieties are, therefore, 12, 13, and 14, respectively, and they are distinguished as carbon twelve (C^{12}), carbon thirteen (C^{13}), and carbon fourteen (C^{14}). The chemical nature and behaviour of an element is determined only by the complexity of its electron cloud, which in turn is dependent on the number of protons, and is independent of the number of the neutrons. Since the three forms of carbon behave alike chemically they are considered varieties of a single element rather than distinct elements. Such varieties of an element determined by a difference in the number of neutrons are isotopes.

Certain isotopes of some of the elements are not quite stable and, from time to time, transformations take place to reduce them to a stable condition. This may involve the capture of an extra electron or a discharge of particles from the nucleus. The emitted particles are discharged with high energy and produce the phenomenon known as radioactivity.

In the case of uranium, for example, three distinct types of discharge are recognized. These are: (1) gamma rays (which are units of electromagnetic force similar to x-rays but generally more energetic), (2) alpha particles (each consisting of two protons and two neutrons), and (3) beta particles (each a highly energized electron). Upon its emission, an alpha particle, being positively charged, immediately captures a pair of electrons and becomes an atom of helium.

The capture of an electron produces a different result. Since it is negatively charged it neutralizes the positive charge of one of the protons, transforming it into a neutron. This changes the atomic number and transforms the atom into a different element without changing the atomic weight.

The rate and mode of disintegration are definite and unique for each unstable isotope and can be measured with very great accuracy. The rate is commonly expressed in terms of the half-life, which means simply the length of time required for any given quantity of the material to be reduced by one half. The following table indicates the mode of disintegration and the half-life of some of the most important isotopes now used in dating the rocks.

TABLE I

Radioactive isotopes (after Tilton and Davis)

Parent Element-Isotope	Daughter Element-Isotope	Mode of change	Half life in billions of years
Uranium-U^{238}	Lead-Pb^{206}	$8\alpha + 6\beta$	4·51
Uranium-U^{235}	Lead-Pb^{207}	$7\alpha + 4\beta$	0·71
Thorium-Th^{232}	Lead-Pb^{208}	$6\alpha + 4\beta$	13·90
Rubidium-Rb^{87}	Strontium-Sr^{87}	β	50·00
Potassium-K^{40}	Argon-A^{40}	electron capture	12·40

In 1907 the Yale chemist, Boltwood, observed that minerals containing uranium or thorium invariably include both lead and helium. He therefore concluded that these are stable end products of the radioactive disintegration of uranium and thorium. After a crystal has formed, these products are trapped and should steadily accumulate as their parent disintegrates. Therefore, if the rate of disintegration were known, the ratio of lead to uranium and of lead to thorium should give a measure of the length of time since the rock crystallized.

For example, using the data given in table 1, and recognizing that

23

U^{238} is presently about 140 times more abundant than U^{235}, we may calculate that one gram of uranium will produce annually about

$$\frac{1}{7,600,000,000} \text{ grams of lead.}$$

At this rate U grams will yield

$$\frac{U}{7,600,000,000} \text{ grams of lead}$$

and in t years it will yield $\dfrac{(t \times U)}{7,600,000,000}$ grams.

Whence,

$$Pb = \frac{tU}{7,600,000,000}$$

or

$$t = \frac{Pb \times 7,600,000,000}{U} \text{ years.}$$

For example, crystals of uraninite from Branchville, Connecticut, show a lead/uranium ratio of 0·050. Solving the equation, $t = 0·050 \times 7,600,000,000$ we get 380,000,000 years, the time since the crystals were formed.

This gives a first approximation, but our problem is rather more complex than we have assumed. For instance, lead is slightly soluble in underground water; if any has been removed in this way from our crystal the calculated age will be too small and if lead has been introduced, it will be too large. Furthermore, there are four distinct isotopes of lead, Pb^{204}, Pb^{206}, Pb^{207}, and Pb^{208}. The first seems to be primary (not radiogenic) and the last three are produced from different parents and at highly diverse rates. We need to know the relative abundance of each of these isotopes in our sample so that the age indicated by each can be independently calculated. Fortunately both these problems can now be solved. By means of a precision mass spectrometer the actual amounts of the four lead isotopes can be accurately determined. And if the ages indicated by the three agree, we can be sure that no lead has been lost and none added; for, since they behave alike chemically, the several lead isotopes would go into solution in equal amounts, and since they have been generated at very different rates, the calculated ages would then disagree.

Furthermore, common lead, such as might be carried in solution by ground water, consists of a mixture of the four isotopes in the following ratios: Pb^{204}, 1 per cent; Pb^{206}, 26 per cent; Pb^{207}, 21 per cent; and Pb^{208}, 52 per cent. Even if such lead has been introduced, it is only necessary to determine the amount of Pb^{204} and deduct the appropriate amounts of each of the other isotopes before making our calculations. All this requires elaborate equipment and critical and time-consuming measurements and, unfortunately, relatively few such precise age determinations have yet been made.

Since 1952 a much simpler method has been extensively used, based on the lead/alpha particle ratios in zircon [103]. It rests on the premise that the disintegration of an atom of uranium, or of thorium, into lead involves the emission of eight alpha particles. If, then, we can measure the rate of emission of alpha particles, we know how fast lead is being formed.

Zircon occurs as crystals widely distributed in granitic rocks and it commonly includes small quantities of uranium and/or thorium which makes the mineral radioactive. For two reasons it is believed that no lead could have been incorporated when the mineral formed, and none could have been introduced into it later from underground solutions: (1) the lead atom is about twice as large as the zirconium atom and would not fit into the tightly packed crystal lattice, and (2) lead, being bivalent whereas zirconium is tetravalent, would require a complex and improbable bonding.

In practice, a small sample of clean zircon crystals is selected and the lead content, in parts per million, is determined by a mass spectrometer, and the number of alpha particles emitted per hour is determined by means of a special type of Geiger counter. The age of the rock is then calculated from the formula

$$A = \frac{Pb \times k}{a}$$

in which A is the age in millions of years, Pb is the amount of lead in parts per million of the sample, k is a constant representing the rate at which alpha particles are emitted from the radioactive parents (uranium and/or thorium), and a is the observed count of alpha particles emitted per milligram of the sample per hour. Because of its relative simplicity and the speed with which the necessary measurements can be made, this method of age determination is now being extensively used.

25

Another method is based upon potassium, which is one of the common and widely distributed elements in igneous rocks. One of its isotopes, K^{40}, is radioactive as a result of either of two methods of transformation: (1) by emission of a beta particle it is transformed into an atom of calcium^{40}; or (2) by capture of one electron it becomes an atom of the inert gas argon^{40}. Knowing the rate of argon formation (table 1) the age of the mineral can be calculated from the A^{40}/K^{40} ratio. In this method a problem arises because of the possibility that argon, being an inert gas, may have partly leaked away. In this event the calculated age would be too small. When from a single rock mass the K^{40}/A^{40} ratio is determined independently for the feldspars and the micas, for example, the age calculated from the feldspars are appreciably less than that calculated from the micas, indicating clearly that there has been leakage from the former. But in rocks that contain K^{40} as well as uranium or thorium, this method can be checked against the Pb/U age determination. Where this has been done there is good agreement between the ages determined by the lead ratio and by the A^{40}/K^{40} ratio in the micas. This indicates that no leakage of argon is suffered by the micas. For this reason the feldspars are neglected and age determinations are based on the micas alone.

Another method is based on the ratio of rubidium^{87} to strontium^{87}. In this method, also, certain precautions are required. For instance, the radioactive Sr^{87} is generally associated with the more abundant common strontium. Caution must therefore be used to select specimens with a low content of common strontium or to make proper corrections for the common strontium in a manner similar to that used for making corrections for lead. The minerals commonly used are two of the micas, either lepidolite or biotite.

The methods described above are suitable for rocks that are many millions of years old, but since the half-life of the radioactive elements used is so long, the amount of decay products formed within a few million years is too small to be accurately measured. A search is therefore being carried on for other radioactive substances having much shorter half-lives.

For objects less than fifty thousand years old a very elegant and precise method of dating is based upon the radioactive isotope of carbon, C^{14}, in objects once living – wood, shells, or bone [105]. This method was developed shortly before 1950 by Willard Libby. Dr Libby found that radiocarbon (C^{14}) is continually formed in the outer atmosphere by the bombardment of cosmic rays that transform nitrogen (N^{14}) into carbon[14]. The latter readily unites with oxygen to form radioactive carbon dioxide (CO_2) which is so readily mixed with the normal CO_2 of the atmosphere that a steady state has long since been attained whereby these two forms of CO_2 exist in the atmosphere in a constant ratio. And since they behave alike chemically they are built into plant tissues in exactly this ratio. Even if plants are eaten by animals the ratio is unchanged, or if the CO_2 combines with Ca to form $CaCO_3$ and is used by marine animals to make shells, the ratio of the two forms of carbon remains the same.

Figure 10. Diagram to illustrate the problem of collating absolute and geologic dates

But the radiocarbon is slightly unstable and is slowly transformed back into nitrogen, its half life being 5,568 years. Once built into organic tissues, therefore, the amount of C^{14} steadily decreases and the ratio of C^{14} to C^{12} gradually declines. After 5,568 years it will be only half as great as in the atmosphere, and after 11,136 years it will be only one-fourth as great. The ratio of C^{14} to C^{12} therefore indicates quite precisely the time that has elapsed since the organism was alive. This method can be applied to bone or shells or wood, or even to the organic muck or peat in old lakes. It can also be tested by applying it to the heartwood of great trees whose ages are shown by growth rings, or by applying it to historically dated objects. In such tests the accordance between the calculated and known dates indicates a high degree of validity for radiocarbon dating.

For the older rocks, however, another serious problem remains. The best minerals for radioactive dating are the micas which occur chiefly in intrusive igneous rocks such as granite or pegmatite dikes, and these can only be dated geologically by their relations to fossiliferous sedimentary rocks. The problem may be illustrated by a hypothetical case, figure 10. The block diagram represents an area many

27

miles across in which three major rock formations are present. The deformed beds (K) are dated by fossils as of Late Cretaceous age and the overlying, undeformed beds (Ol) are likewise dated as Early Oligocene. A large granite stock with radiating dikes cuts the Cretaceous beds and caused their deformation, but it did not affect the Oligocene formation. Radioactive minerals in the granite at locality X give an absolute date of sixty million years BP (before the present). This is the date at which the granite was intruded and crystallized from a molten condition. Here we have two firm geologic dates and one absolute date, but how are they related? As shown by figure 7, two long epochs, Paleocene and Eocene, fall between the Late Cretaceous and Early Oligocene and, as we now know, they represent a time span of at least twenty-five million years. The intrusion of the granite occurred sometime within this interval. How, then, can we pin point the date sixty million years in the geologic time scale? Obviously it cannot be done precisely. We can, however, restrict the possibilities. If the lava had reached the surface it would have cooled rapidly to form a fine-grained felsite; granite is only formed under a thick cover of older rocks which prevents rapid cooling. The structure of the Cretaceous rocks indicates that the region was mountainous when the intrusion was completed, but the structure of the overlying beds proves that erosion had reduced the region to a plain before Oligocene time, removing the cover from the granite, pebbles of which are included in the base of the Oligocene formation. Such extensive erosion must have required some millions of years and we conclude that the intrusion could hardly have been as late as Eocene time; it probably fell somewhere within Paleocene time, but we can go no further with the available information.

Several of the best absolute dates can thus be related only approximately to the geologic time scale, and in the very old rocks of the Cryptozoic eon, where no fossils occur, no geologic time scale has been achieved. In these old rocks an absolute time scale based on radioactive minerals will eventually help us to solve fundamental problems concerning the origin and history of the continents.

Fortunately it is now possible to get good dates from the potassium–argon ratio in formations that can be closely dated in terms of the geologic time scale. Such instances, for example, are from beds of volcanic ash or lava flows in the midst of a fossiliferous sedimentary formation, or from black shales that are fossiliferous or lie within a fossiliferous sequence of beds. Technical difficulties of many sorts, too involved to present here, have been encountered as the techniques for dating the rocks by radioactive isotopes have been worked out, and many of the dates published in the early stages are invalid, but the difficulties are being overcome and quite a number of dates are now established that are consistent with the geological time scale. The chief of these are indicated in the fourth column of figure 7. From these we may conclude that the Paleozoic era began about 600 million years ago, the Mesozoic about 250 million years ago and the Cenozoic era about 60 million years ago. The oldest rocks thus far dated are granites that crystallized about 3,200 million years ago.

Recent comprehensive studies of the absolute time scale by Henry Faul [50], by J. Lawrence Kulp [99], and by Arthur Holmes [78], respectively, are in rather close agreement and contain a wealth of data. Our dates in column 4 of figure 7 are largely drawn from these sources. In the awesome panorama of time represented by our universe, to borrow the words of Bascom, 'man's entire span is one page in a book of 50,000 pages, of which written history is only the last line' [8, p. 199].

Chapter 3

The Universe Around Us

IN THE vastness of space the earth seems isolated and alone; but if it really were so, ours would be a cold and lifeless world drifting in eternal darkness without recorded history or clues to its origin.

The Solar System

The other members of our solar system are relatively near to us (figure 11). Circling about the sun are the nine planets with their satellites, many thousands of asteroids, and an unknown number of meteors and comets. These form a close-knit family and have shared in a common origin.

The sun is the most important to us since it supplies the warmth and light that makes life possible. The moon, our solitary satellite, is the nearest of all and in some ways the most interesting. We may therefore preface this chapter with an account of these two near neighbours.

The Sun

The sun is a true star, self-luminous and entirely gaseous, and more than a million times as large as the earth. If, in imagination, we should place the earth at its centre, the moon in its orbit would be only a little more than half-way to the sun's surface (figure 12).

Like all the other celestial bodies, it is made of the familiar chemical elements, but in the sun their proportions differ greatly from those in the earth, about 98 per cent of the sun's mass consisting of hydrogen and helium. In a very real sense the sun is a vast atomic furnace in which, as in a hydrogen bomb, the fusion of hydrogen atoms to form helium (and possibly other light elements) releases prodigious amounts of energy. This is the source of the radiant

energy that warms and lights our world. It also maintains the high
temperature of the sun in spite of constant loss to outer space. At the
visible surface of the sun the temperature is about 6,000°C, but it

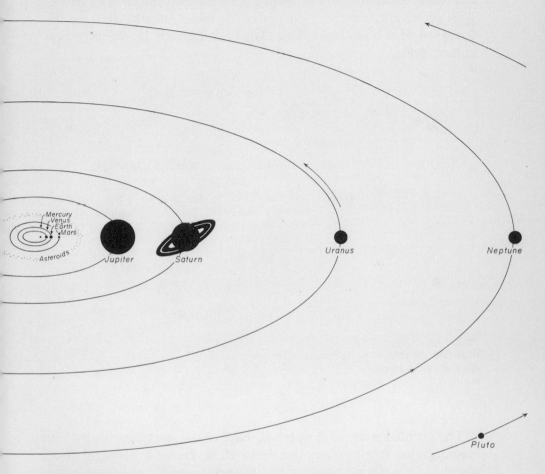

Figure 11. The organization of the solar system. The view is oblique so that the
ellipticity of the orbits is greatly exaggerated. The planets are shown at a
uniform scale and their distance from the sun is shown on a much larger but
uniform scale

increases with depth to the centre where it is estimated to exceed
20,000,000°C. As a result, the entire mass of the sun is gaseous, and
convection currents continually stream to the surface to renew the
heat that is lost into space. At a distance of 93 million miles the earth
intercepts only about one two-thousand-millionth of this energy, yet

that tiny increment is enough to warm and light our world, to keep the atmosphere in motion, to lift the vapours that return as rain and snow, to generate the waves, and to motivate all the forces of erosion and transportation that have shaped and reshaped the earth's surface. This prodigious supply of energy is the more remarkable since we now know that it has never flagged or varied greatly for at least 3,000 million years.

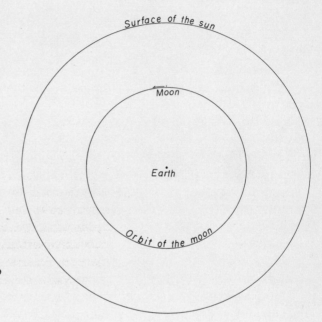

Figure 12. Diagram to illustrate the relative sizes of earth, moon, and sun

The visible surface is the photosphere of the sun (plate 3). At low magnification it appears almost featureless, except for a number of sunspots; but when photographed at high magnification, with most of the light screened out by the spectroscope, it appears as a turbulent sea of flames (plate 4). The temperature here is about four times that of molten iron, and the lighter parts are clouds of white hot gases welling up from the still hotter depths.

From time to time darker areas, known as sunspots, appear, last for a period of months, and then wane and disappear (plate 3). The largest of these are visible to the naked eye (through a dark glass), and were observed by the Chinese long before the invention of the telescope. They appear dark only in contrast to the intense brightness of the surrounding area; if they could be seen against a black background, they would appear white.

Since they strongly affect our atmosphere, sunspots have been the subject of intensive study in recent years, but they still remain something of an enigma. They generally appear in groups, some large and others smaller, and the large ones always occur in pairs some distance apart. The spectroscope shows that the light emitted from a sunspot is polarized and that the polarity is opposite in the two members of a pair. From this it is inferred that the spots are at opposite ends of a strong but local magnetic field beneath the surface [4].

From each sunspot a jet of ionized atomic particles streams at high velocity far out into space and when a spot directly faces us we intercept the jet and experience one of the magnetic storms that from time to time cause displays of the aurora borealis and interfere with the transmission of radio and television signals.

The abundance of sunspots varies in an eleven-year cycle and appreciably affects our climate. During years of maxima, storms are more numerous and severe, and during sunspot minima the climate is more equable. From this it appears that the sun is a somewhat variable star, its output of energy fluctuating in an eleven-year cycle. It seems possible, furthermore, that long-term fluctuations of greater magnitude have contributed to the great climatic changes that are so clearly recorded in the geologic record and are discussed in chapter 10.

Individual sunspots generally appear in intermediate latitudes on the sun and, over a period of months, slowly drift toward the equator. Meanwhile, they appear to move from east to west across the face of the sun because it is rotating in that direction in a period of about twenty-five days.

Outside the photosphere are two envelopes of rarer gases that are visible only during total solar eclipse when the moon blots out the white light of the photosphere. The inner envelope, about ten thousand miles thick, consists of rare gases that glow with a crimson colour, whence it is known as the chromosphere (plate 5). From time to time solar flares leap up from this layer like vast jets of crimson flame.

The outer envelope is the corona (plate 6) which at times of total eclipse appears as a faint halo that extends far out, even reaching the earth. It consists of widely dispersed and largely ionized atomic particles that are streaming at high velocity away from the sun.

33

The Moon

The nearest of all the celestial bodies, and in some ways the most interesting, is the moon (plate 7). Its mean distance is only about 240,000 miles and the great 200-inch telescope on Mount Palomar reveals its surface features as though they were being observed by the naked eye at a distance of only two hundred miles. Its diameter (2,100 miles) is about one-fourth, and its mass about one-eightieth, that of the earth. As a result the force of gravity at its surface is only one-sixth as great as it is here. If we succeed in landing a 150-pound man on the moon he will weigh only twenty-five pounds, and we can imagine the exhilaration he will feel and the long strides he will take; and when he is ready for the return to earth, the thrust required for take-off will be only a small fraction of that needed for the outward journey.

Since the moon has no atmosphere its stark, barren surface is never obscured by haze or clouds. The reason for the lack of atmosphere is well understood. The atoms in a gas behave like a swarm of ping-pong balls in violent motion. When two collide they rebound as perfectly elastic bodies and are thus kept relatively far apart. In the lower reaches of our atmosphere, the atoms are so numerous that none travels far before colliding with another and rebounding; but in the rare upper reaches they are so widely spaced that some fly away without a collision. If the force of gravity is sufficiently great, they eventually fall back, like spent missiles, and rejoin the atmosphere; but if they leave with sufficient velocity they escape the pull of gravity and never return. There is thus a critical escape velocity from a celestial body that depends on (1) the mass of that body, (2) the atomic weight of the gas, and (3) the temperature. The escape velocity on earth is about 7 miles per second but on the moon only about 1·5 miles per second. The atoms of the lightest gases, hydrogen and helium, move with a velocity of more than 7 miles per second and readily escape from our atmosphere, and even the heavy gases could not be held by the moon; if any were ever sweated out of its interior they leaked away into space about as fast as they appeared. In short, the moon simply is too small to hold an atmosphere. It therefore has never had winds or running water; it has neither streams nor valleys nor oceans; and its rocky surface lies naked and changeless. And without an atmosphere to shield it, the sunshine is more intense than in our hottest deserts. During the lunar day the temperature at its surface rises to about 150°C, and during the night it falls as far below zero. Under such extremes, expansion and contraction probably cause the surface of its naked rocks to crumble into gravel and dust. On steep slopes such loose material probably falls down to accumulate as talus, but it cannot be transported farther to produce layers of sedimentary rocks such as we have on earth.

As the temperature rises, the atoms oscillate more rapidly, rebound more violently, and are thus kept farther apart. This is the reason why a gas expands when heated. For this reason, also, if a planet at any time in its history was very hot it would have lost much of its gases even if it were large. The sun, with its enormous gravity, is constantly losing atoms into space because it is so hot.

Two striking features of the lunar landscape are (1) the maria, those great dark areas so readily visible to the eye, and (2) the craters that are visible through the telescope. The maria were so named by the ancients who thought them to be oceans (L. *mare*, sea). Indeed, they would be oceans if water were present on the moon, but actually they are vast flat desert basins lying well below the level of the surrounding brighter areas. They appear dark only because their smooth surface reflects less of the sunlight than do the rough uplands.

The lunar craters (plate 8) are enormous circular pits with relatively flat floors and lofty rims [6; 112]. They range in size from less than a mile in diameter to giants such as Clavius, which is 146 miles across with a rim that towers about twenty thousand feet above its floor. The craters, some thirty thousand in number, virtually cover the surface of the uplands (plate 7), but they are sparsely scattered over the maria. Some of them are more subdued than others because their rims have crumbled down, but some are deep and sharp and obviously are much younger, and in places the younger ones cut the older ones.

For a time it was thought that the lunar craters were volcanoes, but it now seems evident that they were produced by the infall of great meteors. They are not simple impact craters such as a pebble makes when dropped on a surface of soft mud, but are explosion craters formed after the meteor had plunged beneath the surface. The energy carried by a falling meteor is the product of its mass times the square of its velocity [9]; and since they travel at velocities of many miles per second a large meteor carries an enormous charge of energy. When the velocity is checked, this kinetic energy is transformed into heat. This is why upon entering our atmosphere meteorites become 'shooting stars'; the friction of the air reduces

35

their speed and releases heat. Small ones flare white hot and are completely volatilized, but the journey through the atmosphere is so brief that larger ones are only partly consumed before crashing to earth with their surfaces blackened and seared by the heat. Those that strike the moon are unchecked in their fall until they plunge beneath the surface like high velocity missiles and are buried. Then all their energy is suddenly released and they explode like a bomb. According to Beals [9] a meteor travelling at twenty miles per second possesses energy equivalent to sixty-five times its weight in nitroglycerine; and Baldwin [6] has estimated that it would blast out a pit about sixty thousand times its own volume. Since the explosion occurs after burial the pit is circular and, in the absence of atmosphere, the debris, coarse and fine alike, falls back, as in a vacuum, to form a symmetrical rim.

Throughout its long history the earth must have been bombarded by meteors even as the moon has been, but most of the large ones probably fell early in the history of the solar system. On earth the old scars have been removed by erosion, but on the moon we see the cumulative effects of all that ever fell.

Of numerous explosion craters that are still preserved on the earth's surface, the best known is Meteor Crater in Arizona, a great pit some four thousand feet across and five hundred and fifty feet deep (plate 9). It was blasted out of massive sandstone. For a time after it gained attention it was thought to be an impact crater, and several deep wells were drilled in its floor in the hope of finding a great buried mass of meteoric iron. The search was in vain, but the drills penetrated some hundreds of feet of broken and shattered rock, and thousands of small fragments of meteoric iron have been found, scattered over the rim and the surrounding surface as much as five miles away [9]. Furthermore, alteration minerals (coesite) in the walls of the crater bear witness to very intense heat. In short, the meteor exploded into bits and much of it was probably vaporized and dissipated in the air. Chubb Crater in Ungava Peninsula east of Hudson Bay is even larger and was blasted out of solid granite. It is almost two miles across and is now occupied by a lake about eight hundred feet deep [109]. Wolfe Creek Crater in north-western Australia is somewhat smaller than Meteor Crater but is similar in shape, and scattered pieces of meteoric iron found on its rim confirm its meteoric origin [9].

Several considerations prove that the lunar craters are not volcanic. The most telling is that the volume of the material in the rim is just about equal to that of the pit [6]. Also, the lunar craters are remarkably symmetrical whereas volcanic craters are commonly unsymmetrical because of lava flows that have broken through their sides.

The maria are shown by the great telescopes to be remarkably flat plains, broken only by widely scattered craters, and in a few cases by great wrinkles that can only be folds in layered rocks – folds that rise to the height of mountains. Two such ranges of fold mountains are shown in plate 8. Since no sedimentary rocks could ever have formed on the moon it seems obvious that the maria have at least a veneer of vast flat lava flows comparable to the plateau basalts on earth (plate 17).

Of course the meteors that formed the lunar craters must have fallen at random. The craters must once have covered the entire surface of the moon as they do the areas outside the maria. And since the craters in the maria are few, mostly relatively small, and sharply defined, it must be evident that the maria were formed relatively late in lunar history, after most of the great meteorites had fallen, and that the original surface in these areas has been melted down or has subsided before being covered by vast lava flows. They now lie far below the level of the cratered uplands. Indeed, there are several places where part of the rim of a large crater at the margin of a mare has been submerged so that the lava flowed into the crater. Sinus Iridium in the upper left corner of plate 8 is an illustration. It is an embayment bounded on the north by a lofty semicircular rim that appears to be half the rim of a large ancient crater. On the other hand the great crater Copernicus which lies near the southern margin of Mare Imbrium and opposite to Sinus Iridium, is younger than either of the surrounding maria. Great rills of material appearing lighter than the floor of the maria radiate from Copernicus to a distance of four hundred miles or more and are now known to be formed of rock fragments 'splashed' out when the crater was formed. The rills appear lighter because the rough rock fragments scatter the sunlight more than the smooth surface of the maria.

The spectacular photographs secured on 31 July 1964 by the US space satellite, *Ranger VII*, added immensely to our knowledge of the surface of the maria and show details that could never have been discovered by telescopes. The dimple-like pits shown in plates 11 and 12 are not lunar craters but impact pits formed by the fall of

37

chunks of rock blasted out of the great crater, Copernicus, which is located some four hundred miles to the north. (This area is near the end of one of the great rills that radiate from Copernicus.) Most of the falling rocks are buried, but in the largest pit in the upper left quadrant of plate 12 a chunk of rock is still exposed. The mosaic overlay above the right centre of plate 12 shows exceptional details in which pits only about three feet across and 1·5 feet deep can be recognized.

The rounded shoulders and dimple-like shape of the pits may throw significant light on the texture of the surface rock, but at the present the matter is still under study. Their shoulders may have been rounded off by the continual rain of tiny meteorites. It is well known that the earth intercepts some millions of these each day. Most of them are of the size of sand grains and are volatilized in our atmosphere and appear as 'shooting stars'. The moon, revolving about the earth, must intercept a proportionate share of such particles, but since it has no atmosphere they all land on its surface and must serve as a slow but perpetual sand blast. If the surface rock consists of lava flows, the gases escaping in the vacuum that surrounds the moon probably left the surface as vesicular as pumice. If so, the surface would bear the weight of a man but would be crushed by a falling chunk of rock. In any event it is now quite certain that, except for the shallow pits, the surface of the maria is essentially flat.

The origin of the maria is still a subject of controversy. Urey [157] has expressed the belief that they are the result of the infall of super-colossal meteors whose energy fused the surface and left great lakes of molten rock; others believe they are great structural basins into which lava flowed as they subsided. Several considerations seem to this author to favour the latter hypothesis: (1) if they had been formed as explosion craters by meteors of the colossal dimensions implied by Urey, they should be surrounded by enormous rims as are the great explosion craters, but of proportionately greater size; (2) since they are marked by only widely scattered craters they must be relatively young as compared to the highlands that are almost completely covered with craters; (3) in this case the craters in a wide zone surrounding each of the maria should have been buried by the debris blasted out by the supposed supercolossal meteors. It can be plainly seen in plate 7 that such is not the case. On the contrary old craters at the margins of the maria have been invaded by the lavas but are not filled with rocky debris. The choice between these alternative interpretations has far-reaching implications. If the maria are structural basins partly filled by the quiet upwelling of lava, it is evident that the moon at some stage has developed much internal heat (as has the earth), causing fusion of some of the material below the surface which, in welling up, over weighted the crustal zone where the maria exist so that it subsided below the general level.

The Planets

The planets revolve about the sun in nearly circular orbits that lie in a common plane (figure 11) and all travel in a counter-clockwise direction as seen from the north polar view. Their movement is majestic in its simplicity and regularity. We on earth glide serenely along in our annual journey about the sun oblivious to the fact that we are travelling at $18\frac{1}{2}$ miles per second! And so perfect is the organization of the system that eclipses of the sun and moon can be precisely predicted indefinitely into the future.

The planets fall into two quite distinct groups. The minor planets – Mercury, Venus, Earth, and Mars – are relatively small and are solid; the major planets – Jupiter, Saturn, Uranus, Neptune, and Pluto – are vastly larger and are almost or entirely gaseous.

Mercury, the nearest to the sun, is only three thousand miles in diameter, and is too small to hold an atmosphere. It probably has a surface like that of the moon, but is too remote and too close to the sun for us to see craters if they exist. Mercury rotates so as to keep one side always facing the sun, and since it is only about 35 million miles away, and has no atmosphere to shield it, this side must be very hot.

Venus is slightly smaller than the earth (diameter 7,450 miles) and its mass is approximately four-fifths as great. But conditions on this planet are vastly different from those on the earth. The atmosphere of Venus is perpetually clouded so that the actual surface of the planet is never visible. Spectroscopic analysis of the reflected sunlight indicates that it is composed largely of carbon dioxide (CO_2) with lesser amounts of methane (CH_4) and ammonia (NH_3). No evidence has been seen of water and no free oxygen could exist in the presence of methane and ammonia [98]. The nature of the clouds is still an enigma but it has been suggested that they consist of dust particles.

The spectacular space probe of *Mariner II* in December, 1962,

39

revealed that although the upper layers of the atmosphere are cool, the temperature increases with depth and is about 800°F at the surface of the planet [83]. This surprising condition is attributed to the so-called 'greenhouse effect' resulting from the thick and relatively opaque atmosphere which allows the heat from the sun to penetrate to the surface of the planet but prevents its radiation back into space. Of course this temperature would prohibit any forms of life that we can imagine.

The *Mariner II* space probe also indicated that Venus, like Mercury, keeps one side constantly facing the sun. This may explain the added facts that the planet has no appreciable magnetic field and no Van Allen radiation belts such as those that girdle the earth. The significance of these observations is discussed on pages 65 and 111.

Mars is only a little more than half the diameter of the earth (4,200 miles) and is barely large enough to hold a tenuous atmosphere which, like that of Venus, consists largely of carbon dioxide (CO_2) with little, if any, water and no free oxygen. No clouds appear in its atmosphere but small white polar caps come and go with the seasons and are believed to be accumulations of hoar frost of frozen carbon dioxide. Photographs taken by the US satellite *Ranger IV* on 14 July 1965 reveal a barren cratered surface remarkably like that of the moon with no evidence of erosion. This indicates that the atmosphere of Mars has never been appreciably denser than it is at present.

Jupiter, the greatest of all the planets, has an apparent diameter of 88,600 miles and a volume more than a thousand times as great as the earth, but its low specific gravity (1·36) proves that it is almost entirely gaseous. Spectroscopic analysis of the sunlight reflected from the upper layers reveals ammonia as the dominant gas with methane in second place, but there is no evidence of water and free oxygen cannot be present, and the deeper part of the planet is believed to consist largely of hydrogen and helium. Wildt [169] has estimated that there is probably a solid core somewhat larger than the earth, consisting of compressed hydrogen and helium. Since the planet is so far from the sun, the surface temperature ranges between −100° and −140°C, and the clouds that mantle it are inferred to consist of frozen crystals of ammonia (just as the high cirrus clouds on earth are formed of ice particles).

Saturn, the great ringed planet, has an apparent diameter of 74,000 miles, but its mean density of only 0·72 indicates that it is completely gaseous. Its upper layers resemble those of Jupiter in being formed largely of methane and ammonia. No evidence has been seen of water, free oxygen, or nitrogen. The bulk of the planet is believed to consist of hydrogen and helium.

The more remote planets, Uranus, Neptune, and Pluto, are so far away that spectroscopic analysis of their reflected light is difficult and unsatisfactory, and we have little knowledge of their composition beyond the fact that they are gaseous bodies. At their vast distances from the sun they receive but little warmth and their surface temperatures are estimated to be more than 200°C below zero.

From this brief survey it is evident that the earth is a very minor planet circling the sun at the optimum distance to receive the amount of warmth and light needed for life. And in many ways it is a unique planet—the only one having abundant water and an atmosphere of nitrogen and free oxygen. We shall return to these peculiarities so vital for living things in chapter 8.

Satellites

Most of the planets have satellites. The earth has but one (the moon) but Mars has two, Jupiter twelve, Saturn nine, Uranus five, and Neptune two. Each satellite revolves around its planet in a nearly circular orbit and, with few exceptions, they revolve in the plane of the planetary orbits and in the same counter-clockwise direction. As exceptions, the eighth, ninth, and eleventh satellites of Jupiter revolve clockwise, and the orbits of the satellites of Uranus and Neptune lie at a large angle to that of the planets. These irregularities are believed to indicate that these satellites originally belonged to other planets and were captured by their present parents.

The asteroids are small solid objects ranging in size from a diameter of nearly five hundred miles down to the limit of visibility and below. They travel in independent orbits that occupy a wide belt between the orbits of Mars and Jupiter. There is a curious progression in the size of the orbits of the planets whereby, with one notable exception, each planet is nearly twice as far from the sun as the next nearer one. The exception would disappear if a planet occupied the position of the belt of asteroids. It seems probable that a planet once occupied this position and was disrupted by the tidal stresses produced as it repeatedly passed giant Jupiter. None of the asteroids is large enough to be seen satisfactorily, even with the largest telescopes, but recent observations have revealed that Eros, one of the largest of them, varies in brightness in a manner suggesting that it is a tumbling object of unequal dimensions. It comes nearer to the earth than any other of the asteroids, and in 1975 will pass within 14 million miles of us.

Meteors

The 'shooting stars' that streak across the night sky are meteors. Each is a solid body (a meteorite) heated to incandescence by friction as it plunges into our atmosphere. Some millions of them fall to earth daily, but most of them are no larger than sand grains and are completely vaporized before they reach the surface. Occasionally one of the larger ones gets through before being completely vaporized, and lands as a solid object, a meteorite (plate 10). They usually have a blackened surface with smoothed concavities, 'like a snow ball that has been licked by a warm tongue'. This is due to the heat produced by friction as they pass through the atmosphere – heat so intense as to vaporize the outer part, but so brief that it scarcely warms the interior. The Weston Meteorite was seen in flight, appearing first over Rutland, Vermont, as a 'fireball' about one-fourth the diameter of the moon and travelling at high velocity toward Connecticut where it was seen to fall. It was estimated to have a velocity of more than three miles per second at a height of some eighteen miles above the earth and appeared to have a diameter about two-thirds that of the moon before it broke up with a loud explosion and came raining to the ground near Weston, Connecticut, as a swarm of meteorites, several of which buried themselves below the sod in a pasture field. The one shown in plate 10 weighed about 33 pounds. The only meteorite known to have hit a human being crashed through the roof of a house in Sylacauga, Alabama, in 1954, and struck a woman on the thigh. It weighed about $8\frac{1}{2}$ pounds. Meteor Crater in Arizona (plate 9) resembles the explosion craters on the moon.

Meteors are of two sorts, one metallic and the other stony. The former consist of metallic iron with a small admixture of nickel. One of their most distinctive features is their very coarsely crystallized condition which shows up as the so-called Widmanstätten figures on polished slices. The stony meteorites are made of a variety of silicate minerals.

According to Fireman [51],

the metallurgical evidence indicates that (from an originally hotter condition) the iron meteorites cooled very slowly under high pressure until they reached a temperature of approximately 300°C; they remained at this temperature for at least fifty million years and then became cold. On the other hand, the study of the diffusion of the noble gases in the stony meteorites indicates that they were cooler than −150°C and under low pressure for almost all of their 4·5 billion year history.

In short, the meteorites are inferred to be fragments of a planetary body, the outer part of which was made of silicate minerals (as in the earth) and the interior of iron and nickel. Some fifty million years after formation it was disrupted to form the meteors that have been circling through cold space ever since. This was presumably the missing planet next beyond Mars and, from its composition, it was one of the solid minor planets. The meteorites appear to be fragments of asteroids that have escaped from the asteroidal belt.

At present there is very great interest in meteorites for several reasons. In the first place they give us samples of what the deep interior of an earth-like planet would be like, and their average composition probably approximates the average composition of the earth; and the ratio of metallic to stony meteorites should indicate the size of the metallic core of the earth. In the second place it is now possible (by means explained in chapter 2) to determine the date, in years, when the stony meteorites crystallized, and of the many that have been thus studied all indicate a date of near 4,500 million years BP. If they are fragments of a planet that was disrupted early in the history of the solar system they afford the best evidence we have of the time of the birth of the earth. This age is neatly confirmed, moreover, by the relative abundance of the three species of radiogenic lead (Pb^{206}, Pb^{207}, and Pb^{208}) as they exist on earth. Since they were formed at different and well-known rates we can calculate the time it would take to produce the existing ratios. It turns out to be approximately 4,500 million years.

Meteors travel in independent and highly elliptical orbits about the sun and commonly occur in swarms. The orbits of some of these swarms cross that of the earth and they reappear at regular intervals and from a fixed direction. It appears probable that since the disruption of the planet that lay beyond Mars, some of the fragments

passed near enough to Jupiter to be drawn from their normal course
into their present highly elliptical orbits.

Comets

Comets (plate 13) appear from time to time as faint, luminous objects
in the night sky, grow brighter as they approach the sun, and then
fade again in a period of months as they recede in highly elliptic
orbits. Each displays a dense nucleus or 'head', surrounded by a
gaseous envelope that streams out into a 'tail' that may be millions of
miles long.

In its journey about the sun a comet grows brighter and its tail
grows longer during its approach. The tail meanwhile is constantly
directed away from the sun, trailing behind as the comet approaches,
then swinging through a wide arc as the comet passes the sun, and
rushing ahead like the flame of a blow-torch as the comet recedes.
This behaviour clearly indicates that the tail is formed of particles
driven away from the head of the comet by the radiant energy of the
sun. Spectroscopic analysis of the light shows that the tail consists of
ionized gases, chiefly CO_2 and CN, and from this it is inferred that
the head of the comet consists of a solid mass, or masses, of the ices
of methane (CH_4), ammonia (NH_3), and carbon dioxide (CO_2) [13].

It may be noted in passing that meteorites resemble the minor
planets in their composition and that comets have much more in
common with the gaseous major planets.

Comets have been the subject of fear and superstition by primitive
people and were considered a portent of evil during the Middle Ages.
They sometimes cross the orbits of the planets and on rare occasions
one has come near collision with a planet, but their mass is known
to be trivial and there is no evidence that a comet ever affected the
majestic course of a planet. In 1886 Brook's Comet, having a previous period of twenty-seven years, came so close to Jupiter that it
was drawn into a smaller orbit in which it has since returned at
seven-year intervals, yet it failed to disturb the motion of even the
smallest satellites of Jupiter.

Our Galactic System

The ancients observed the belt of faint light that girdles the night
sky and called it the Milky Way. The great telescopes later resolved
this faint light into a myriad of individual stars too faint to be seen

by the naked eye because of their distance. Together with all the visible stars they form a vast system having the shape of a thin lens that is rotating upon its short axis. Because of the Milky Way it is termed a galaxy (Gr. *galacticos*, milk).

Light, travelling at 186,000 miles per second takes only about eight minutes to reach us from the sun, which is 93 million miles away; but from the nearest of the stars, Proxima Centauri, it requires about 4·2 years – and most of the stars are hundreds of thousands of light-years away.*

Our galaxy has an equatorial diameter of about 100,000 light-years and a polar diameter about one-tenth as great, and we are about 26,000 light-years from its centre [132]. It includes about 100,000 million stars each of which revolves in its orbit about the polar axis of the system. Although the system revolves as a unit, like a giant pinwheel in a fireworks display, the angular velocity decreases steadily with distance from the centre (as it does in our solar system), so that stars at the periphery make one revolution in about 230 million years whereas those near the axis require only about 120 million years for one revolution [120].

As we look out through the thin dimensions of the system the stars appear widely spaced and relatively bright, but as we turn our gaze toward the periphery the stars appear to be more and more numerous and more closely spaced, but most of them are faint because of their distance, and finally the most remote ones are lost in the faint glow of the Milky Way and can be distinguished only with the aid of the great telescopes. One has a comparable sensation when standing near a railroad track and studying the telegraph poles. Looking directly across the line the poles are near at hand and appear tall and widely spaced, but as one looks farther and farther down the line the poles become more closely crowded but shorter and shorter until they become indistinguishable in the distance.

Remote Galaxies

Thus far we have not seen all of our wonderful universe; far out beyond the Milky Way, 'like islands in a sea of space' are a thousand million or more other galaxies comparable to ours. The nearest of

* It is inconvenient to express distances among the stars in terms of miles, and the unit generally used is the light-year, which is the distance light can travel within a year's time. One light-year is a distance of almost six million million miles.

these and the only one visible to the naked eye is the Great Nebula in Andromeda (plate 14). It is about 900,000 light-years away and even through small telescopes it appears to be a faint fuzzy star; but the great telescopes resolve it into a vast system of individual stars. Other galaxies are much farther away, and with every increase in the size of our telescopes more and more come into view, so it is evident that we have not yet reached the limits of the universe. The great 200-inch telescope on Mount Palomar can detect such objects as much as two thousand million light-years away [132], and it is estimated that more than a thousand million galaxies of stars are now within its range.

The appearance of these galaxies depends on the angle at which we view them. When seen from a polar view (plate 15) they are circular but when viewed obliquely (plate 14) they appear elliptical, as does the great one in Andromeda. Others seen edge-on appear very slender (plate 16). By comparison of many, it is evident that each galaxy is a thin lenticular system of stars.

The stars within a galaxy are not evenly spaced, however, but are grouped into clumps or linear 'arms' which appear to be spirally twisted about the axis of rotation, as indeed they are. From this appearance it could be inferred that the galaxies are rotating about their short axis. Indeed only the centrifugal force due to rotation could prevent the stars in such a system from being drawn together into a single mass. This inference is completely confirmed by the spectroscope. When it is trained on opposite limbs of a galaxy seen from the edge view (plate 16), the shift in all the spectral lines proves that on one extreme the stars are approaching us at high velocity and at the opposite extreme they are receding at the same velocity.

Within recent years a still more remarkable discovery has come to light – these remote galaxies (not the stars in our own galaxy) are all receding from us at almost incredible speeds. And the farther they are from us the faster they are moving. For some of the nearest the calculated velocity is about one thousand miles per second, but for the most distant ones studied the velocity of sixty thousand miles per second [136] approaches one-third the speed of light! And since in all directions they are moving away from us it is now widely believed that the entire universe is expanding. If this is true, we can reverse the process, in imagination, and calculate that at a time some seven thousand million years ago all the galaxies were condensed into one great mass which then exploded with incredible violence and sent the fragments spinning away into space to evolve into widely spaced galaxies of stars. From such dizzy speculation we can only wonder if this was the beginning of creation or if we are only witnessing the expanding phase of a cycle of explosion and contraction of the universe in which stars and galaxies are born only to be drawn back eventually into a common melting pot and then be reborn again in another colossal explosion.

Although belief in an expanding universe is now widely held by those more competent than this writer to judge, it may not be presumptuous to express a word of caution. The supposed expansion rests on a single line of evidence—the 'red shift' in the spectral lines of the light coming to us from the remote galaxies. This means that the vibrations in the light rays have been lengthened. It can be proved experimentally that recession would produce this effect; but is there possibly some other, unknown cause that would produce the same effect? Arthur Compton has deduced that since a beam of light is a stream of discrete photons of energy, a photon can collide with a free electron and rebound elastically. In this case each object may add to or subtract from the energy of the other depending on their relative motions at impact. If the electron is stationary, the photon will rebound or glance off, expending part of its energy, and this would have the effect of increasing the wave length [33]. It is well known that elementary particles of many kinds are widely scattered through space and that their total mass is great. Can the 'Compton effect' increase the length of the vibrations as light travels millions of light years through space? If so, the 'red shift' would increase with the distance even if the source were stationary.

There is one other consideration to ponder. If we are part of an exploded and expanding universe, then since the galaxies are receding from us in all directions we must be relatively near the point of origin. What a strange coincidence if, after all, we are near the centre of the universe.

In any event, from the awesome view we now have of the universe, it is clear that the earth is only a mote in a vast sea of space following a star of very modest size toward an end that is beyond our comprehension. We may at once feel humble because of the earth's minor role in the universe and exalted that the human mind can comprehend this much.

Chapter 4

The Planet Earth:
1 The Lithosphere

A Model of the Earth

IT WILL simplify the following discussion if we begin with a model
showing what we know of the earth's interior (figure 13).

The crust, which includes all the rocks we know from direct obser-

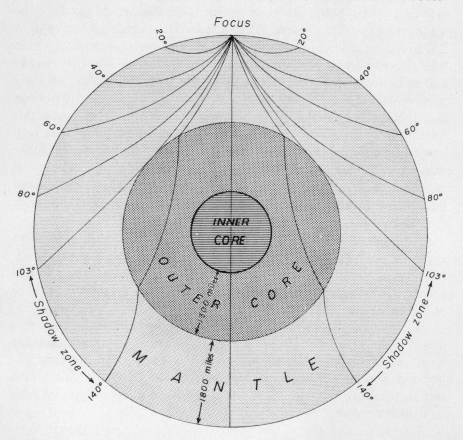

Figure 13. Diagram to illustrate the major structure of the earth

48

vation, is relatively thin. On the scale of our model it would fall within the thin surface line. It is therefore represented on a larger scale in figure 14. The term crust is inherited from the early days of geology when the earth was thought to be molten except for a thin crust of solid rock at its surface; its present connotation is explained on page 56.

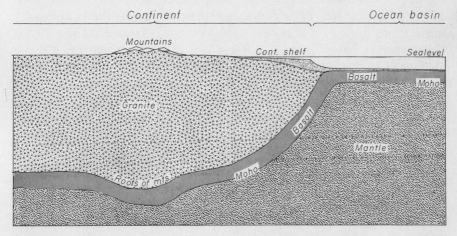

Figure 14. Diagram to illustrate the structure of the earth's crust

The mantle underlies the crust, extends to a depth of about 1,800 miles, and includes about 85 per cent of the volume of the earth. It is inferred to consist of silicate rock rich in iron and magnesium and to be denser and heavier than the crustal rocks.

The core is made of metallic iron of which the outer 1,400 miles is molten and the rest is solid.

Exploring the Deep Interior

Since the deepest wells do not penetrate even to the bottom of the crust our knowledge of the deep interior obviously rests upon inference. It is derived largely from a study of the seismic vibrations generated by earthquakes or from explosions at the surface. Waves of vibrations from such disturbances radiate in all directions into the earth and, if strong enough, they emerge at distant points on the surface where they can be recorded on seismographs. These deep seismic vibrations are of two sorts. Alternate pulses of compression and expansion produce compression waves in which particles oscil-

49

late back and forth in the line of propagation. Meanwhile, shear waves are generated in which particles oscillate at right angles to the line of flight. Compressional waves can be transmitted through either solid or fluid media, but shear waves are possible only in solids.

The speed with which seismic vibrations travel depends on the rigidity of the medium, and since the rigidity increases with the confining pressure the velocity of the seismic waves increases gradually with depth even in a homogeneous medium. As a result the vibrations do not travel in straight lines but curve outward toward the surface as indicated in figure 13. The reason for this is suggested by the behaviour of an automobile when the wheels on one side encounter mud or snow. The drag slows this side of the car and permits the opposite side to outrun it, deflecting the car toward the slower moving side.

The time lag between the instant of disturbance and the arrival of the vibrations at a distant station gives a measure of the average speed of the shock waves. Since different kinds of rock differ widely in rigidity each will impart a characteristic velocity to the vibrations that traverse it. The actual velocity has been determined experimentally for the major rock types. This is done by detonating a powerful explosion at the surface of a large area underlaid by a single type of rock and noting the time of arrival of the shock waves at stations at predetermined distances on the same body of rock. Thus, for example, it is known that in loose sediment the velocity of the compressional waves ranges between 1·5 and 2·5 km (0·9 to 1·5 miles) per second (depending on the depth and the degree of compaction of the sediment); it ranges between 3·0 and 3·5 km (1·8 to 2·1 miles) in sedimentary rocks (depending likewise on the depth and the degree of their consolidation); in granite it ranges from 6·2 km (3·7 miles) at shallow depths to 6·7 km (4·0 miles) per second at greater depths; and in basic rocks such as basalt and gabbro it is about 6·7 km per second. Finally, when the vibrations go deep enough to enter the mantle their velocity suddenly jumps to 8·1 or 8·2 km (4·86 to 4·92 miles) per second. Obviously the mantle rock is much more rigid than any of the crustal rocks.

Shear waves travel only about half as fast as the longitudinal waves and arrive later at any distant station. By this means seismologists can readily calculate the distance to a remote earthquake (or to an atomic bomb burst).

Obviously the seismic vibrations can tell us much about the nature of the rocks that lie hidden below the surface and we may now apply these principles to the study of the deep interior of the earth. In the first place the sudden increase in velocity when the seismic vibrations enter the mantle indicates that it is made of material more dense and rigid than any of the crustal rocks; and since the velocity then increases gradually with depth down to about 1,800 miles, we can infer that the mantle is relatively homogeneous throughout its depth.

However, when the vibrations enter the core, two striking and significant changes occur. First, the compressional vibrations are abruptly deflected deeper before gradually curving outward again. As a result they leave a 'shadow zone' between the distance of about 103° and 143° from the focal point of disturbance in which neither compressional nor shear vibrations appear. We must infer that at a depth of 1,800 miles they have encountered material that is less rigid than the mantle even under greater confining pressure. In the second place no shear waves appear in or beyond the shadow zone; they have been completely damped out upon entering the core and this can only mean that they have encountered fluid. In short, the outer core is molten. This also explains why the compressional waves were deflected downward at the interface between mantle and core; the molten material is, of course, less rigid than the mantle rock.

Finally, the compression waves that pass within less than eight hundred miles of the centre of the earth gain velocity and arrive on the opposite side sooner than they should if the core were uniform throughout; they evidently have passed through material more rigid than the fluid outer core. This is one of the bases for the belief that the inner core is solid.

So much for the physical state of the deep interior of the earth; its composition is inferred from other lines of evidence. There are three reasons, for example, for believing that the mantle consists of dunite or something closely similar. Dunite is a dark, dense rock made largely of the mineral olivine, a complex silicate very rich in iron and magnesium. It is heavier and more rigid than either granite or basalt.

Dunite is not normally found at the surface, but in several places where volcanoes have erupted through the deep ocean floor, chunks or masses of dunite appear in the lava, having been carried up as fragments from great depths. It appears probable that they are actual samples of the mantle. In the second place, dunite has the right weight and rigidity to account well for the velocity with which seismic vibrations travel in the mantle. Finally, experimental study of silicate melts by N. L. Bowen at the Geophysical Laboratory in Washington led him to conclude that if a molten earth having approximately the composition of gabbro had slowly cooled, the first mineral to crystallize out would be olivine, the mineral of which dunite is formed. As this mineral crystallized the remaining melt would be enriched in silica. He reasoned that if the earth at some stage were molten, it began to solidify deep in the interior where the pressure is enormous, and dunite formed progressively to produce the mantle until finally the residual melt near the surface was so enriched in silica as to form the granitic and basaltic rocks of the crust.

The case for a dunite mantle now seems highly convincing, but it must be noted that an alternative hypothesis has been advanced by some geophysicists. It is known that the atoms are spherical in shape, and that in crystals they are held together by powerful binding forces in a definite arrangement known as a space lattice. The atoms of each chemical element have a unique and measurable atomic radius, those of some elements being much larger than those of other elements. It is conceived that if the pressure were great enough to partially overcome the binding forces the atoms could be crowded more closely together; or small ones might be squeezed into the voids between larger ones; or new minerals might be formed having a closer atomic packing. Such crowding would make the material denser without altering its chemical composition. A change of this nature is a phase change. As a useful simile we may think of a barrel of oranges which, of course, do not fit tightly together. We might add to the weight of the barrel (1) by crushing the oranges, or (2) by adding smaller fruit that would fall into the voids between the oranges. Some students have thus reasoned that the mantle may be denser than the crustal rocks because of a phase change produced by the great pressure that exists in depths. This concept faces a serious difficulty, however. Since the pressure increases gradually with depth, such a phase change should occur at a fairly uniform depth all over the earth. On the contrary, the boundary between crust and mantle is four to five times as deep under the continents as it is under the ocean floors (figure 14). A difference in chemical composition therefore seems much more probable than a phase change.

An attempt is now under way to drill a well through the crust and bring up cores of the mantle rock for direct observation. This is the

Mohole Project, under the sponsorship of the National Academy of Sciences [8]. It is not feasible to drill on the continents where the crust is so thick; the best hope is to drill through the deep ocean floor where it is less than five miles thick. This, however, presents formidable technological problems. The drill rig, for example, must be mounted on an ocean-going vessel and the ship must be kept in a fixed position far from the sight of land, in spite of ocean currents and storm waves. Furthermore, the drill stem will be about seven miles long—two miles to reach the ocean floor and five more to reach through the crust. The drill must be withdrawn and returned into the hole at frequent intervals in order to set casings in the well and to renew the drill bit when it is dulled. The magnitude of this problem will be appreciated if we reduce the scale of the operation. Bascom [8] has illustrated the problem by the following simile. Imagine yourself atop a twelve-storey building dangling over its edge a small cold chisel attached to a slender wire. This will represent the bit and the drill stem. A half-inch hole in the ground will represent the well. It is dark and the wind is blowing gently. Your problem is to lower the chisel into the hole twelve storeys below and to withdraw and re-insert it repeatedly in total darkness. This is only one of the many technological problems to be solved. One other may be noted. If the water is two miles deep and the drill stem is made of $5\frac{1}{2}$ inch steel pipe, the stem will weigh about 250,000 pounds by the time it reaches the ocean floor and will buckle under its own weight and will crush the drill bit unless the whole string of tools be suspended from the vessel and very delicately controlled so as to exert only the pressure required to make the bit cut into the rock.

In the spring of 1960 three test wells were drilled near the Guada-lupe Islands about 150 miles west of Mexico where the water is about twelve thousand feet deep. The purpose was to develop techniques and to test the feasibility of drilling in deep water. Each well was started in the sediment that blankets the ocean floor. When each well penetrated basalt at a depth of about 560 feet drilling was stopped. It was then supposed that the wells had reached the fundamental basalt layer of the crust. Subsequent study of the fossils in the core has proved, however, that the oldest sediment resting on the basalt is of Miocene age [131], and, more recently, determination of the potassium–argon ratio in the basalt also indicates that it is of Miocene age [93]. It, therefore, represents a relatively young submarine lava flow and the probability seems great that older sedimentary rocks will be found below. One of the significant results of the Mohole Project may be the discovery of how much of the supposed basalt layer of the crust is actually basalt and how much is ancient, indurated sedimentary rock.

A much larger vessel will be required to carry the equipment for drilling down to the mantle, and at the present writing, negotiations are under way to secure such a vessel. The drilling techniques have been tested and found adequate and we can now hope that within a few years deep wells will penetrate the crust and bring up undoubted samples of the mantle rock. As a by-product of the Mohole Project, the techniques for drilling in deep water will be of great use in the search for submarine petroleum fields; but the immediate objectives are more fundamental. If the project is successful it will throw light on two of the greatest unsolved problems of the earth – the geologic history of the ocean basins and the source of the elemental forces that have formed the continents and uplifted the mountains on our ever-changing world.

The Metallic Core

The evidence of a metallic core is threefold. In the first place the average specific gravity of the earth (5·5) is almost twice that of any rocks that we know. Even granting that the enormous pressure in the deep interior would compress any material and make it denser than it is under surface pressures, it still seems probable that part of the deep interior is made of something heavier than rock; and if compression were responsible for the increased specific gravity in the core, the change should be gradual rather than abrupt as it is known to be at the interface between mantle and core. Furthermore, since the core is molten in spite of increasing pressure, it must be made of material of different composition from that of the mantle. It must have higher specific gravity and a lower melting point than the mantle rock. Iron would fit both these requirements.

The second line of evidence comes from meteorites which, if not actual fragments of a disrupted planet that once occupied a position between Mars and Jupiter, are fragments of smaller earthlike bodies such as the asteroids. The average composition of meteorites should therefore approximate the average composition of the earth. They fall generally into two classes: (1) stony meteorites made of silicate minerals; and (2) metallic meteorites made of iron with an admixture of nickel. As noted above, the core amounts to about fifteen per cent of the volume of the earth and the mantle eighty-five per cent. The ratio of metallic to stony meteorites is rather higher than this. Meteorites thus strongly imply that a considerable part of the earth should consist of iron. Furthermore, if, at any stage, the earth were molten, the iron, being heavier than silicates, should have settled to the centre.

Assuming, therefore, that the core is metallic, we may infer something as to the temperature deep within the earth. Before the present century it was generally assumed that the interior heat was inherited from an original molten stage; but since the discovery of radioactivity it seems evident that heat is being generated constantly by radioactive elements in the rocks. It escapes at the surface by conduction, but rock is a very poor conductor and the heat must tend constantly to build up in the deep interior. From the core there are two possible modes of escape: (1) It may pass with almost infinite slowness by conduction through hundreds of miles of silicate rocks that make up the mantle and the crust; and (2) since we know that the mantle rock can flow, it seems possible that if heat builds up sufficiently, convection currents are generated in the mantle similar to those that rise over a flame in a vessel of thick syrup. If so, the hottest part of the mantle would slowly well up to near the surface where heat could be passed through the crust by conduction. We shall return to the concept of convection currents in the mantle.

Our immediate concern is the probable temperature of the metallic core. Under surface pressures iron melts at about 1,500°C but from laboratory experiments it is known that with increasing pressure the melting point rises and should reach about 3,000°C under the pressure that exists at the bottom of the mantle. However, it should not greatly exceed 4,000°C under the pressures that exist at the centre of the earth. And since the inner core is not molten we must infer that the temperature in the outer core is probably between 3,000°C and 4,000°C.

The Crust

The sharp distinction between crust and mantle was discovered in 1909 by a Hungarian geophysicist, Andrija Mohorovicic. From an analysis of the records of many earthquakes scattered over central Europe he found that seismic vibrations that had gone deeper than about twenty-five miles arrived at distant stations sooner than expected, indicating that at greater depth their velocity had been abruptly increased by about two kilometres per second. The basement under the continent consists predominately of granitic rocks which are exposed in many places, and the velocity of seismic waves indicate that such rocks persist to a depth of about twenty-five miles. The sudden increase in velocity at that depth proves, however, that the deeper rocks are much more rigid than granite. The boundary between these two types of rock soon came to be known as the Mohorovicic discontinuity or, in common parlance, the Moho. Further study in other regions has given cumulative and conclusive evidence that this is a general phenomenon – each of the continents is underlaid by a vast plate of granitic rocks resting on the mantle. On this basis the crust is now defined to include the rocks above the Moho. Unlike the continents, the ocean basins are underlaid by basalt or rocks of comparable weight and density, with a relatively thin veneer of sediments (figure 14).

If we could strip the earth of its oceans and see its bare rocky surface as we do the moon, the continents and ocean basins would be its most conspicuous features. The continents would be seen as vast relatively flat plateaus standing about three miles above the ocean floors. Compared with these major features the mountains would appear local and almost trivial, like the decorations on a cake. In spite of erosion that is constantly wearing down the lands, moreover, the continents have thus stood high above the ocean basins for at least two or three thousand million years.

The reasons for this is now at least partially understood. Since the crust floats on a mantle capable of yielding, the granitic plates that form the continents ride high because they are relatively light as compared with the basalt that floors the oceans. They float in equilibrium even as the great tabular icebergs float partly above water in the polar seas. Thus we creatures of the lands find ourselves like penguins riding icebergs of granite. It is only incidental that water stands about a half mile below the average level of the continents.

Rocks of the Crust

The crust has grown by the rise of material sweated out of the depths in a molten condition. In places the rising magma has reached the surface to explode into volcanic activity or to spill out more gently in vast lava flows; but for the most part it has come to rest before reaching the surface and, in cooling slowly, has crystallized to form granular rocks such as granite and basalt. All such rocks 'born of fire' are termed igneous (L. *ignis*, fire) and large masses that have crystallized at considerable depth are termed plutonic, after the Greek god, Pluto, ruler of the underworld.

As we now know, the mantle is solid, and melting has occurred only locally so that igneous activity is confined to particular regions, but the geologic records show that regions now quiet have at times in the past been the scene of great igneous activity. The heat required for melting is almost certainly due to radioactivity, but the reason for the localization of the melting has long been a moot question. It now seems probable that it may be due to the slow rise of convection currents in the mantle. The melting point rises with an increase in pressure and falls with a decrease. In the earth the confining pressure due to the weight of all the overlying rock increases rapidly with depth. At a depth of five miles, for instance, it exceeds fifteen tons per square inch; at ten miles it is more than thirty tons; and at twenty-five miles it is about eighty tons per square inch; and at a depth of one thousand miles it is almost inconceivable. Even at high temperature, therefore, mantle rock that is solid at great depth would tend to melt when brought to higher levels.

Because the melting point varies from mineral to mineral a rising mass of mantle rock probably would soften as the minerals with the lowest melting point become fluid. Under the enormous pressure the liquid parts would tend to be squeezed out as water may be squeezed from a sponge. For two reasons the fluid would then tend to rise. In the first place melting involves expansion and the liquid phase is lighter than the solid; and in the second the pressure can only be relieved by upward movement. The molten material under colossal hydrostatic pressure is thus forced upward along fractures into the crust.

The behaviour of the magma as it approaches the surface depends on its composition, its temperature, and the amount of water and other volatiles contained, as well as the nature of the rocks into which it is intruded. Figure 15 indicates the chief spatial relations of masses of igneous rocks.

If the magma stands for long ages within a magma chamber before cooling enough to crystallize, different components may separate as cream separates from milk or oil from water, and components of

57

different composition may segregate in different places. Thus, from a common magma source several different varieties of igneous rock may be formed. Rocks that are rich in SiO_2 are called acidic. Acidic magmas generally include a relatively large amount of volatiles and if they reach the surface they generally form explosive volcanoes because the sudden release of pressure allows the gases to expand into bubbles which then burst their walls as the lava is blasted into the air. This reduces it to small fragments – lapilli and volcanic 'ash'

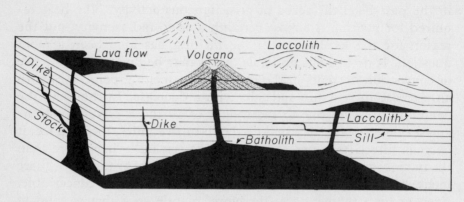

Figure 15. Idealized diagram to show the chief forms of igneous rock masses. Batholiths are the largest and have no known floor. Laccoliths are blisters with an arched roof and a floor. Dikes are sheet-like fillings of crevices and may run in any direction. Sills are thin sheets forced between layers of bedded rocks. A stock is a cupola arising from a batholith

– which fall back to build a volcanic cone with a crater at the summit. Since this makes a weak cinder-like deposit, when the cone has reached considerable height the rising lava column commonly breaks through the sides and flows out to spread down the slopes.

Magmas rich in the bases, iron, magnesium and calcium, are termed basic. They generally have a lower melting point and carry less volatiles than the acidic magmas and commonly are more fluid and may spread widely in sheets only a few feet thick. Successive flows issuing at intervals of a few to many years may thus build up a thick and widespread deposit of layered beds of lava (plate 17). Such are the plateau lavas that in several parts of the world have covered very large areas. The Columbia River Plateau, for example, covers parts of five of the north-western states and has an area of some two hundred thousand square miles (figure 16). Here basaltic lavas flowed out over a region of considerable relief, first filling the low places and eventually covering the highlands to build a broad, nearly flat plateau. The Columbia and Snake rivers have since cut deep canyons that reveal a thickness of as much as four thousand feet of lava disposed in extensive layers that range generally from fifteen to forty feet thick. Buried soils and fossil vegetation between layers

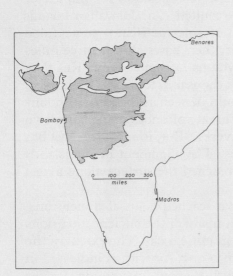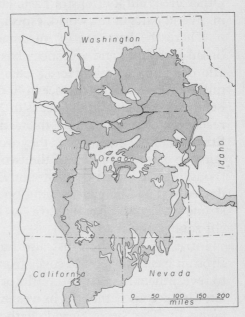

Figure 16. Maps showing the extent of two great fields of plateau basalt. Left, the Deccan Plateau of India, after Wadia; right, the Columbia Basalt Plateau of Oregon and Washington, which is of Miocene age (darker shading), and similar basalt flows of Pliocene age in Oregon, northern California, Nevada, and Idaho, after the geologic map of the United States

prove that the flows came at intervals of many years and that intermittent eruptions occurred over a span of several million years. The lava came not from a central vent but from many vents, probably along great fissures in the crust and the lava must have been very hot and fluid to have spread so widely. The total volume of the lavas has been estimated at twenty-four thousand cubic miles. Most of the flows occurred during Miocene time, but locally, as in the Snake River Basin, they continued into near recent time and in the Valley of the Moon in Oregon the surface appears as fresh as a modern lava flow.

59

The Deccan Plateau in peninsular India resembles the Columbia Plateau and has an area of at least two hundred thousand square miles, but here the lava was extruded late in Cretaceous time or in the Eocene epoch. A similar vast outpouring of basaltic lavas in late Triassic or early Jurassic time covered some three hundred thousand miles of Brazil and ranges in thickness up to two thousand feet. Other great outpourings of basic lavas are known in the older rocks in several parts of the world, especially in Precambrian rocks.

Where the lavas are of intermediate composition a complex of broad lava flows and volcanoes has resulted. The Hawaiian Islands afford a fine example. Here a chain of volcanic islands some 1,600 miles long rises from the ocean floor, their bases almost three miles below sea level and in the peaks of Mauna Loa and Mauna Kea they reach an elevation about thirteen thousand feet above the sea. Stripped of the ocean water they would be seen as the loftiest mountains on earth, the peaks of the two great volcanoes rising some two thousand feet higher than Mount Everest. But, in part, the lava has flowed out and spread in low slopes. The alignment of the islands strongly suggests that the lava has reached the surface along a vast rift zone in the crust.

Intrusives into the crust also have reached colossal dimensions. Erosion has removed the cover from many of the ancient intrusions to reveal them as great batholiths of granitic rocks. The extent of the late Cretaceous batholiths in western North America is indicated in figure 17. The Sierra Nevada batholith is about four hundred miles long and eighty miles wide and the Coast Range batholith extends for some 1,100 miles along the western margin of Canada. Detailed study of such great granitic masses shows that none is the result of a single intrusion. Each is a complex of intrusives that were driven into the crust during a long span of time. The most impressive display of batholithic intrusions are seen, however, in the so-called 'shields' of the continents (figure 18). Each of the continents has at least one nucleus of very ancient, largely granitic, rocks now exposed by long erosion. It is here that the most ancient dated rocks are found. Here the structure records mountains of great magnitude and complexity; but the mountains are long since gone and their roots have been laid bare by long erosion. They are now the most stable parts of the continent as well as the oldest, and they form broad low plateaus very gently arched up at the centre like ancient battle shields, whence the name. Until 1883 it was generally supposed that they were parts of the primaeval crust of the earth. But in that year A. C. Lawson working in the southern part of the Canadian Shield found that remnants of the oldest sedimentary formations were intensively deformed and intruded by the underlying granite [104]. In

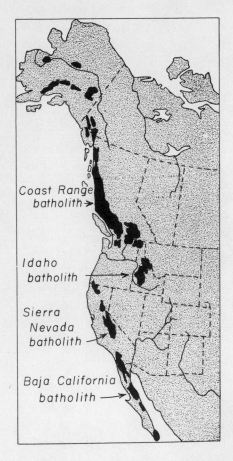

Coast Range
batholith →

Idaho
batholith →

Sierra
Nevada
batholith

Baja California
batholith →

Figure 17. Map showing the distribution of mid-Cretaceous batholiths in western North America

short, the granite is younger, not older, than the covering sedimentary rocks. A shield consists of a complex of many batholithic intrusions that once formed the cores of ancient and departed mountain systems. In 1883 this was a sensational discovery, but subsequent study has proved that in all the shields the granite is intrusive and younger than the oldest of the overlying sedimentary rocks. No single place is known where any portion of the primaeval crust of the earth still exists.

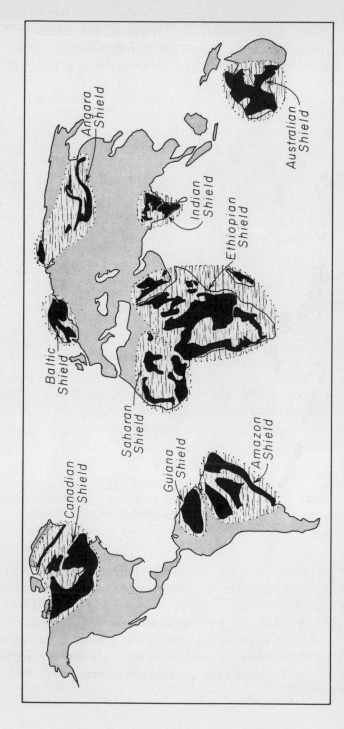

Figure 18. Map showing the ancient shields of the continents. Black indicates outcrops of the ancient Precambrian rocks

One is tempted to imagine that during the early history of the earth the upwelling of magmas took place on a fantastic scale, but this is probably not justifiable. The ancient rocks of the shields represent more than five-sixths of all geologic time and we see here the cumulative effects of billions of years. The crust has grown – and is still growing.

The dating of these ancient granites has revealed another fundamental truth about the earth – the oldest rocks are within the shields and as we go toward the margins of the continents the intrusives are progressively younger (figure 19). In short the continents have grown larger throughout geologic time by lateral accretion [44; 171]. The shields are the ancient nuclei of the continents and although once the scene of great diastrophic changes they have now become the most stable regions of the land surface. The reasons we shall seek in chapter 11.

Igneous rocks comprise the primary category of rocks of the crust, but there are two others. The first of these includes the sedimentary rocks. Throughout geologic time the exposed igneous rocks have been under the attack of the forces of weathering and erosion and the products have been carried away as sediment (mud, sand, and gravel) by wind and running water. From the uplands it is transported to lower elevations to be widely spread as layers of mud and sand. Much of it eventually reaches the sea where waves and bottom currents sort and spread it, but it may also accumulate in structural basins on the land. Such layers of sediment eventually become compact and solidify into bedded layers of stone (sandstone, shale, limestone, etc.). From time to time in the past many parts of the continents have been submerged beneath shallow seas that crept in over the lowlands, and the sedimentary rocks thus laid down on the continents now form much of the land surface. Animals and plants buried in the accumulating sediments were commonly preserved as fossils that give us a vital record of the history and evolution of life on the earth (see chapter 12). Over great areas the sedimentary rocks form a relatively thin veneer over the granitic basement (commonly not over a few thousands of feet thick), but in great structural basins that slowly subsided over a period of millions of years their thickness is measured in tens of thousands of feet. Most of the sediment carried to the edge of the continents is deposited within a hundred miles or so of the shore where it accumulates to great thickness building out the continental shelves. Part of it is carried far out to sea, however, and

Figure 19. Map to show evidence of peripheral growth of the North American continent. The dots mark localities where ages have been determined by radio-active isotopes. In a large area in the centre of the Canadian shields the dates range from 2·5 thousand million to 3·2 thousand million years. A small area farther north also exceeds 2·5 thousand million years in age. A wide belt surrounding the central area gives dates between 1·0 and 2·5 thousand million years. In the marginal belt the ages are generally less than six hundred million years. Adapted from figures by Engel [44]

the ocean floors are covered by a relatively thin veneer of sediments.

A third category of the rocks of the crust are the metamorphics. These may represent either igneous or sedimentary rocks that have been altered by heat and/or pressure and have suffered recrystallization or other mineralogical and structural changes that mask or alter their original nature. Metamorphism takes many forms. Common examples are the recrystallization of limestone into marble, the cementation of sandstone to form quartzite, and the alteration of clay shale into slate. Where pressure is very great as within the depths of growing mountains, the original mineral crystals, oriented at random, are regrown with their least dimensions at right angles to the compressional force. As a result granitic rocks become layered and have a banded appearance (plate 18). Such layered granular rock is gneiss. Under comparable stresses mudrocks (shales) tend to recrystallize as micas and become slate, and if sufficiently altered form schist. Finally, it now appears likely that, under static conditions, heat and permeating volatiles may cause recrystallization in depth of a wide variety of sedimentary or igneous rocks into granite which is lithologically indistinguishable from primary igneous granite [55].

The concept of granitization is still a subject of controversy and has been hotly debated in recent years but seems to be gaining favour. Proponents of the idea cite instances where a regional complex of sedimentary or igneous rocks can be traced laterally with increasing alteration until it grades into granite. If this concept proves to be valid we may need to consider, after all, that part of the shield granite may not be plutonic and could even include portions of the original crust now altered beyond recognition, and the granitization may have occurred locally at times in the distant past.

The Earth as a Magnet

Early navigators depended on the North Star for their bearings at night and were severely handicapped by cloudy skies and fog. The invention of the magnetic compass was therefore a great boon to navigation. The place and date of this discovery is unknown, but the earliest design consisted of a magnetized needle floated on a sliver of wood or straw, and since it pointed north and south it was supposed in some manner to be attracted by the North Star. It came into use at least as early as the twelfth century, but it was not until 1600 that William Gilbert showed that the earth is a magnet with north and south magnetic poles and that, since opposite poles of magnets attract each other, the south pole of the compass needle is directed toward the north magnetic pole of the earth. The earth's magnetic poles do not correspond closely in position with the axis of rotation, however, so the compass needle does not point toward the north pole but to the north magnetic pole which lies near Prince Albert Island in longitude 100° west and about 70° north. This is about 1,054 miles south of the north pole. Accordingly the compass needle points true north only along the 100th meridian.

The reason for the earth's magnetism has long been a complete enigma but in recent decades it has assumed unexpected importance. The earth's magnetic field, for example, is responsible for the recently discovered Van Allen belts, discussed in chapter 6. It is the basis, moreover, of the new discipline of paleomagnetism that poses far-reacting concepts about the history of the earth and the position of the continents. It has been discovered, for example, that fine magnetic particles of sediment carried in suspension align themselves like the compass needle and settle with one pole directed toward the earth's north magnetic pole, being thus locked into position in the rocks. Their present orientation in the rocks of any past age (e.g. the Permian System) should therefore indicate the position of the magnetic poles at that time, or at least the orientation of the land mass with respect to the magnetic poles. The conclusions now being drawn from such evidence are at once puzzling and spectacular as indicated in chapter 11.

Our present knowledge of the deep interior of the earth has led to a plausible explanation of the earth's magnetism. According to modern theory [41] the earth is a dynamo by which its iron core is made a colossal magnet. It has long been known that if an insulated wire is wrapped around a soft iron bar the bar is magnetized by induction when an electric current passes through the wire. It loses its magnetism when the current is turned off but is immediately magnetized again when the current is turned on. This is the principle used in many industrial applications, notably the powerful magnets with which scrap iron is handled. Now if any electric current exists in the earth's mantle or its liquid core the rotation of the earth must carry it round and round the solid iron core. The source of such electric current or currents is unknown but is conceived to be due to chemical irregularities in the constituents of the earth which separated positive and negative charges and thus initiated currents of electricity as in a storage battery. If so, the rotation of the earth would make of it a dynamo transforming the energy of motion into more electricity, and thus maintaining its effectiveness as a dynamo.

Although the original current is too feeble to be effective on a small scale, electromagnetic theory indicates that its effectiveness increases exponentially with the size of the dynamo and on the scale of the earth it would be self-sustaining [41].

The lines of force in an electromagnetic field are easily illustrated by laying a sheet of paper over a small bar magnet and dropping iron filings over the paper. The filings immediately align themselves with the lines of force (figure 20). Of course this shows the lines of force

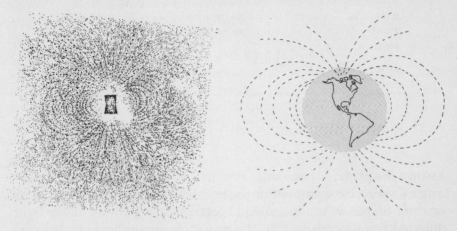

Figure 20. Left, iron filings sprinkled on a sheet of paper overlying a small bar magnet orient themselves with the magnetic lines of force. Right, diagram to indicate magnetic lines of force about the earth

in a single plane, but they also exist in all planes at right angles to the axis of the magnet, emerging at the poles of the magnet and curving around from one pole to the opposite. Thus the earth is the centre of an electromagnetic field that extends far out in space and is responsible for the Van Allen belts discussed in chapter 6.

Chapter 5

The Planet Earth:
2 The Hydrosphere

It was assuredly not chance that led Thales to found philosophy and science with the assertion that water is the origin of all things. . . . From that day to this the unique position of water has never been shaken. It remains the most familiar and the most important of all things.

HENDERSON, *The Fitness of the Environment*

AMONG the planets of our solar system the earth is unique in possessing an appreciable amount of water. Mercury is almost certainly as dry and barren as the moon and spectroscopic analysis of the light reflected from Venus and all the major planets indicate little or no water vapour. It has been suspected that there may be a little moisture in the tenuous atmosphere of Mars, but the planet certainly has no standing water. In contrast, about sixty-five per cent of the earth's surface is covered by oceans which have an average depth of some fifteen thousand feet and a volume of about 300 million cubic miles. From this vast reservoir water vapour rises into the atmosphere to fall as rain or snow over the lands, feeding the streams and springs, maintaining the moisture in the soil, and filling the reservoirs of water underground.

In his fascinating book, *The Fitness of the Environment*, Henderson has shown the significant role of water in conditioning the earth as an abode for life [74]. Some of the following paragraphs have drawn heavily on that source. It is no accident that of all the planets in our solar system Earth is the only one with abundant life, and that if there be any living things on Mars, they are only lowly plants. It appears probable that some of the remote stars in the universe have planets peopled by living creatures, but if so, we may be sure that they resemble Earth in having abundant water.

The Great Thermostat

When heat is applied to an object its temperature rises, and as it cools again to its original temperature an equivalent amount of heat must escape. The amount of heat involved is a measure of its heat capacity or, technically, its specific heat. The fundamental unit in which heat is measured is the calorie, which is the amount required to raise the temperature of one gram of pure water $1°C$. Since this is chosen as the standard, the specific heat of water is $1 \cdot 0$. The important fact is, however, that each substance has its individual heat capacity, as suggested in table 2, and that water is almost unique in having such a high value.

TABLE 2
*Specific heat of representative
substances, after Henderson*

Ammonia	1·23
Water	1·00
Alcohol	0·50—0·70
Chloroform	0·24
Marble	0·22
Glass	0·20
Quartz	0·19
Iron	0·10
Lead	0·03

The heat capacity of water is about five times as great as that of the minerals of which rocks are made and ten times as great as that of the metals. Accordingly, a given amount of heat will raise the temperature of a unit quantity of rock about five times as high as it would an equal quantity of water. This is one of the reasons why on a summer day bare rock or a paved street becomes so much hotter than the surface of an adjacent pond or lake, and why a scrap of metal in the street is so much hotter than the pavement. It also explains, in part, why on a hot day the land heats up faster than the adjacent sea, producing a sea breeze blowing landward, and why on a cold day the land cools faster, reversing the wind direction toward the sea. The mild, equable climate of oceanic islands is due to the stabilizing influence of the surrounding water. For the same reason the fluctuations of temperature are not nearly as great in coastal areas as in continental interiors.

The high specific heat of water also has a dramatic effect on the

69

temperature of living creatures, since their bodies are about nine-tenths water. An iron man's temperature would fluctuate about ten times as fast and as far as that of a human being.

The heat exchange involved in a change of phase, from solid to liquid or from liquid to vapour, is known as latent heat. To melt a gram of ice, for example, requires the absorption of eighty calories of heat, and to freeze it again requires the liberation or removal of an equivalent amount of heat. This is a measure of the latent heat of fusion of water. As a result, when the temperature hovers about the freezing point, water is a powerful stabilizer of temperature giving off heat when ice is forming and absorbing heat when the ice melts. As shown in table 3, the latent heat of fusion of water is almost uniquely high, being exceeded only by that of ammonia.

TABLE 3

Latent heat of fusion (in calories)
of representative substances, after Henderson

Ammonia	108
Water	80
Copper	43
Glycerine	42·5
Benzine	30·1
Sulphuric acid	24
Iron	23–33
Menthol	18·9

The latent heat of evaporation is even more remarkable. To evaporate one gram of water requires the expenditure of 536 calories of heat, and when one gram of water vapour condenses again, an equivalent amount of heat is released. This means that the evaporation of one gram of water absorbs as much heat as would be required to raise the temperature of 536 times as much water by 1°C. For this reason, also, water exerts a profound influence on climate. As the temperature in a warm region rises, evaporation increases and a vast amount of heat is absorbed, and when the moisture is carried by the winds into cooler regions where it condenses into rain, an equal amount of heat is released. As indicated in table 4, the latent heat of evaporation of water far exceeds that of any other substance. Nothing else in nature would be an effective substitute.

According to Henderson, evaporation in the equatorial region removes about 2·3 metres of water from the surface of the oceans annually. This absorbs more than 1,000 million million calories of heat per square kilometre. The effect of this evaporation is to moderate the temperature in the tropics, and when the moisture is carried by the atmosphere into higher latitudes to condense as rain or snow, all this heat is released again, moderating the temperature of the colder regions. Thus the moisture in the atmosphere serves as a vast thermostat regulating the temperature over the earth's surface.

TABLE 4

Latent heat of evaporation (in calories) of representative substances, after Henderson

Water	536
Ammonia	295
Ethyl alcohol	236·5
Acetone	125·3
Nitric acid	115
Benzene	109
Aniline	93·3
Ether	90·4
Carbon dioxide	72·2
Chloroform	67

The mammals have taken advantage of this unique quality of water in developing their amazing thermostat, the sweat gland. Anyone who has worked in the desert will remember the experience of stopping to rest in the shade of a tree or a ledge of rock, wet with sweat, and shortly to find himself shivering. The rapid evaporation of sweat in the dry desert air has absorbed heat so fast that one feels chilly even in the presence of the desert heat. It is for this reason also that one may be reasonably comfortable in a warm room through which a breeze is blowing whereas he would be miserable in a room of equal temperature in which the windows are closed so that evaporation is inhibited. A 150 pound man weighs 68,250 grams (of which about 48,000 grams is water and 20,250 is bone and tissue). To reduce his temperature by 10°C (or to prevent it from rising by 10°C) will require the removal of about 520,000 calories. This will be accomplished by the evaporation of about 970 grams, or just over 2 pints, of sweat. Of course, a vigorously exercising man on a hot day will drink several times this much water, most of which is discharged as sweat.

Another important quality of water is its high vapour tension which determines the amount of vapour that can be held in the atmosphere when in contact with the liquid phase. The vapour tension of water varies enormously with the temperature as indicated in table 5. Thus the amount of water vapour that can be held in the atmosphere is very great at high temperature and slight at low temperature. As a result, evaporation is rapid in warm places, but as the temperature drops the moisture tends to be precipitated as rain. The very great range of its vapour tension therefore makes water the most important factor in meteorology.

TABLE 5

The effect of temperature on the vapour tension of water, the temperature expressed in degrees centigrade and the tension in millimetres of water, after Henderson

0°	4·58
10°	9·18
30°	31·55
50°	54·97
80°	355·47
100°	760·00

Finally, water has another unique quality of vast importance. Other liquids increase in density as the temperature drops to the melting point so that the solid phase is heavier than the liquid. Water obeys this rule until the temperature falls to 4°C and then it begins to expand. As a result, ice is lighter than water and floats at the surface. If water continued to shrink at low temperature, as other liquids do, the ice formed during cold weather would sink to the bottom where it would be insulated by the water above. Thus in the course of time most lakes in the temperate zone would remain largely frozen, the polar seas would be solid ice, and even the ocean basins would be largely filled with ice. On the contrary, because ice floats, that which freezes during the winter is largely melted again during the summer, icebergs drift away from the polar regions to melt in warmer seas, and even the floe ice in the Arctic region does not exceed a few tens of feet in thickness. Moreover, in the presence of ice the temperature of the surrounding water remains almost constant; added heat merely melts part of the ice and the removal of heat merely causes part of the water to freeze.

In two other respects water serves as a great thermostat for the earth. Ocean currents profoundly modify the climate of the lands. The Gulf current in the Atlantic, for example, carries warmth to all of western Europe while the cold Labrador current sweeps southward along the eastern coast of Canada (figure 35, page 99). London lies on the latitude of the Strait of Belle Isle, Berlin is opposite Goose Bay, Labrador, and northern Norway lies opposite the centre of the Greenland ice cap. Thus the most densely populated part of western Europe lies in the same latitude as the almost uninhabited barrens of Labrador and southern Greenland. One is tempted to speculate on the climatic changes that would ensue in Europe if the Isthmus of Panama were submerged so that the warm equatorial current could sweep through into the Pacific instead of being turned north to form the Gulf current. The effect would undoubtedly be profound. In the Pacific Ocean the Japan current brings warmth and moisture to the coast of Oregon and Washington and from there north along the southern coast of Alaska which is in the latitude of eastern Siberia.

At present about ten per cent of the land surface of the earth is desert, and the great deserts lie mostly in the interior of the great continents. If the continents were partly submerged so that interior seas spread over the lowlands, dividing the land into smaller units, such seas would be vast reservoirs to supply moisture and moderate the temperature. The geologic record shows clearly that this has actually happened many times in the past and that at such times the climate has been more equable and climatic zones much less strongly differentiated than they are at present.

Thus, in many ways water serves as a great thermostat modifying the climate of the earth. In stark contrast stands the naked moon with a temperature range of about 300°C – its rocky surface being heated to about 150°C during the lunar day and cooling to 150°C below zero during the night.

In summary, water serves as a powerful agent to regulate and moderate the temperature of the earth, and to control the temperature in living bodies. In these respects it is unique; no other substance in nature would serve as an adequate substitute.

Yet another important quality of water is its efficiency as a universal solvent. No other fluid has equal capacity to dissolve virtually every known solid. This is one of the reasons why water is such an important agent in the weathering of rocks, reducing them to fragments that can be carried away by wind or running water. For this reason also the oceans are a vast reservoir of dissolved minerals and foods required by the teeming hordes of living creatures in the sea. It is vital also in the metabolism of all living creatures, for all the food

73

enters our bodies in aqueous solution and all the waste products of metabolism are removed in solution. Water is the universal solvent capable of carrying in solution at least small quantities of all the elements needed by living organisms.

Realms of the Sea

At present, marine waters more than fill the ocean basins and flood the margins of the continental platforms. The submerged margins constitute the continental shelf. At the seaward margin of the shelf the bottom slope breaks off more steeply down over the continental margin and then gradually flattens out to merge with the deep ocean floor. The sediment derived from the land is spread across the continental shelf by the waves and bottom currents and most of it eventually comes to rest here or at its seaward margin. The shelf is thus, in general, a vast constructional terrace (though in areas of tectonic disturbance it is in part structural).

In the sea, depth is a major factor determining the living conditions and the physical forces that operate. For this reason the sea is divided into depth zones as indicated in figure 21.

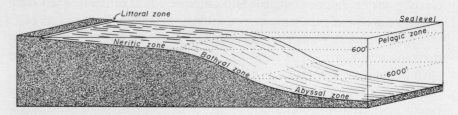

Figure 21. Depth zones in the sea

The littoral zone lies between extreme high and low tide limits and is alternately flooded and exposed as the tide rises and falls. It is relatively narrow even where the coast is low and the tides are high. Along sea cliffs it is a mere line, and even where the sea advances over a flat and gently sloping surface the waves and currents cut a concave profile to below low tide limit that keeps the intertidal zone narrow. Its greatest width is seen in the large deltas where sediment is introduced faster than the sea can transport it and the land is built out. In such places three sub-zones may be recognized; (1) the salt marsh flooded once each month by the highest tides, (2) the beach or shore face, and (3) the mud-flat which is exposed only at low tide (figure 22). In large deltas the salt marsh may attain a width of twenty-five to thirty miles but elsewhere it is generally less than a mile wide; and where the tidal range is great, as in the Bay of Fundy, the mud flat may be as much as four or five miles wide so that at extreme low tide the sea is scarcely visible from the shore. With such local exceptions the littoral zone is rarely more than a quarter of a mile wide.

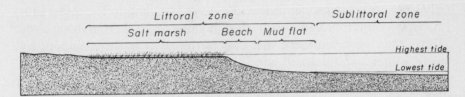

Figure 22. Profile across the tidal zone

For most organisms this is an inhospitable environment, alternately flooded by salt water and exposed to the atmosphere. Occasionally it is drenched by fresh water during heavy rains or when streams are in flood. It also suffers the maximum of short-term temperature changes. In the temperate zone it may be covered with ice in mid-winter and be quite warm on a summer day; and in both temperate and torrid zones mass mortality occurs occasionally when extreme low tide falls during the hottest part of a summer day and animals are literally cooked in their shells.

The salt marshes are covered by a few kinds of plants that can tolerate either fresh, brackish, or salt water, but most plants cannot endure such drastic changes. Barnacles, oysters, blue clams and certain snails survive by resting with their shells tightly closed when the tide is out, and certain crabs, boring clams and many worms burrow into the mud and sand for protection. Creatures that can thus protect themselves have relatively few predator enemies and thrive in great abundance, but the number of kinds so adapted is relatively small.

The neritic zone extends from the low tide limit to the break in slope at the edge of the continental shelf. Before the present century oceanographers generally assumed that storm waves and bottom currents were effective to a depth of six hundred feet and that the continental shelf was graded to this level. For this reason the one hundred fathom line is conspicuously marked on marine charts. It is now evident, however, that the break in slope does not follow this line closely but ranges in depth from about three hundred feet to more than six hundred feet depending on the degree of exposure to the great storm waves of the open ocean, the contour of the land, the prevailing climate, and the amount of recent crustal warping.

For the most part the floor of the neritic zone is a monotonous plain sloping very gently seaward. Off the mid-Atlantic coast of the United States the average slope to a depth of three hundred feet is only about five inches per mile and a diver standing in the midst of it probably could not distinguish enough slope to guide him toward the shore. The loose sediment that covers the shelf is shifted about by storm waves and tidal and wind-driven currents. Depressions serve as traps to catch the sediment until they are filled, and elevations are planed down as the loose sediment is picked up and shifted to lower places. Thus the sea floor is kept nearly flat.

Local irregularities occur, especially near shore where strong tidal currents keep open channels in the sea floor and large sand bars or barrier islands are thrown up by the waves and long-shore currents; and where the sea is encroaching on an irregular land surface, rocky ledges and islets may have escaped erosion and depressions may not yet be filled. The most widely distributed irregularities are the limy reefs formed by corals and algae in the warm seas. Such irregularities notwithstanding, the neritic sea floor is for the most part nearly flat and its seaward slope is very gentle.

The neritic zone has been the cradle of evolution for marine life. It provides the optimum living conditions and has a more varied population than any other part of the sea. Temperature changes are not great; sunlight penetrates to the bottom so that plants thrive, providing food and shelter for many kinds of animals; the movement of the water insures an adequate supply of dissolved oxygen and at the same time brings a constant supply of microscopic food to animals that are sedentary; and the inflow of water from the land brings an abundance of dissolved mineral requirements.

At present the neritic zone ranges in width from less than twenty-five to more than two hundred miles and its total area is about ten million square miles. But its area has varied within wide limits throughout geologic time and the effects of such changes have been far reaching. At present the continents are largely emergent and the neritic zone is confined almost entirely to their margins, but during most of the geologic periods the continents have been partially submerged by a relative rise in sea level that created vast inland seas (figures 47–57). For the most part these were shallow and added greatly to the area of the neritic zone. Toward the end of each period the inland seas slowly retreated and the continents were largely emergent, as at present. The expansion of such inland seas greatly increased the realm of shallow marine creatures and at the same time frequently afforded connections between faunal provinces that had long been separated, and permitted the mingling and resultant competition among previously isolated organisms. The subsequent retreat of the inland seas caused mass migration and crowding of the organisms in the restricted marginal or shelf seas.

The effects of such geographic changes on the land life were equally great. At times of emergence land bridges were sometimes formed between lands that had long been isolated. During Pliocene time, for example, such a land bridge across Behring Strait allowed proboscidians and other large mammals to reach North America from the Old World, and late in the same epoch the Isthmus of Panama became a land bridge between North and South America after millions of years of isolation. During the low stand of sea level resulting from the accumulation of the Pleistocene ice caps, the Strait of Dover was laid bare and England was connected to the mainland of Europe. At the same time many of the islands of the East Indian archipelago were united to the mainland of South-east Asia so that large mammals could cross, dry shod, what is now the floor of the South China Sea. Migrations between lands long isolated by the sea must have upset the balance of nature by introducing predators and diseases for which the endemic organisms had no adequate defence.

The climatic effects of wide fluctuations of the epiric (inland) seas were also great. The presence of large inland seas and low lands tended to moderate the temperature and increase the rainfall over the continents. Conversely the formation of land bridges interfered with ocean currents that tend to equalize the temperature. At present, for instance, the Isthmus of Panama holds back the westward flow of water in the tropical Atlantic and diverts it northward as the Gulf Stream where in the temperate zone it is deflected back toward Europe.

Even the outer part of the neritic zone is subdivisible into faunal provinces by climatic zones, and the nature of the bottom sediment

77

causes wide differences in the local faunas; and near shore, where it enters embayments, many distinct environmental niches can be recognized. Along the Gulf Coast of the United States, for example, Shepard and Moore [146] have recognized sixteen local environments each having a distinctive fauna. Thus, for a number of reasons, the neritic zone has a more prolific and more varied assemblage of living creatures than any other part of the sea.

The bathyal and abyssal zones occupy the floor of the deep ocean basins and are separated by an artificial, but widely accepted, boundary at a depth of one thousand fathoms. Thus the bathyal zone occupies the upper part of the continental slope and the abyssal zone includes the lower part of the slope and all of the deep ocean floor. From both the geologic and biologic points of view this distinction now seems to have little importance and in the following discussion both zones will be considered together.

The surface waters to a depth of about six hundred feet constitute the pelagic zone. Here all the living creatures must either swim or float. Here two groups of microscopic plants (diatoms and coccoliths) and two groups of microscopic animals (radiolarians and globigerines) thrive in great abundance and together with the meroplanktonic young of other creatures, serve as the ultimate food supply for the larger animals. Their abandoned shells rain down to form the organic oozes of the deep ocean floor.

Exploration of the Ocean Basins

The deep ocean floor lies masked in eternal darkness three miles, more or less below the surface. It is small wonder that it remains the last great frontier on earth to be explored. Indeed, we know vastly more about the surface of the moon than we do about the ocean floor. Until after 1930 only two methods were available for its study: (1) its depth could be sounded by lowering a cable from an ocean-going vessel; and (2) surface samples of the bottom sediment could be secured by dippers attached to the ends of cables. It was a notable achievement by these tedious methods to map dangerous shoals and prepare marine charts for the guidance of ocean-going vessels; but for deep water the soundings were too widely spaced to give a valid idea of the bottom topography and, except for several great 'deeps', the ocean floor was thought to be relatively flat. Since about 1930, however, several new techniques have been developed and we now know that the relief on the ocean floor equals that of the lands. Some of the new methods of study deserve brief discussion before we attempt to summarize the results.

The Sonic Depth Recorder

One of the most important devices is the sonic depth finder which was highly developed during World War II. It discharges sound impulses directed vertically to the ocean floor and catches the echoes as they rebound to the surface (figure 23). Sound travels in water at

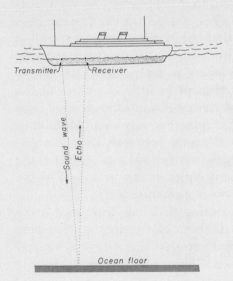

Transmitter   Receiver

Sound wave   Echo

Ocean floor

Figure 23. Diagram to illustrate the use of the sonic depth recorder

a velocity of about 5,800 feet per second, and the time lag between the instant of discharge of the sound and the return of the echo gives the measure of the distance to the bottom and back. These are electrically recorded and plotted on a moving belt and thus give a continuous profile of the bottom from a moving vessel (figure 30). In recent years sonic depth finders have been carried not only by special research ships but by many naval and commercial vessels, and our knowledge of the bottom topography is growing by leaps and bounds.

Coring Devices

A parallel advance has been made in devices for bringing up cores of the bottom sediment. The first such device was the Piggot gun developed about 1936 by C. S. Piggot [124]. It consisted of a weighted tube attached to the end of a cable that when lowered rapidly to the bottom could be driven several feet into the soft bottom sediment and when withdrawn contained a core of the deposits. It was applied with spectacular results when a string of thirteen cores were taken from the floor of the North Atlantic along a line between Newfoundland and Ireland [16]. Their study revealed information that could not have been secured by any other means. For example, five distinctive zones were recognizable each of which clearly was deposited simultaneously across the Atlantic Basin. One of these is a layer of volcanic ash and four are marked by fragments of rock dropped from melting icebergs. A study of the foraminifera entombed in the sediment shows that the surface water was cold at the time the glacial material was dropped, and much warmer in the intervals between. And with these layers as datum lines the relative rate of accumulation of bottom sediment in different parts of the ocean was evident, and the ratio of terriginous mud to organic ooze could be determined. This confirmed quantitatively what might have been inferred, namely that at abyssal depths relatively near the continental margin the sediment is largely terrigenous mud and that the rate of accumulation there was many times as fast as it was in the middle of the basin where organic ooze predominates.

The Piggot gun had one shortcoming that has now been overcome. As its tube was driven into the bottom, friction on the inside tended to compress the soft sediment so that the core was shorter than the hole from which it was taken. This difficulty was overcome about 1947 by the Swedish oceanographer B. Kullenberg in association with Hans Pettersson [122]. The Kullenberg piston corer, illustrated in figure 24, consists of a long metal piston attached to the end of a cable and surrounded by the coring tube. Above the tube is a heavy weight which during the descent is suspended from a release arm that is held in position by counter weights hanging a little below the end of the piston. When the counter weights come to rest on the bottom the release arm frees the weight which presses the coring tube down into the sediment. Since the piston is already in contact with the bottom the hydrostatic pressure of the surrounding water and sediment keeps the core inside the tube from being compressed. With this device it has been possible to secure undeformed cores as much as eighty feet long. The coring tube is lined with a glass or plastic sleeve that is withdrawn with the core, sealing it to prevent distortion or drying until it can be studied in the laboratory.

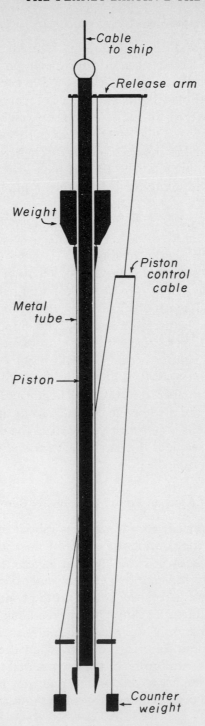

Figure 24.
The Kullenberg corer

Underwater Photography

Maurice Ewing and his colleagues at Lamont Laboratory were the first to adapt underwater cameras for use in photographing the deep ocean floor and they are now widely used in oceanographic research. The camera, with flashlights attached, is focused at a predetermined distance and lowered by cable. A counterweight hanging below the camera is so arranged that when it comes to rest on the bottom the shutter is opened and the flashlight is discharged at the instant when the bottom is in focus. Such cameras have also been attached to the cable carrying grappling devices so that a photograph is made just before bottom samples are taken [117].

Another spectacular invention is the bathyscaphe, a capsular vessel large enough to carry two observers, and to withstand the enormous pressure at great depths in the sea. It is provided with powerful searchlights and a porthole through which observations can be made. In 1960 the bathyscaphe *Trieste* successfully reached the floor of the Challenger Deep south of Guam at a depth of thirty-five thousand feet [123]. Since the pressure at this depth amounts to some sixteen-thousand pounds per square inch the problem of designing a port-hole that would neither break nor leak might seem insurmountable. It was ingeniously solved. The window is a plug of clear plexiglas about a foot thick tapered toward the inside and fitted into a tapered porthole so that the greater the pressure from the outside the tighter it is pressed into its seat. Observers within the bathyscaphe not only can observe the sea floor but can observe and photograph the strange living creatures of the deep.

Topography of the Ocean Floor: Submarine Canyons

For almost a hundred years a few great submarine canyons have been known to cross the continental shelf off the mouths of great rivers. One of the best known is the Hudson River Canyon (figure 25). Its position seems to indicate that it is an extension of the valley of the Hudson River out across the shelf and the continental margin. The origin of such submarine canyons long remained, and perhaps still is, a challenging enigma. They were originally assumed to be subaerial valleys cut at some time in the past when the shelf was exposed, either because of local uplift of the continental margin or of lowered sea level. But when it was discovered that they increase in depth and width as they descend to depths of three thousand feet or more, such

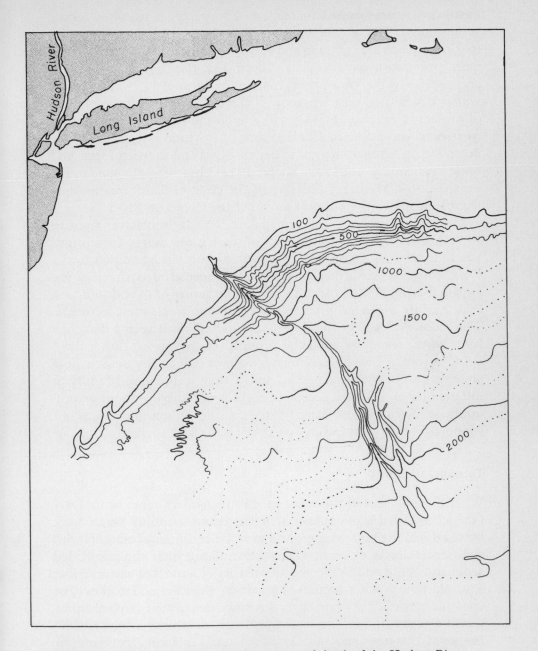

Figure 25. Contour map showing the extent and depth of the Hudson River canyon. Beginning near the edge of the continental shelf the canyon has been traced to the ocean floor at a depth of more than 2000 fathoms (12,000 feet). Contour intervals 100 fathoms. Simplified from a figure by Heezen, *et al.* [72]

83

changes of level seemed incredible. The problem assumed larger proportions when in the 1930's it was discovered that such submarine canyons are common and widely distributed. Modern surveys with sonic depth recorders have shown that the continental shelves and especially the continental margins are trenched by many and widely distributed canyons, some of them beginning off the mouths of present rivers and others heading upon the shelf with no relation to streams on the land. Furthermore, they commonly descend far down the continental margin to depths of several thousand feet, and some of them are immense. Shepard [145] has recently shown, for example, that Monterey Canyon off the coast of California is comparable in size to the Grand Canyon of the Colorado River.

Monterey Canyon is cut into granite but Hudson River Canyon and others along the Atlantic shelf of the United States are cut into nearly horizontal sedimentary rocks that range in age down to the Cretaceous. It is clear that the valleys have been eroded, that they are largely independent of the lithology and structure of the bottom, and that they are a general phenomenon common to all the continents. The more we learn of them the more incredible it seems that they have been carved by subaerial erosion. If they were thus carved simultaneously, the sea level must have been reduced by an incredible amount during their formation, and if they were carved locally at different times, we must accept an equally incredible amount of local uplift (followed by depression) of the continental margins that is not supported by erosion features on the present land surface.

Turbidity Currents

When the problem of the submarine canyons became so acute Daly [32] advanced the hypothesis that currents of muddy water have flowed down the bottom slope and over the continental margins with sufficient velocity to erode valleys. Postulating that the suspended sediment would add to the average density of a mass of water so that it would flow down a bottom slope under the clear water above, he used the term density currents. But since density currents are produced also by differences in temperature or salinity, Johnson [88] proposed the now generally accepted term turbidity currents for those due to suspended sediment. When first presented, Daly's hypothesis was an exciting idea but it seemed to most geologists (including Daly) to be in the realm of wild speculation. The sequel is a classic example of the way science advances. Daly began his memorable address before the Geological Society of America with these words: 'Ladies and Gentlemen, the hypothesis I am about to present is so preposterous that even I do not believe it!' And having thus disarmed his audience, he continued: 'But the submarine canyons exist and we don't know how they were formed. We must therefore consider every imaginable explanation until we hit upon the correct one. I propose to explore one such explanation today.' Probably no other idea has had a more profound effect on geologic thought in this generation.

In 1937 the Dutch geologist, Ph. H. Kuenen [94] proved experimentally that muddy water will flow down a bottom slope under clear water and may attain considerable velocity, and in subsequent papers he has contributed much to the idea and to the interpretation of ancient deposits laid down by turbidity currents for which the term 'turbidites' is now widely used. In the meantime Lake Mead above Hoover Dam on the Colorado has become a vast natural laboratory for the study of turbidity currents [57]. Gould has shown that when the Colorado River is in flood the sediment-laden water streams southward under the lake, following the old river channel, and during the flood of 1947 it flowed the full distance of 145 miles from the head of the lake to the dam, being compensated by a return flow of clear water at the surface. Here the bottom profile is gentle and the current is slow. At the time of the flood of 1947 it required $4\frac{1}{2}$ days for the muddy water to reach the dam which it approached at a velocity of only about 0·83 feet per second. Far from eroding the bottom these gentle turbidity currents are silting up the old channel which was already at grade before the dam was built, but they do prove that turbid water will flow along a bottom slope even if the incline is very gentle. In Lake Mead the average slope is less than five feet per mile.

That violent or spasmodic turbidity currents at times flow down the continental margins was first demonstrated by Heezen and Ewing in 1952 [68]. On 18 November 1929, a severe earthquake generated by faulting near the continental margin south of the Grand Banks and Newfoundland shook the Maritime Provinces and all of New England and broke several transatlantic submarine cables. This happens to be the region of the greatest concentration of submarine cables in the world. Although the precise moment of each cable break was known, no significance was attached to the data

85

until some twenty years later when Ewing and his colleagues at Lamont Laboratory undertook their study. Their results are epitomized in figure 26. At the time of the Grand Banks earthquake several

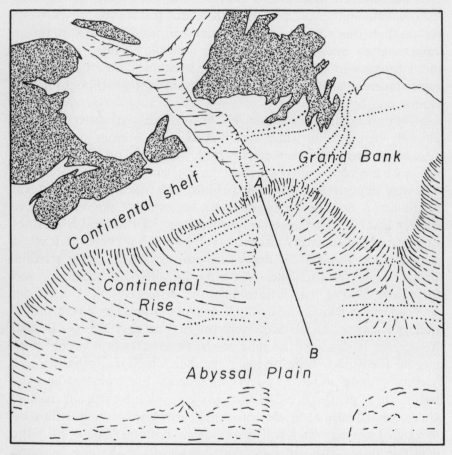

Figure 26. Area of the Grand Banks turbidity flow of 18 November 1929. The earthquake dislodged a large mass of sediment that had accumulated at the continental margin. Starting as a landslide it picked up water and much of it went into suspension forming a turbidity current that rushed down the continental slope and far out along the ocean floor. The line A—B indicates the position of the profile shown in figure 27. The dotted lines represent submarine cables. Adapted from figures by Heezen and by Heezen and Ewing

of the cables which lie upon the nearly horizontal continental shelf were not damaged, but seven which cross the steep upper part of the continental margin were broken simultaneously and others spaced farther down the slope were broken in sequence over a period of thirteen hours and seventeen minutes, and large sections of the cables (as much as two hundred miles long) were carried away and have never been found. Heezen and Ewing concluded that the destruction began with an enormous landslide that stretched for about 150 miles along the upper margin of the continental slope where sediment had accumulated to an unstable profile and that this at once broke the seven upper cables. Then as the moving mass of sediment raced down the steep slope it picked up water and much of it went into suspension, producing a vast turbidity current 150 miles across that went rushing down into the ocean basin breaking one cable after another as it passed. Knowing the exact moment of each

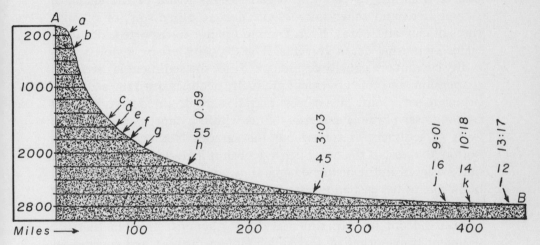

Figure 27. Profile showing the progress of the Grand Banks turbidity current. Letters *a* to *l* indicate the positions of twelve submarine cables. Cables *a* to *g* were broken simultaneously; *h* to *l* were broken in sequence over a period of 13 hours and 17 minutes after the earthquake. The figure next above each of these stations indicates the velocity of the current in knots as it passed the station; the figures written vertically indicate the elapsed time in hours and minutes between the moment of the shock and the breaking of the cable

break and the distance of each cable from the source, it was easy to calculate the average velocity of the current between cables (figure 27). The results were spectacular and to some seemed incredible [143], for the calculated velocity exceeds any known on the lands. At cable *h* which is near the base of the steepest slope and about one hundred miles from the source the calculated velocity is fifty-five knots (almost a mile a minute). It decreased exponentially as the slope flattened out but was still forty-five knots at a distance of two hundred miles where the depth was fifteen thousand feet and the bottom slope only twenty-five feet per mile; and at cable *K* which is four hundred miles from the source and on a slope of only four feet per mile the velocity was still twelve knots. Obviously the current must have continued much farther before finally dying out.

At the time this idea was advanced it was simply a hypothesis; even though based on what appeared to be convincing evidence. But it could be tested by study of the bottom sediments in the area concerned, and this Ewing and his associates proceeded to do during the next several years.

The normal deep sea sediments are distinctive, consisting of very fine, non-laminated clay and organic oozes made of the shells of foraminifera and other microscopic pelagic organisms, or of mixtures of clay and oozes. Even fine sand is not transported into deep water by normal ocean currents. The deposits left by a violent turbidity current are equally distinctive. Since the sediment is carried in suspension, and the movement gradually declines until the sediment begins to settle out, the coarsest particles are dropped first followed by progressively finer material. Thus within a short period a single layer of sediment is spread out that grades from coarsest at the bottom to finest at the top. Such a deposit is a graded bed. A series of bottom cores on the disturbed area showed just such a sandy, graded bed while to the east and west of the region swept by the current the bottom consisted of normal abyssal clay. From the data available in 1952 and from his experimental data, Kuenen estimated that the sediment transported by this single violent current had covered an area of about 100,000 square miles of the ocean floor to a depth averaging between forty and one hundred centimetres [96]. Cores taken later [69] strongly confirm this estimate. Of a chain of seven cores taken along an east–west line across the area swept by the current, cores 1 and 2 taken near the western side revealed a graded bed of sand respectively 70 centimetres and 130 centimetres thick, resting on normal abyssal clay. Core 7 taken just east of the path of the current showed only abyssal clay at the surface. Three attempts to take cores in the intermediate area were unsuccessful and, since the coring tube came up bent and empty, it was inferred that the sandy layer was too compact to be penetrated by the corer and, in the lack of a clay plug from below, the sand trickled out of the tube as it was raised. Sceptics of this interpretation argued that if the flow was initiated by a vast landslide a large part of the slumped material should remain as a great mound below the slumped area. Using highly sensitive depth recorders, just such a deposit has since been discovered and was reported by Heezen and Drake in 1962 [73].

Additional evidence of the ability of turbidity currents to carry sand into deep water was soon discovered near Bermuda. About thirty miles south-east of the Islands, and at a depth of nearly three miles, a core was brought up showing a graded surface layer of calcareous sand about 5·5 feet thick near the bottom of which were shells of molluscs that live only in shallow lagoons, and pieces of the calcareous alga, *Halimeda*, that lives only in the presence of sunlight. The source of these objects could only have been in shallow water about the Bermuda Islands, whence they were transported suddenly down a thirty mile slope and deposited on the deep ocean floor.

Several other turbidity flows associated with breaks in submarine cables have since come to light. A notable case was described by Heezen off the mouth of Magdalena River in Columbia [70]. Here a submarine cable lying about fifteen miles off shore and at a depth of 4,200 feet has been broken fourteen times within the span of twenty-five years. Here massive landslides from the steep slope just off the river mouth have been triggered not by earthquakes but by harbour construction. During the night before one of the cable breaks, for example, a long section of the jetties being built at the river mouth disappeared.

A particularly interesting example of turbidity flow near the Fiji Islands was reported by Houtz and Wellman in 1962 [80]. Kadavu Pass lies between the Island of Viti Levu and Kadavu. Here the steep slope from the islands leads down a trough to a depth of about seven thousand feet. From the town of Suva on the south shore of Viti Levu a submarine cable runs obliquely south-west down into the trough and then follows its axis to the south-west. Coral reefs fringe the Island of Viti Levu and outside the reef there is a narrow belt of shallow water beyond which the bottom slopes south-west-ward at an angle of about 5°.

On 14 September 1953, a severe earthquake shook the region, its epicentre being near Suva. Following the quake the submarine cable was broken and a length of about sixty miles of it was swept away or buried so that it has never been found, except for three pieces having a combined length of about three miles. These pieces were twisted and tangled and one of them was entangled with a length of steel hawser that presumably had been dropped at some time from a passing vessel. One of the pieces of cable had the insulation abraded from one side only, indicating that it had lain partly buried as the current swept over it and before it was ripped out (figure 28). Although the steel hawser was deeply rusted between the twisted wire strands, its surface was bright and free of rust, apparently the result of sandblasting by the passing sediment. Houtz and Wellman experimented on rusted parts of the cable by pumping a jet of water saturated with bottom sediment over it and found that a current of short duration must have had a velocity of at least ten miles per hour and probably as much as twenty miles per hour in order to abrade the rust away.

Figure 28. Idealized sketch of a piece of submarine cable from which the insulation was abraded from one side before it was ripped out of the ocean floor by the turbidity current near Suva in the Fiji Islands

Many profiles across the Atlantic Basin and a large number of cores taken by the staff at Lamont Laboratory during recent years have revealed vast graded plains extending as much as four hundred miles out from the continent that are largely formed of turbidites which have buried the original relief and smoothed out the ocean floor (figure 29). The cores indicate that these plains are underlain by a complex of thin lenses of graded sandy deposits interbedded with abyssal clay. These relations indicate that, at least during late geologic time, turbidity currents have repeatedly spread sand far from the continental margins and have been a major factor in the sedimentation of the ocean floor [72]. Indeed the extent and thickness of these deposits poses an unsolved problem. If turbidites had been carried into the ocean throughout geologic time at the rate they have recently been accumulating, the Atlantic basins should now be filled. It is suspected that the recent high rate of transport by turbidity currents is related to the fluctuations of sea level during Pleistocene glaciation. But it is certain that turbidity currents are not dependent on glaciation and can occur wherever sediment is built out into a deep basin until it becomes unstable. Since the discovery of this process ancient turbidities have been recognized among the geosynclinal deposits of many different ages.

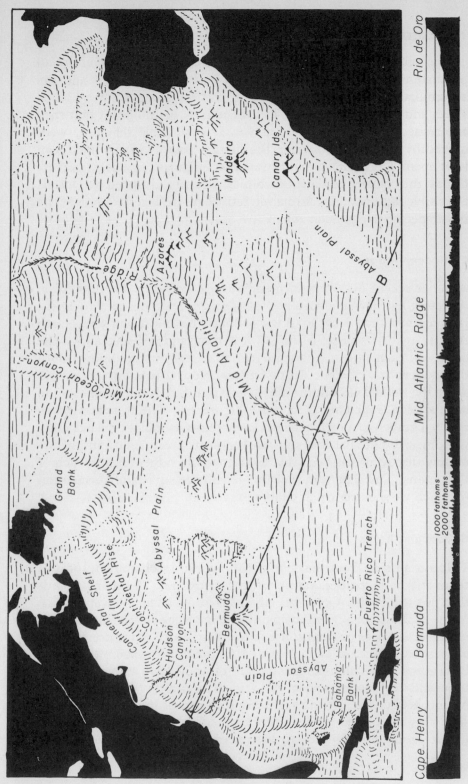

Figure 29. Physiographic diagram of the North Atlantic Ocean basin. Simplified from a map by Heezen, *et al.* [72]. The profile below follows the line A—B from Cape Henry, Virginia, to Rio de Oro, Africa, with a vertical exaggeration of 40 to 1. After Heezen

It is still not certain that the submarine canyons have been carved by turbidity currents. They now serve as sediment traps and the accumulating sediment is from time to time flushed out by landslides and turbidity currents, but there is as yet no proof that they are being deepened in this manner. It is possible that they were carved by subaerial erosion in the distant past and have thus been kept open. They remain one of the great enigmas of geology. Nevertheless the concept of violent turbidity currents advanced by Daly as a possible agent of their formation led to the discovery of one of the most spectacular phenomena of the oceans.

Mid-ocean Ridges

Another recent discovery of great interest concerns the mid-ocean ridges. It has been known since the *Challenger* expedition late in the last century that a broad ridge follows the middle of the North Atlantic with its crest rising several thousands of feet above the basins on each side of it, but its real character was not known until the modern use of sonic depth finders. Now it is known to extend along the middle of both the North and South Atlantic oceans and to have a deep trench along its crest (figure 29). The trench is apparently a graben let down between great faults as though the ridge is a vast linear bulge that is under tension at its crest. A still more surprising discovery has been that a comparable ridge exists in each of the oceans. The significance of this is still the subject of speculation to which we shall return in chapter 11.

Guyots and Atolls

Volcanoes rising from the deep ocean floor are well known, some of them still active, others now dormant or extinct. The many islands that dot the Pacific Ocean are all volcanic or have a volcanic base. Many of these are aligned in chains and have issued from great welts on the ocean floor or from zones of faulting. Some of the oceanic volcanoes are immense. The Hawaiian Islands, for example, form a chain some 1,600 miles long and rise from a depth of about seventeen thousand feet below sea level. The twin peaks, Mauna Loa and Mauna Kea on the island of Hawaii, tower more than thirteen thousand feet above sea level and, measured from their base, are the tallest mountains in the world, exceeding the height of Mount

Everest by more than two thousand feet. The lava issuing from the ocean floor differs in composition from that of most volcanoes on the continents, being more basic (i.e., richer in iron and magnesium) and it falls into the broad category of basalt. None of the oceanic volcanoes include granitic rocks.

Special interest attaches to truncated volcanic cones whose flat tops now lie several thousands of feet below sea level. There is convincing evidence that they were at some time in the past truncated

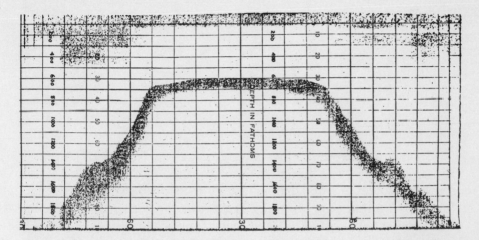

Figure 30. Depth recorder profile across a guyot located south of Eniwetok Island in latitude 8° 50′ N, longitude 163° 10′ E. It was secured by Hess on 6 October 1944. Since the vertical scale is greatly exaggerated, the lateral slopes appear too steep. After Hess [76]

by marine erosion only a little below sea level and have since subsided. They were first recognized in 1942 when Harry H. Hess, then a naval officer in command of the *USS Cape Johnson*, had a sonic depth recorder installed on his vessels and took depth profiles as the ship crossed and recrossed the Pacific [76]. Within two years he had discovered twenty such submerged, truncated cones for which he proposed the name guyots after a famous Swiss oceanographer (figure 30). Study of published hydrographic charts soon indicated about 140 additional guyots. Subsequent profiles made by sonic depth finders borne by naval and commercial ships and by research vessels of several oceanographic institutions have since revealed a large number of guyots in the mid-Pacific and a considerable number in the North Atlantic and elsewhere [61].

The profile of a typical guyot is shown in figure 31. The flat tops range from four or five miles to more than twenty miles wide and are normally bordered by a gently sloping shelf below which the sides of the cone have an average slope of 20° or slightly more. The marginal shelf is considered to be the result of longer erosion by the waves while the flat top was being cut. Pieces or pebbles of basalt dredged from the tops of several guyots confirm their volcanic nature.

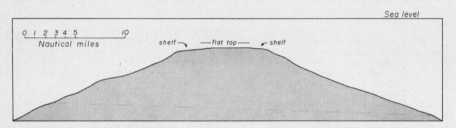

Figure 31. Typical profile of a guyot

When first discovered, guyots were thought to be very old, even of Precambrian age, but dredgings from both the Hess and Cape Johnson guyots brought up shallow water fossils of mid-Cretaceous age [61] proving that their summits stood near the surface at that time. Both now lie about six thousand feet below sea level (figure 32).

Closely allied to the guyots are the atolls of the mid-Pacific. Ever since the memorable voyage of Darwin aboard the *Beagle* it has been recognized that the coral reefs had grown up from a volcanic base, but it was not known whether the base was conical or truncated, nor was it known how thick the calcareous cap might be. During Operation Crossroads at Bikini in 1946 a string of seismographs was set up across the lagoon to pick up the seismic vibrations created by the atomic bomb. The shock waves having passed through the calcareous cap were reflected back, confirming the expected basaltic floor beneath and indicating its approximate depth. They also indicated that it was a flat surface. In the following summer three deep wells were drilled on Bikini Island and they revealed two highly significant facts [100]. First, the deepest well, penetrating to a depth of 2,556 feet, revealed that all the calcareous deposit consisted of detritus of shallow water shells such as those now growing on the atoll. Second, the fossils proved that the deposits ranged in age from recent at the top through Pliocene, Miocene, and Oligocene to Late Eocene which was the deepest material penetrated. In short, the

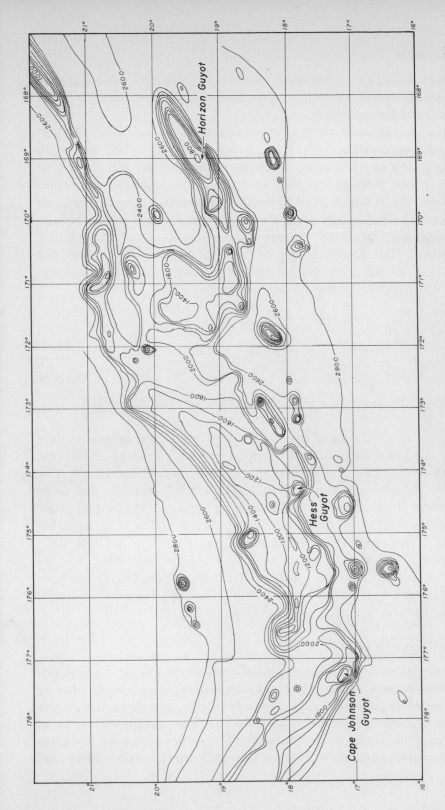

Figure 32. Contour map of an area in the mid-Pacific north-east of Guam showing numerous guyots and sea-mounts. Contour interval in fathoms. After Emery, et al. [42]

95

volcanic base had been sinking almost continually since Eocene time and so slowly that corals and other reef making organisms were able to build as fast as it sank.

In 1952 two deep wells were drilled on Eniwetok Atoll, the first reaching hard rock at a depth of 4,610 feet and the second at a depth of 4,630 feet [101]. From the bottom of the second a core of olivine basalt about fourteen feet long was brought up. Fossils in the cores confirm the findings at Bikini; the calcareous deposits were all formed in very shallow water and they range in age down through Pliocene and Miocene to Eocene which rests directly on the volcanic basement. The accordant depths of wells on opposite sides of the atoll also strongly infer that the base is a sunken guyot. A profile section of Eniwetok Atoll is shown in figure 33.

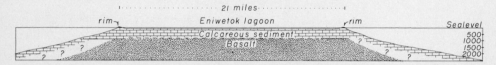

Figure 33. Profile section across Eniwetok Atoll, after Emery, *et al.* [42]

In the tropical zone of the mid-Pacific, atolls predominate but are associated with guyots and flat-topped benches known as seamounts; north of the zone of active coral reefs only guyots are found. The guyots do not stand at a uniform depth and it is possible that some are older than others or that they have subsided at unequal rates. From the limited information now available, however, it appears that many of them were truncated during Cretaceous time and have since been slowly sinking. On this basis Menard has concluded that 'an area of several millions of square miles in the central Pacific has been sinking as a unit during the whole of Cenozoic time and the total subsidence has averaged a mile more or less' [111].

Island Arcs and Trenches

One of the most striking features of the western Pacific is a series of great island arcs arranged like festoons with their convex sides facing the ocean (figure 34). These islands bristle with volcanoes, some active and others now dormant or extinct. They are also the locus of frequent and intensive earthquakes. These island arcs are the summits of great submarine ridges separated from the mainland by seas of varying depth and each is bordered on the convex side by an enormous trough or trench in the ocean floor. The trenches are long but relatively narrow and closely parallel the island arcs, and they greatly exceed in depth the rest of the ocean floor. The Challenger Deep in the Mariana Trench south of Guam, for example, lies almost

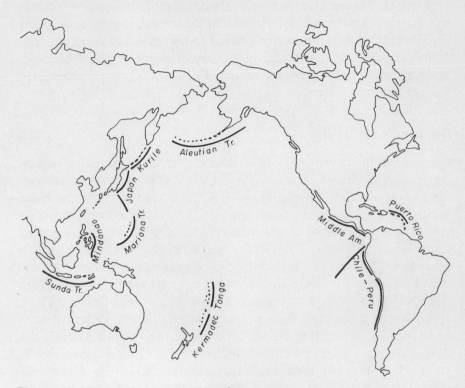

Figure 34. Island arcs and ocean trenches

seven miles below sea level (35,600 feet), the Mindinao Trench east of the Philippines is a close second with a depth of 34,428 feet, and the Kurile Trench is third with a depth of 34,020 feet. These depths contrast with a maximum of around fifteen thousand feet for the broad ocean basins.

Island arcs and trenches are more common in the western Pacific than elsewhere, but the Leeward Islands east of the Caribbean in the Atlantic are bordered by the deep Puerto Rico Trench, and the Sunda arc and Sunda trench face the Indian Ocean.

On the east side of the Pacific a chain of great trenches lies close

97

against the mountainous continental margin without the intervention of island arcs, the Middle American Trench following the coast of Mexico and Central America almost to Panama, and the Chile–Peru Trench extending for some two thousand miles along the coast of South America.

Some of the trenches have a V-shaped profile but others such as the Puerto Rico Trench are almost flat bottomed, the flat floor being due to a deep fill by sediment carried in by turbidity currents. The island arcs and trenches (figure 34) are clearly the result of large-scale deformation in the earth's crust. Their significance is considered further in chapter 11.

Currents in the Oceans

Currents in the ocean are produced by the wind, by the tides, and by differences in density of water masses [95]. The general oceanic circulation is well known (figure 35). In low latitudes where the trade winds blow persistently from the east a broad surface current is driven westward until it encounters a land mass and is deflected either north or south. Then in the belt of the westerlies it is driven eastward. Thus in the North Atlantic the general circulation is clockwise and where the warm surface water is restricted in Florida Strait the Gulf current flows at a velocity of four to five knots. Then, spreading as it flows northward, it loses velocity and is deflected eastward to bring warmth to western Europe. In the South Atlantic the flow is counter-clockwise. In the Pacific, likewise, there are two great eddies, the northern one bringing warmth and moisture to the western side of North America all the way from California to Alaska which is much warmer than corresponding latitudes in northern Japan and eastern Siberia, while in the South Pacific the circulation is counter-clockwise.

The effect of such ocean currents on the distribution of marine organisms has been great. Many of the benthonic forms pass through a free swimming or floating larval stage and as a result have been transplanted from island to island across wide expanses of deep water. Others can be transported while attached to seaweed or drift wood. As a result the reef corals of the tropical Pacific are almost cosmopolitan in that vast realm though but few of them ever reached the Atlantic. Many of the shallow water molluscs are widely distributed among the Pacific islands.

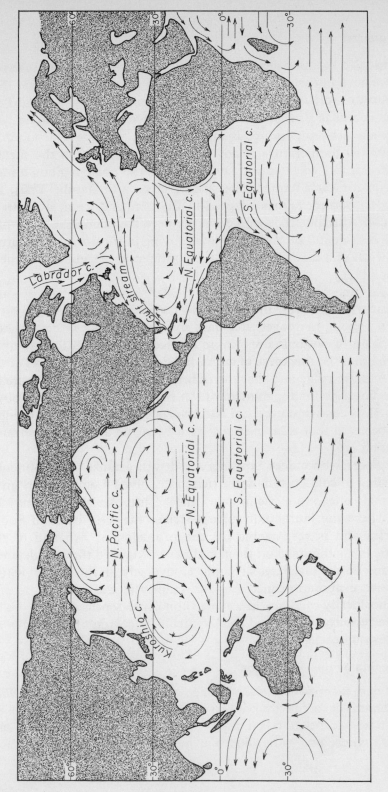

Figure 35. Major surface currents in the ocean

99

A second mode of general circulation has resulted from the low temperature in the polar regions. The cold water, being denser than warm water settles to the bottom and moves very slowly toward the equator; and as a result the water at great depths is near the freezing point and its temperature is fairly uniform the world around. In general the temperature at any latitude decreases from the surface downward but when traced laterally from the polar regions toward the equator each temperature zone increases in depth. Thus, for example, bottom faunas adapted to the temperature at a depth of six hundred to one thousand eight hundred feet along the outer part of the continental shelf of Norway are living in the same temperature at a depth of a mile or so along the continental margin off southern Europe [126].

Tidal currents in the shallow water near shore are well known and play an important role in the transportation of bottom sediments. It is now known, moreover, that they may be effective in deep water. The chain of bottom cores across the North Atlantic, for example, showed that the thickness of each zone decreases on the flanks of the mid-Atlantic ridge and that the thinning is paralleled by a decrease in the finest grained increment of the bottom sediment which obviously has been winnowed out and transported away from the ridge. It is believed that tidal currents have been the agent of this transportation [16].

In places where deep currents are driven against the continents, upwelling of cold bottom water rich in dissolved food elements gives rise to an uncommon richness of marine life. An example may be seen where the Humboldt current strikes the west coast of South America and is responsible for the profusion of fish and of the aquatic birds that feed on them and have produced the vast deposits of guano on the Galapagos Islands. Conversely, in the tropics where excessive evaporation increases the salinity at the surface, density currents locally carry warm water to abnormal depths.

The recently discovered role of turbidity currents was discussed on previous pages.

Sediments of the Ocean Floor

With two exceptions a wide border of the ocean floor about each continent is covered with fine terrigenous mud derived from the land. The first exception is off areas such as Yucatan Peninsula and Florida where only lime mud is available. The second is in places where spasmodic turbidity currents have carried fine sand and silt far out to sea.

In the abyssal region the most widespread sediment is red clay which covers about a quarter of the floor of the Atlantic and Indian Oceans and nearly half of the Pacific. The source of the red clay is less obvious than that of other types of deposits, and it certainly is not simple. It probably includes wind-blown dust, volcanic ash, meteoric dust, and terrigenous sediment of colloidal dimensions. The red colour is produced by the oxidation of the contained iron. The cold water spread from the polar regions contains sufficient free oxygen, and the slow descent of finely divided particles probably allows for oxidation before they reach the bottom.

The remainder of the ocean floor is largely covered by the so-called organic oozes made of the minute shells of microscopic pelagic organisms that thrive near the surface. The most widespread of these is Globigerina ooze (plate 19) which covers some 50 million square miles of the floor in intermediate depths. Only two of some fifty families of the foraminifera have become adapted to pelagic life and although they include relatively few species, individuals thrive in unnumbered millions. At time of reproduction the living protoplasm abandons the tiny calcareous shells which rain down like snow flakes to the bottom where they arrive empty.

Another group of organisms forming calcareous deposits is the Coccoliths, a group of extremely minute single celled plants that form tiny shells which, like the globigerines, are abandoned at time of reproduction.

Less widespread are the siliceous deposits made of the microscopic shells of diatoms (plants) and of radiolaria (animals).

In the cold water below a depth of about fifteen thousand feet the concentration of carbon dioxide causes such tiny calcareous shells as the globigerines and coccoliths to go into solution, leaving only the red clay to accumulate. At lesser depths the bottom deposits show all gradations from pure organic oozes to calcareous muds, depending on the rapidity of the introduction of terrigenous muds.

The thickness and the nature of the sediment on the ocean floor should throw light on such fundamental problems as the history of the ocean basins and the permanence of continents and oceans. Unfortunately almost nothing was known about either until within the last quarter century and even now we have only made a start toward their investigation. This problem is discussed in chapter 11.

Chapter 6

The Planet Earth:
3 The Atmosphere

THE ATMOSPHERE is a relatively thin blanket of air surrounding the earth (figure 36), but its importance for living things is absolute. By day it shields us from the heat and the lethal rays of the sun and at night it prevents excessive loss of warmth to outer space. Without it the diurnal changes of temperature would be comparable to those on the moon where during the day it rises to exceed the boiling point of water and at night falls to about 250°F below zero. It also carries the moisture and the ultimate source of food for every living thing.

In both mass and composition it differs widely from that of all the other planets in the solar system. At sea level it exerts a pressure of about fifteen pounds per square inch and consists largely of nitrogen (78 per cent) and oxygen (21 per cent), with only traces of a few other gases. The chief of these are the inert gas, argon (0·93 per cent), and carbon dioxide (0·003 per cent). Carbon dioxide is the essential food for plants which, through photosynthesis, they build into organic compounds. These, in turn, form the ultimate food of animals, which are incapable of building organic compounds from the raw chemical elements. Animals are absolutely dependent on oxygen since they derive the energy for their vital processes from the oxidation of organic compounds. But an atmosphere of oxygen and carbon dioxide alone would be lethal to both animals and plants. Experimental studies of the effect of higher concentrations of carbon dioxide on animals have recently been carried out at the Brookhaven National Laboratory on Long Island and Dr Donald D. Van Slyke (personal communication) reports as follows:

A concentration of three per cent of CO_2 has, on a healthy man, no marked effect, except to increase somewhat his respiration. A concentration of five or six per cent can be breathed for a long time, but causes discomfort, perhaps including headache and nausea. A concentration of ten per cent of CO_2 breathed for a few minutes causes dizziness, nausea and in some cases, unconsciousness. I think that the concentration of CO_2 that can be tolerated for a long time by mammals cannot be very much more than ten per cent, although mice can breathe a mixture of oxygen and thirty per cent CO_2 for about an hour before they succumb.

Pure oxygen, on the other hand, would be disastrous to all forms of life. In hospitals pure oxygen is used temporarily for patients suffering from certain types of illness but, during its early use, tragic

Figure 36. Segment of the earth to show the relative thinness of the atmosphere. Line *a* marks the upper limit of the troposphere and line *b* the top of the stratosphere. The dotted line indicates the extreme outer limit of the atmosphere

accidents occurred occasionally as a lighted cigarette or a chance spark caused the oxygen tent to burst into flame. Oxygen has such strong affinity for carbon and hydrogen (the chief constituents of organic matter) that at the temperature of a lighted match uncontrollable combustion occurs in the presence of pure oxygen. If our atmosphere consisted of pure oxygen such an explosion would sweep the surface of the earth in a blinding flash, consuming every living thing. The nitrogen, which is an almost inert gas, serves as a buffer to dilute the oxygen to a safe level. Thus the earth's atmosphere is amazingly suited to meet the requirements of living things.

Beside the permanent gases discussed above, the atmosphere carries a highly variable amount of water vapour which, of course, is essential for all forms of life.

The reason for the unique composition of the earth's atmosphere is discussed in chapter 8.

The volume and density of the earth's atmosphere are also unique among the planets and are at an optimum for life. Venus is most nearly equal in size to the earth but its atmosphere is so dense and opaque that the surface of the planet is never visible. The heat rays from the sun penetrate to the rocky surface but are unable to escape again through the opaque cover. The resultant 'greenhouse effect' has caused the temperature to build up to about 800°F [83], which is twice that of a lighted match and would be intolerable for any kind of life we can imagine. We are familiar with this principle on a small scale on the earth where a cloud cover reduces the loss of heat so that the temperature does not fall as low on a cloudy night as on a clear one.

At the opposite extreme from Venus is Mars which is much farther from the sun and has a very tenuous atmosphere. There the loss of heat is so rapid that the polar regions turn white during the winter season with a hoar frost of frozen carbon dioxide. If this inference is correct, the temperature must be approximately that of 'dry ice'. Compared with such extremes as Venus and Mars the earth's atmosphere is an almost ideal blanket to maintain the optimum conditions for life.

Layers of the Atmosphere

Until the present century, study of the upper atmosphere was limited to what could be learned by ascending to mountain tops or by the use of balloons and kites. Since the pressure drops so rapidly with elevation it was then believed that the atmosphere extended only a few miles above the highest mountains and maintained a fairly uniform composition as it decreased in density. It was also supposed that the temperature dropped progressively until it reached the cold of outer space.

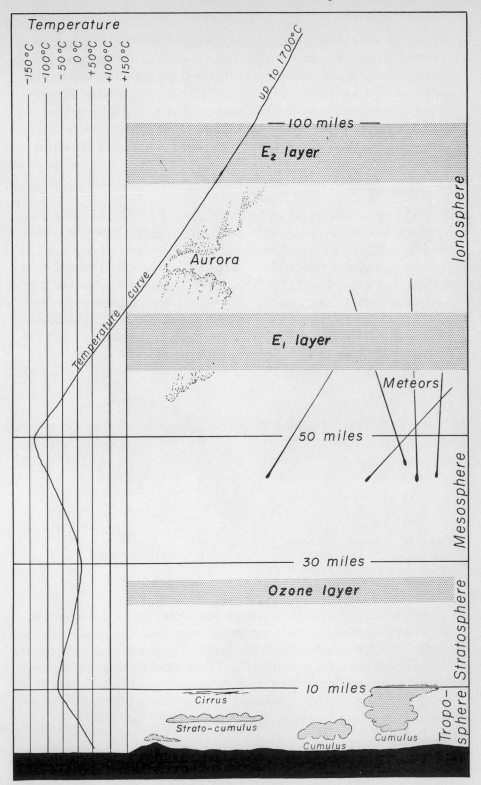

Figure 37. Layers of the atmosphere. Adapted from Nicolet [115]

Space probes during the last two decades, on the contrary, have revealed surprising complexities. The rapidly expanding literature is mostly too technical for review in this volume and we shall attempt only a general account with special concern for factors that affect the living environment. A major discovery is that the atmosphere includes several distinctive layers that differ in composition and in temperature and other characteristics. The relation of these layers is indicated in figure 37.

The Troposphere

The troposphere extends to a height of about ten miles in the tropics but decreases in thickness toward the polar regions where it is only about five miles thick. It contains about nine-tenths of the mass of the atmosphere and virtually all of the water vapour. It includes all the clouds and is the layer in which the planetary circulation controls our weather. The name troposphere refers to its active movements (Gr. *tropos*, turn or change). The atmospheric pressure decreases to about 1·6 pounds per square inch at the summit and the temperature drops to about 63°C below zero [115].

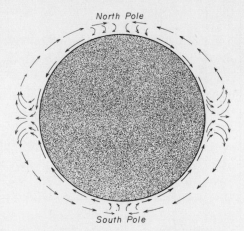

Figure 38. Diagram to indicate what the planetary circulation of the atmosphere would be like if the earth were not rotating

The decrease in thickness toward the poles results from the contraction of the gases as the temperature falls. The upper air over the tropical zone flows away down the gradient, producing a permanent belt of low pressure in low latitudes. The heavier air then flows under to restore the balance. If the earth were not turning on its axis, this would produce a simple circulation toward the poles aloft and toward the equator at lower levels as suggested by figure 38.

But because the earth is rotating the Coriolis effect causes any current of air (or of water) to be deflected toward the right in the northern hemisphere and toward the left in the southern. This induces the complex planetary circulation represented in figures 39 and 40. For an interesting explanation of the Coriolis effect see McDonald [108].

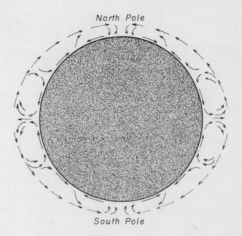

Figure 39. Vertical circulation of
the atmosphere on a rotating earth

Because of the Coriolis effect the poleward flow aloft is moving almost due east in the northern hemisphere by the time it has reached latitude 30°, while in the southern hemisphere it is flowing west (figure 40). Here it tends to bank up, producing a permanent belt of high pressure in which part of the air descends and then spreads both north and south. This produces a belt of calms known as the 'horse latitudes' in which the descending air, having lost most of its moisture aloft becomes thirsty as it is warmed again and causes rapid evaporation. Most of the world's deserts lie in these zones. The return flow toward the equator is then deflected westward to form the 'trade winds'. Meanwhile, the flow toward the poles at low levels is deflected eastward to form the belt of the 'westerlies' in the temperate zones. Part of the air aloft has continued toward the poles where it builds up a permanent belt of high pressure from which, from time to time, great masses of cold air pour down along the surface into lower latitudes where the Coriolis effect sets them spinning, clockwise in the northern hemisphere and counterclockwise in the southern. These are the well-known 'highs' that so greatly effect our weather in the temperate zones.

This general planetary circulation is modified and complicated by many local factors. Where the prevailing wind crosses a mountain range, for example, it is chilled and drops most of its moisture as it ascends the windward slope, and it descends on the leeward side undersaturated, and, as it is warmed, it tends to produce strong

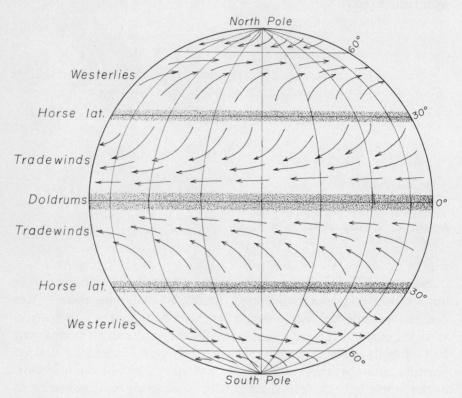

Figure 40. Plan view of the planetary circulation of the atmosphere

evaporation. Thus north–south trending ranges are generally marked by excessive rainfall on one flank and aridity on the opposite. Local inequalities of temperature at the earth's surface also influence the air currents. Since a land surface warms more rapidly during the day than a body of water, and cools more rapidly by night, a sea breeze commonly flows landward along the shore during the afternoon, and a land breeze flows seaward at night. The monsoon winds of India have a comparable explanation. During the summer the interior of Asia is permanently warmer than the Indian Ocean and the wind blows landward, while during the winter the land is colder and the wind blows seaward. Tornadoes and hurricanes likewise are generated by more local warm spots where the heat causes the air to rise and be displaced by cooler air rushing in from all sides. Here again it is the Coriolis effect that causes them to twist. Even the local thunder clouds are produced by ascending currents generated by local warm spots. On a summer day the difference in temperature between a ploughed field and a grassy prairie or a lake is sufficient to cause ascending and descending currents that give the effect of turbulence to a low-flying airplane.

During a heavy thunderstorm the updraught may be great enough to carry the condensing raindrops upward to freezing temperature where they become hailstones. Large hailstones have fallen part way only to be carried up again through the level of condensation into the freezing zone several or many times before falling to the ground.

The Stratosphere

The stratosphere extends above the troposphere to a height of about thirty miles above the earth's surface. Here the air is very tenuous and clouds are generally lacking. Jet planes flying in this region readily attain high speed because the air resistance is slight. Their flight is smooth also because of the general absence of turbulence, but special devices are necessary for them to scoop up enough of the rarefied atmosphere to provide for combustion of their fuel.

Until it was explored by high-flying airplanes and rockets and balloons, the air in the stratosphere was supposed to be still and the temperature was believed to drop steadily with altitude. Both assumptions were wrong. The temperature gradient is reversed in the stratosphere and rises gradually to about 17°C at an elevation of thirty miles. Furthermore, during World War II high-flying planes discovered a strong but rather narrow stream of air in the lower part of the stratosphere that has come to be known as the jet stream. It flows from west to east, above the temperate zone, following a sinuous and frequently changing course, its velocity varying from less than one hundred to more than three hundred miles per hour. For some unknown reason it influences the course of the highs and lows in the underlying troposphere. Where it swings far to the south during the winter months the cold masses of high pressure follow it southward and when it moves farther north they also remain farther north.

In the upper part of the stratosphere the composition of the atmosphere changes in an important respect. Here the incoming ultraviolet light from the sun breaks some of the oxygen molecules apart (O_2 to $O+O$) and the isolated atoms of oxygen quickly attach themselves to another molecule of oxygen to form ozone ($O_2+O=O_3$). The ozone absorbs much of the ultraviolet light. Thus the relatively thin ozone layer shields the earth from these lethal rays [11].

The Mesosphere

The temperature reaches a peak at the top of the stratosphere and then declines again up to an altitude of about fifty miles where it is about 130°C below zero. It then begins to rise again. This zone of falling temperature is the mesosphere.

The Ionosphere

In the words of Blumenstock,

The ionosphere is the earth's frontier with outer space. Upon this buffer region falls an immense electromagnetic cannonade: light rays, ultraviolet and infrared radiation, radio waves and corpuscular streams from the sun, similar rays from other stars, cosmic rays from interstellar space beyond the solar system. All these impacts produce a great variety of effects on the molecules and atoms of the upper air. The ultraviolet radiations, for example, knock electrons from the air particles, split molecules into atoms, and leave ionized molecules and atoms. Cosmic rays shooting in the nuclei of air atoms at huge energies produce a vast energetic debris. [15].

Although it extends out to a distance of perhaps five hundred miles before grading away into the emptiness of outer space its gases are so tenuous that they comprise only a tiny fraction of the mass of the atmosphere. Nevertheless, the ionosphere plays a vital role in conditioning the earth for life. If the heat and lethal rays from the sun reached the surface, life might well be impossible.

Until recent space probes it was generally supposed that the temperature in the upper atmosphere would fall gradually until it reached the cold of outer space. To the contrary, it is now known that the temperature gradient rises steeply in the ionosphere and at a height of three hundred to four hundred miles the temperature is of the order of 1,200 to 1,700°C, exceeding that of molten iron. The rising temperature should not have been surprising, however, since virtually all our heat comes from the sun and it strikes the upper atmosphere with maximum intensity. The heat of the upper atmosphere is only one of the barriers our spacemen have to face.

The ionosphere was so named because its gases are so largely ionized. Instead of the neutral molecule O_2, for example, oxygen occurs as free atoms, O, which carry a positive electric charge. Nitrogen likewise occurs not as N_2 but as free atoms, N, and carbon dioxide is broken down into CO and O. In the lower part of the ionosphere there are several distinctive layers of highly charged particles that make possible radio and television transmission. The impulses sent up from transmitters cannot penetrate these electrically charged layers, but are deflected back to earth and thus can be picked up by receivers over a large area.

The Van Allen Radiation Belts

Far out beyond the atmosphere lie two remarkable belts of high energy atomic particles that were discovered through space probes engineered by James A. Van Allen during the 1950's and now bear

Figure 41. Diagram to show the relation of the Van Allen radiation belts to the earth

his name. Although not part of the atmosphere they do affect the atmosphere and deserve brief consideration here [159; 84].

The relations of these belts is indicated in figure 41. Although they girdle the earth, neither extends to the poles. They are belts of high energy particles trapped in the earth's magnetic lines of force and are without sharply defined borders. The inner belt reaches maximum intensity at about two thousand miles above the earth and is about one thousand miles thick at the middle, the intensity dying out gradually above and below; the outer belt shows maximum intensity at a height of about fifteen thousand miles and is as much as four thousand miles thick at the middle. According to present understanding the lines of force in the earth's magnetic field in these zones trap high energy electrons and protons jetted from the solar flares. Being unable to escape, these charged particles spiral around the lines of force and race back and forth from one edge of the belt to the opposite until the concentration builds up to a critical level when part of them leak away along the lines of force at the edges of the belt and plunge down into the ionosphere. Here they encounter the atmosphere and yield part of their energy in the form of heat which produces the glow we see as the auroras. Space probes have shown that the temperature in the auroras runs as high as about 2,500°C, which considerably exceeds that at lower latitudes which are shielded by the Van Allen belts.

These belts of high energy particles will prove a hazard to astronauts headed for outer space – a hazard that may be avoided by launching them from the polar regions.

1. A manuscript in stone. The even layers of sedimentary rock seen here are part of a sequence more than a mile thick exposed in the walls of the Grand Canyon of the Colorado River. The view is upstream from a point about five miles above the mouth of the Canyon

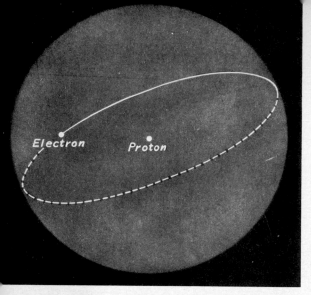
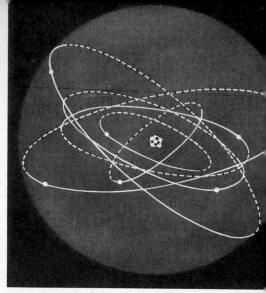

2. Diagrams to illustrate atomic structure. The nucleus of the hydrogen atom (left) consists of a single proton, and the single electron rotating about it at a given distance defines the spherical boundary of the atom, which is lightly shaded. The nucleus of the carbon atom (right) is made of six protons (white) and six neutrons (black), and the electron cloud includes six electrons arranged in three concentric shells

3. *Left:* Photosphere of the sun with two groups of sunspots. Below, a greater enlargement of the central sunspot group.

4. *Right:* Spectroheliogram of a portion of the sun, photographed in red light of the hydrogen   line, showing flocculi and several small sunspots

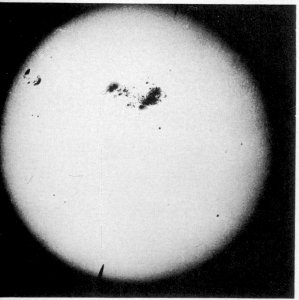

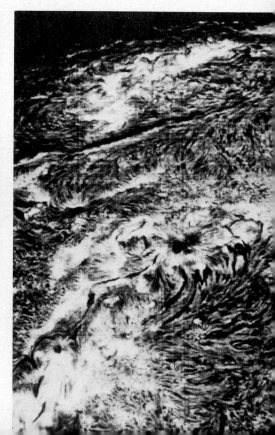

5. Photograph of the chromosphere, solar flares, and halo at time of total solar eclipse. The largest solar flare is 272,000 miles high

6. The solar corona seen at the moment of total solar eclipse

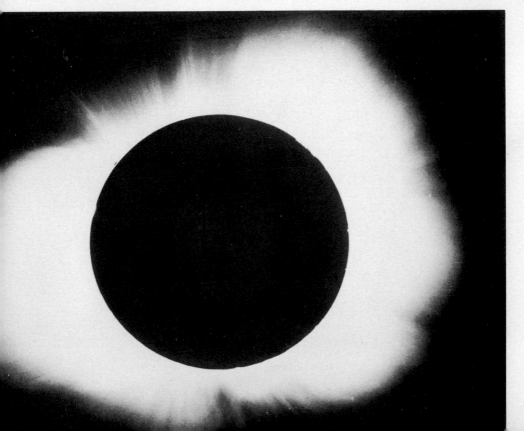

7. Photograph of the moon at first quarter showing lunar craters and maria

8. Fold mountains on the floor of two of the maria. Above, a portion of Mare Imbrium. Below, a portion of Mare Serenitatis. These folded mountains are several hundred feet high. The great crater, Plato, has a diameter of sixty miles and its rim rises several thousands of feet above its flat floor

9. Meteor Crater from the air. The view is west toward San Francisco Peaks

10. The Weston meteorite which fell in a field about twenty-five miles west of New Haven, Connecticut, during the morning of 14 December 1807. This is a stony meteorite

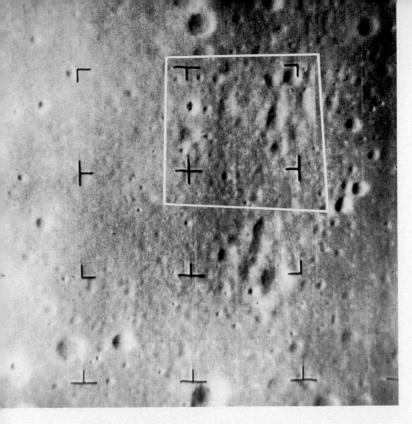

11. Photograph of an area of about thirty square miles of the surface of Mare Imbrium from an altitude of 11.2 miles by U.S. satellite *Ranger VII*. A close-up of the area outlined in white is shown in plate 12

12. Photograph from an altitude of 3.7 miles only 2.5 seconds before the crash landing of *Ranger VII*

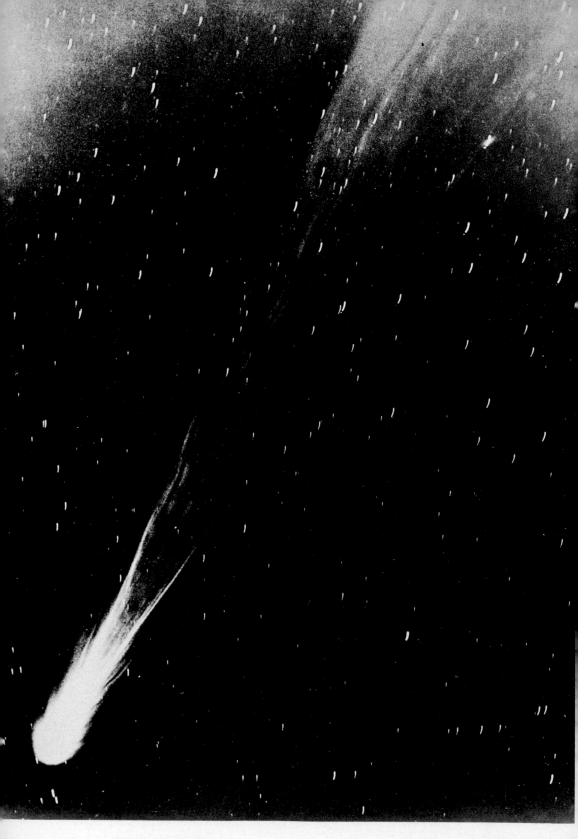

13. Brook's Comet

14. The Great Nebula in Andromeda, seen in oblique view

16. Spiral galaxy in Coma Berenices, seen in edge view

15. Spiral galaxy in Ursa Major, seen in polar view. Our galaxy is believed to be similar

17. Plateau basalt exposed in the river bluff at Vantage, Utah

18. Deformed gneiss in the Aiguille Range Series at Vallon de Van, France

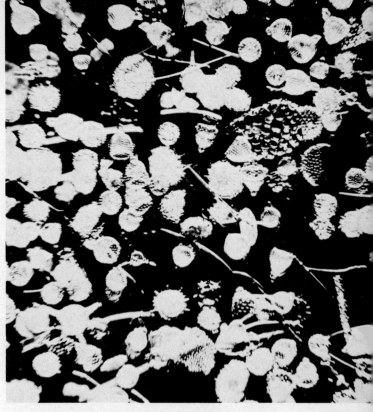

19. Deep-sea oozes. Above, radiolarian ooze greatly enlarged. These silicious shells are barely visible to the naked eye. Below, Globigerina ooze (x 10) as dredged from a depth of 2,898 feet about a hundred miles west of Martinique

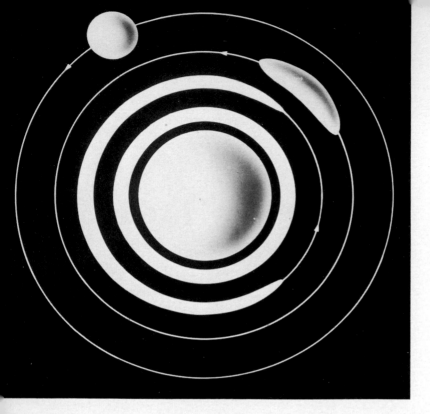

20. Diagram to represent Laplace's hypothesis of the origin of the solar system

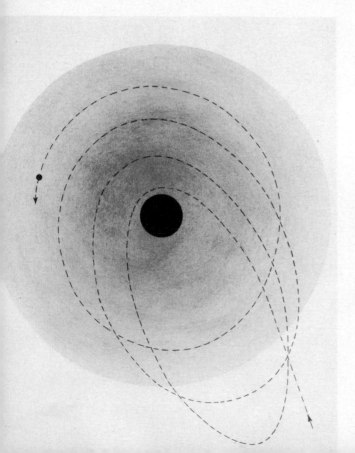

21. Diagram to explain how the 'resisting medium' would reduce the ellipticity of a young planet according to Chamberlin. In plunging into the resisting medium it is travelling slower than the substance of the medium but in its outward journey it is travelling faster than the medium and is slowed and does not travel so far from the sun. In its next return it is carried farther out by the medium. It is not to be supposed that its orbit would be changed so rapidly as here indicated

22. Peneplaned summit of the Laramie Range near Buford, Wyoming. This granite surface lies at an elevation of about eight thousand feet. A small monadnock appears in the distance at the left

23. Canyon of North Platte River. After flowing for a long distance across the intermont basins the river cuts through the Casper Range in this narrow gorge with granite walls as much as 750 feet high

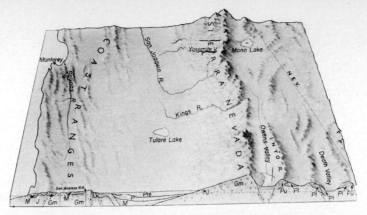

24. Block diagram of the Sierra Nevada region. (After Dunbar)

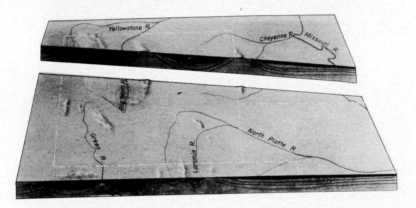

25. Block diagram showing structure and relief in the Rocky Mountains at the beginning of Oligocene time when the intermont basins (shaded) were filled and the ranges were peneplaned except for scattered monadnocks. The major streams then flowed over a veneer of sediments without regard for the buried structures. (From Dunbar 38 after Atwood and Atwood)

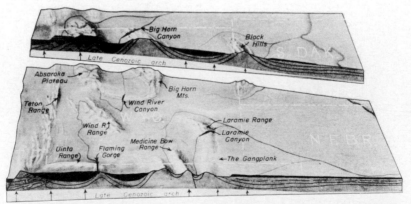

26. Modern relief in the area shown in plate 25 after gentle regional uplift which brought the peneplaned surface to an elevation of about eleven thousand feet along the continental divide. The basin fill was largely removed by erosion but the old ranges formed of hard rock stand out in bold relief. The main streams flow in very shallow valleys across the basins and then cut through the ranges in spectacular gorges (After Dunbar 38)

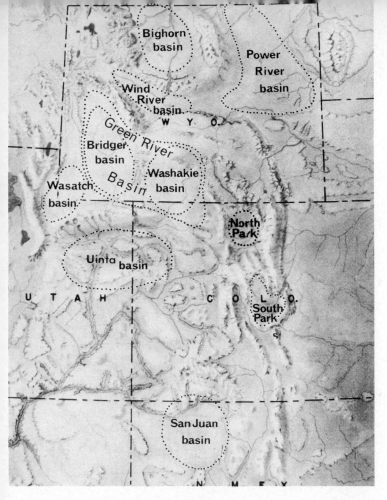

27. Map showing the modern relief in the Central and Southern Rocky Mountains. (After Dunbar)

28. Palaeogeographic map of North America in mid-Cretaceous time. (After Dunbar from Schuchert)

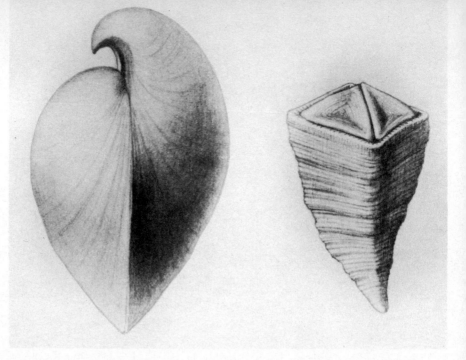

29. Immigrants into western North America from Europe by way of the Arctic Sea. Left, the large brachiopod, *Stringocephalus;* right, the unusual coral, *Goniophyllum*

30. Ordovician lava flows exposed in a sea cliff near Coal River on the west coast of Newfoundland. Such flows were widespread across Newfoundland in Ordovician time

31. Late Cretaceous dinosaurs in western United States. (From a great mural by Rudolf F. Zallinger in Yale Peabody Museum)

32. Ancient sand dunes in the Coconino sandstone of mid-Permian age near Flagstaff, Arizona

33. Laminated anhydrite from the Castile formation in the Delaware Basin of west Texas. The dark layers were deposited in the rainy season and the light layers during the arid season. (x 1/3)

34. The Pleistocene ice sheets. Data from Flint (53). The polygonal design indicates floe ice

35. Above, glacially smoothed and striated floor on the Milford chlorite schist near New Haven, Connecticut. Below, a glacial boulder found on the surface shown above. This is the under side of the boulder which has been flattened and scratched while frozen in the bottom of the glacier

36. A modern scene in eastern Greenland near the source of the Dangaard-Jensen glacier

37. *Overleaf:* Valley glaciers on Andree Island on the east coast of Greenland

38. Varved clay from a proglacial lake bed at South Hadley, Massachusetts. At the right a small detail approximately natural size showing gradation of the light grey silty layers deposited during the summer into the dark winter layers of clay

39. Glacially polished floor beneath the Dwyka tillite near Kimberley, South Africa

40. Mount Lefroy in the Canadian Rockies formed of fossiliferous marine limestone of Cambrian age

41. Glacial boulder from the Gowganda tillite in the Huronian 'system' at Cobalt, Ontario

42. A slice of metamorphic rock showing deformation by solid flow. The dark layer was originally impure sandstone and the light rock was limestone. These were originally even horizontal layers. When subjected to heat and horizontal pressure the sandstone layer was recrystallized into complex silicate minerals and compressed into folds as the limestone yielded, being thinned where the folds were stretched and thickened where compressed. About one half natural size

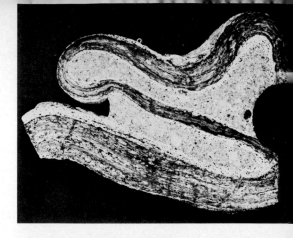

43. Pliocene fossils (snails and clams) from Castell Aquato, Italy. Yale Peabody Museum. Such fossils in Italy were recognized by Da Vinci as seashells that once lived where now dug up but many refused to accept this explanation at the turn of the sixteenth century

44. Third lower molar of the American Mastodon, *Mammut Americanum,* from Peru, Indiana. It was a similar tooth that Governor Dudley considered that of a human who was drowned in the Deluge

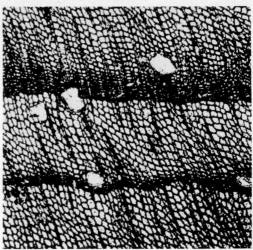

45. A block of petrified wood from the fossil forest of the Yellowstone. The cell walls have been replaced by silica and the cell cavities are filled with clear silica. Yet the growth rings and medullary rays show as clearly as in a modern log. Next to it is a photograph of a transparently thin section cut from the end of the specimen at the left and enlarged about ten diameters. It shows part of three growth rings

46. *Below:* Silicified snail shells and a clam shell of Middle Ordovician age. At the right a chunk of limestone containing such fossils. At the centre below a piece of the same that has been largely dissolved by hydrochloric acid exposing the contained

47. At the left a chunk of Devonian sandstone with natural moulds of brachiopod shells. At the right an artificial cast of the same made by coating the moulds with liquid latex. The latex was peeled loose and turned over to the right

48. *Below left:* Natural mould of a pinnule of the large fern, *Neuropteris decipiens.* A concretion which had formed about the leaf was placed on edge and cracked open revealing the hollow mould just as it appears here. From the Carbondale formation at Mazon Creek, Illinois

49. *Below right:* Natural mould lined with a film of carbon showing part of a leaf of the fern, *Alethopteris aquilina,* from the Coal Measures at Saarbrucken, Germany

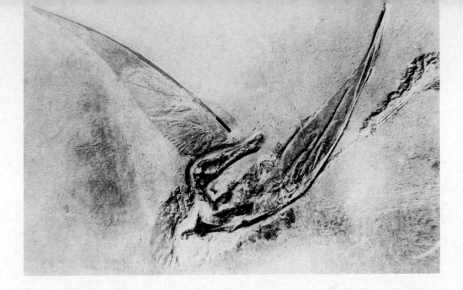

50. A small pterosaur, *Rhamphorhynchus phyllurus*, with its leathery wing membranes and tail flukes preserved as natural moulds on a layer of Upper Jurassic limestone at Solenhofen, Bavaria. The skeleton is permineralized

51. Natural mould of the oldest known bird, from the Upper Jurassic limestone at Solenhofen, Bavaria

52. *Left:* Footprints of a small dinosaur which had crossed a mud flat pitted by raindrops of a passing shower. This is the under surface of a sandstone layer deposited over the tracks and shows casts of the tracks. From the Newark red sandstone of Late Triassic age at Turners Falls, Massachusetts

53. *Right:* A fossil stonefly, *Lemmatophora typica,* from a bed of Lower Permian limestone near Abilene, Kansas. The insect, about the size of a housefly, shows colour spots on its wings. Microscopic hairs are preserved

54. *Below:* Walcott's fossil locality in the Burgess shale of Middle Cambrian age on the slope of Mt. Wapta, British Columbia

Chapter 7

Origin of the Solar System

Globed from the atoms falling slow or swift,
I see the sun, I see the systems lift their forms.

TITUS LUCRETIUS (95–55 BC)

MAJOR features of the modern world described in the preceding
chapter can be observed and measured, and with a few exceptions
they are accepted with a high degree of confidence. But to envisage
the origin of our solar system some four and a half thousand million
years ago requires a different approach. No one was present to
record those far-off events and the conditions under which our
world was born have long since disappeared.

In this event the scientist must turn detective, seeking clues upon
which to base a logical inference. Thus he develops a theory or
hypothesis of what has happened. It may or may not be the correct
explanation but it directs the search for more evidence, pro or con. If
facts are discovered that cannot be explained, the hypothesis may be
modified so as to account for them, or it may have to be abandoned
and new hypotheses tried out until the right one is discovered. The
first hypothesis is commonly invalid, not because it is illogical but
because unknown factors in the situation were left out of consideration. But as more evidence is gathered the correct hypothesis will
become highly convincing even though the evidence be largely circumstantial. This is the way crimes are solved; and it is the way most
of the difficult discoveries in science have been made.

Many of the great advances in medicine have grown out of hypotheses based on circumstantial evidence. Dr Finlay's suggestion that
yellow fever is carried by mosquitoes remained only a hypothesis for
nearly twenty years, but it stimulated Dr Walter Reed and his
colleagues in Havana to test it by exposing volunteers to the bite of
infected mosquitoes. Vaccination to prevent disease developed out of
a simple hypothesis advanced by Dr Jenner about 1770. He had
learned that dairymaids in the Vale of Gloucester were immune to

smallpox and since they were commonly in contact with cows affected by the harmless cowpox he came to suspect that, in some manner, infection by cowpox had given immunity against smallpox. Between 1796 and 1798 he put his hypothesis to the test by inoculating patients first with the germs of cowpox and later with smallpox. The sequel is well known. Smallpox had been one of the great scourges of mankind but has now almost disappeared. Moreover, the principle of vaccination has since been applied to many other diseases. Hypotheses have been equally fruitful in many other fields. The concept of universal gravitation was a pure flight of Newton's imagination inspired by the fall of an apple, but when tested and proved, it turned out to be one of the great achievements of the human mind. We shall never be able to see an atom, but when Niels Bohr conceived of the atom as a positively charged nucleus surrounded by a swarm of negatively charged electrons, his hypothesis started a chain reaction of discoveries that have revolutionized our concepts in both chemistry and physics. Other examples of the use of hypothesis and theory in the discovery of truth could be multiplied ad infinitum for this is the chief means by which science advances in penetrating the unknown. Almost every step in our modern space technology, for example, is based on theoretical considerations. We need not apologize therefore for reviewing the attempts to gain an understanding of the origin of the solar system and of this planet upon which we dwell.

The Nebular Hypothesis of Laplace

The first attempt to account for the origin of the solar system on a rational basis is generally attributed to the distinguished French astronomer, Simon Pierre Laplace, and dates from the year 1796. The germ of the idea had been suggested a few years before by the German philosopher, Immanuel Kant, but it was Laplace who developed the theory in such simple and lucid form that it soon gained wide acceptance and for the next century went almost unchallenged.

Laplace assumed as a starting point that at some time in the remote past all the matter of our solar system existed in the form of a hot gaseous nebula, much larger than the orbit of the outermost planet, and slowly rotating. From this primaeval condition he tried to show how the nebula evolved automatically, in accordance with simple physical principles, into the present solar system.

He assumed that it must have lost heat to outer space and in cooling it gradually shrank. This, he showed, must have caused acceleration of its rotation and the gradual increase in centrifugal force in the equatorial plane. Thus, he argued, the nebula was slowly transformed into the shape of a thin lens and eventually the centrifugal force at the periphery equalled the force of gravity. At this stage a peripheral belt of the nebula was shed as a gaseous ring while the rest shrank away from it (plate 20). The ring, of course, continued to circle about the parent nebula with the angular velocity it had at the moment of separation. Then, as shrinkage of the nebula continued, a second ring was shed in the same manner, and eventually a third, and so on until a ring had formed for each of the planets.

Meanwhile mutual attraction among the particles within a ring eventually caused it to break and to draw together into a sphere that continued to orbit along the path originally occupied by the ring. As an analogy one may think of the way in which a thread of syrup hanging from a spoon will draw back into a rounded droplet. The forces involved are different, the syrup being drawn into a sphere by surface tension whereas the gaseous ring is drawn into a sphere by gravitative force, but the results are similar.

In this view each planet began as an enormous sphere of hot gas revolving in a circular orbit and spinning on its own axis. If large enough it, in turn, shed rings as it shrank, to form satellites about itself.

This simple scheme seemed to account logically for the most obvious features of the solar system as they were known in the nineteenth century. In particular it could account for the spacing of the planets, their nearly circular and concentric orbits, their revolution in a common plane, the organization of the satellite systems, and the residual heat of the sun. Nevertheless, Laplace was aware of difficulties, and he relegated his hypothesis to the position of a note in a larger work and presented it, in his own words, 'Avec la défiance que doit inspirer tout ce qui n'est point un result de l'observation ou du calcul.' Yet the simplicity of the scheme made such a wide appeal that it was not until the beginning of the present century that serious shortcomings came to be appreciated. These were forcefully set forth by T. C. Chamberlin and F. A. Moulton, geologist and astronomer respectively, at the University of Chicago [25].

One of the most obvious objections to the hypothesis concerns the present condition of the sun. If it were the residue of the original

nebula and had shrunk to its present size since the formation of
Mercury, the sun should be a thin lens spinning rapidly and ready to
shed another ring. Quite to the contrary, it is essentially spherical
and turns leisurely on its axis in a period of about twenty-five days.

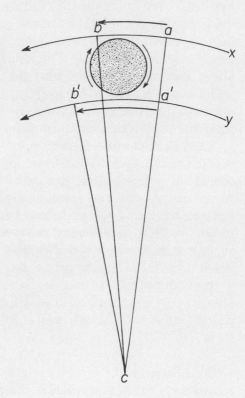

Figure 42. Diagram to indicate
why Laplace's hypothesis should
have caused retrograde rotation of
the planets. Since the angular
momentum is constant, particle *a*
travels with less angular velocity
than particle *a'*, which has a smaller
orbit. According to Kepler's laws
the triangle *abc* must have the same
area as triangle *a'b'c*. Thus while
particle *a* travels the distance *ab*,
particle *a'* travels the distance *a'b'*.
Applying this principle to all the
particles in a planet should give it
the rotation indicated

A second shortcoming concerns the angular momentum of the
solar system. The angular momentum of a planet is the force pro-
pelling it along its orbit; it may be expressed quantitatively as the
product of its mass times the area swept over in a unit of time by an
imaginary line connecting it to the centre of attraction about which it
revolves (figure 4). Furthermore, it is a constant; if the radius of
revolution be decreased the angular velocity will increase and vice
versa. Since we know the mass of each of the planets, their distance
from the sun, and their angular velocity, we can readily calculate the
angular momentum of each, and can determine what their angular
velocity would be if they were shifted to smaller or larger orbits.
Such calculations by Russell [135] prove that the entire solar system

does not possess enough angular momentum to have caused a ring to be shed at any stage in its development. Indeed, they show that if all the angular momentum of the entire system were concentrated in the sun it would rotate in a period of about twelve hours (instead of twenty-five days) but would remain almost spherical since centrifugal force at the equator would be only about five per cent of the force of gravity. In short, it would be far from the possibility of shedding a ring.

Yet another obstacle faces Laplace's hypothesis. If the planets were formed by the condensation of a gaseous ring, the direction of rotation should be opposite to the direction of revolution (figure 42). This follows from the fact that a certain angular momentum was inherited from the moment of separation of the gaseous ring, but a particle on the near side of the young planet is travelling in a smaller orbit than an equal particle on the remote side and, according to Kepler's laws, must therefore travel with somewhat greater angular velocity. The net result of this principle operating on all the particles must give the young planet a backward spin. This, of course, does not agree with the conditions in the solar system in which the planets rotate and revolve in the same direction.

There are other serious objections to Laplace's hypothesis but these alone are sufficient to discredit it, and it is now long since abandoned.

Hypotheses of Tidal Disruption

In view of these considerations Chamberlin and Moulton [25], shortly after the beginning of the present century, began exploring a radically different concept. They assumed that the sun travelled alone until it almost collided with another star. Then as the two stars passed within a few million miles of one another each was partly torn asunder by tidal forces generated by their mutual attraction. As the passing star receded rapidly into space with its retinue of fragments, the pieces torn from the sun fell back into elliptical orbits about it, and out of these fragments, born of a stellar catastrophe, the solar system evolved.

Chamberlin and Moulton were impressed by the explosive forces that exist in the sun by virtue of its great heat, and they conceived that tidal bulges generated during the short interval of close approach exploded into a series of enormous 'bolts' or jets of hot gas that were drawn out in the wake of the passing star (figure 43). Part of this material was rapidly dispersed to form a vast gaseous envelope about the sun, but the largest 'bolts' were so great as to have enough inter-

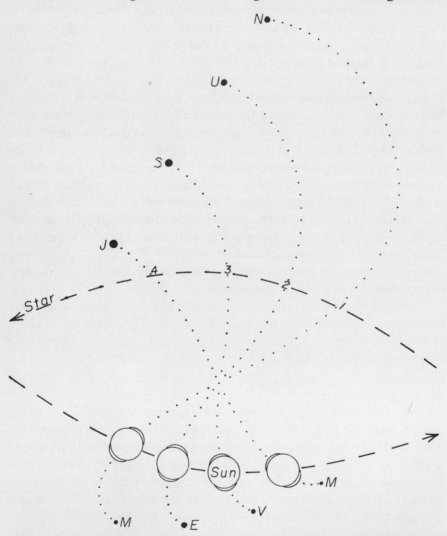

Figure 43. Diagram to represent the Chamberlin–Moulton hypothesis of tidal disruption of the sun by the close approach of a passing star. This assumes that the major planets originated from the tidal bulge on the near side of the sun and the minor planets from the opposite tidal bulge. The dotted lines indicate the supposed courses of the planetary nuclei on leaving the sun. The planets are supposed to have left the sun in sequence as the star passed: Neptune and Mercury first, when the star was in position 1; and Jupiter and Mars last, when it was in position 4. After Chamberlin, 1928

nal gravity to hold together. Then as such a jet of gas cooled, it condensed into liquid droplets which, in turn, solidified to form tiny meteorites. On the assumption that these solid particles were the building units of which planets were made, they were termed planetesimals and this became known as the Planetesimal Hypothesis.

A few of the largest bolts of gas were assumed to have formed swarms of planetesimals large enough to have a gravitative field that gradually drew them together to form the nucleus of a planet. Then as it continued to revolve about the sun it grew in size by sweeping up the scattered planetesimals along or near its path, which came raining in like a perpetual fall of meteorites until most of the scattered debris had been gathered up. The satellites were assumed to be lesser condensations that were too far from the orbits of the young planets to be intercepted but were near enough to be captured.

A serious problem for this hypothesis was to account for the nearly circular orbits of the planets and the satellites. The postulated bolts of gas jetted from the sun must have been drawn in the wake of the passing star until it had receded far enough to allow them to fall back and, because of this tug, they must have missed the sun on their return and have fallen into highly elliptical orbits.

To transform these into nearly circular orbits Chamberlin and Moulton postulated that a considerable portion of the gas ejected from the sun spread to form a vast cloud that revolved in spherical form with the sun. As a result the planetesimals formed during its condensation travelled in circular orbits. This formed a 'resisting medium' through which each of the planetary nuclei had to plough its way during each journey about the sun. In this case the young planet, on its outward journey from perihelion (nearest point to the sun) would be travelling faster than the resisting medium and would be slowed down as it swept up the material in its path; and on the return journey it would be travelling slower than the resisting medium and would be accelerated by all the particles picked up. The net result would be to reduce the ellipticity of its orbit with every journey about the sun (plate 21).

Aside from the question whether this *ad hoc* explanation is adequate, it creates a further problem. In a vast swarm of planetesimals travelling at high velocity, the mutual attraction between two of them would have been trivial as compared with the disruptive force resulting from a collision, and they should have been pulverized to form a cloud of dust before aggregates assumed enough mass to create an effective gravitative field. Hence the entire mass of material ejected from the sun should have dissolved into a vast nebula of gas and dust [147]. Of course, the major planets are almost entirely gaseous and could never have been made of planetesimals unless, as Urey has suggested, the temperature at their distance from the sun was so low that hydrogen and helium froze into sleet.

In view of these considerations two British astronomers, Sir James Jeans and Sir Harold Jeffreys, proposed a radical modification of the hypothesis of tidal disruption [86; 87]. They emphasized that the even surface of the sun proves that the explosive forces are trivial as compared with its enormous gravity. They reasoned, therefore, that in the event of the close approach of a passing star the tidal bulges did not explode into discrete 'bolts' but rose into a steady jet of gases that eventually reached out to the distance of the outermost planet. Such a relatively slender 'filament' of hot gas was, of course, unstable and as it cooled and condensed it broke into several segments, each of which was to form a planet.

Of course, each of these must have fallen back in a highly elliptical orbit, and to transform it into a nearly circular course, Jeans and Jeffreys invoked the resisting medium of gas about the sun just as Chamberlin and Moulton had done.

To account for the satellite systems they assumed that in its first journey the young planet at perihelion passed so near the sun that it suffered tidal disruption and the formation of a gaseous filament that segmented to form a satellite system, thus repeating on a smaller scale the mode of formation of the planets. But this posed a further problem: if the attraction of the sun was sufficient to disrupt the young planet at perihelion on its first revolution, why did it not disorganize or destroy the satellite system on the second revolution. It was necessary to assume that the orbit had been altered by the 'resisting medium' to such an extent that the planet passed much farther from the sun on its second revolution than it had on the first.

More formidable criticisms have now discredited the Gaseous-Tidal hypothesis. Spitzer [147] has calculated that a hot gaseous filament of the dimensions postulated by Jeans and Jeffreys would have expanded so fast under its own internal pressure that it would have dispersed and spread into a gaseous cloud about the sun instead of contracting into planets.

A major criticism that applies also to all theories of tidal disruption concerns the distribution of angular momentum in the solar system.

The significant fact is that the angular momentum of Jupiter exceeds that of all the rest of the solar system. That is to say, it would have required more force to launch Jupiter into its orbit than to place all the other planets in orbit and set the sun spinning on its axis. In an attempt to account for this remarkable fact Russell [135] once tentatively suggested that the primordial sun was a double star with one large and one small component and that Jupiter represents the smaller component which had its own momentum at the time of tidal disruption. But to conserve it while the larger component was being disrupted, and to place it in a circular orbit in the midst of the other planets involves so many improbable conditions that the idea was quickly abandoned.

For these and other reasons too numerous and too technical to present here, it now seems impossible to account for the organization of the solar system by any theory involving tidal disruption of the sun. Current speculation has therefore reverted to the premise that it evolved out of a gaseous nebula but in a manner completely unlike that envisioned by Laplace.

The Dust Cloud Hypothesis

Modern telescopes have revealed that vast nebulous clouds of gas and dust particles are common in our galaxy. Some of them glow with the reflected light of stars that are within or near them but many occupy voids between the stars and appear dark because they block out the light of distant stars beyond them. The total mass of such diffused material is now known to be great.

It seems probable that such 'dust clouds' are accumulations of particles driven out into the voids of space by the radiant energy of the luminous stars, and that when they have grown large enough, mutual attraction of the scattered particles eventually causes them to condense to form new stars. In any event such vast nebulous dust clouds are common celestial objects.

In 1944 C. F. von Weizsäcker [167] developed a new theory based on the premise that our solar system evolved from such a dust cloud. It postulates a time in the remote past when the sun was at the centre of such a nebula that was slowly rotating and extended out somewhat beyond the present orbit of Pluto. In this situation individual particles in the nebula revolved about the sun in free Kepler orbits. Thus the angular velocity differed progressively with distance from the sun. This he argued must have created turbulent eddies arranged in concentric zones about the sun (figure 44).

Such eddies must have had retrograde rotation for the reason explained by figure 42; but von Weizsäcker postulated that turbulence between the zones of primary eddies produced counter eddies rotating forward. These he likened to roller bearings between the concentric shells of the nebula. He argued further that condensation began in the 'roller bearings' and that they gradually grew and developed gravitative fields capable of capturing all the material of

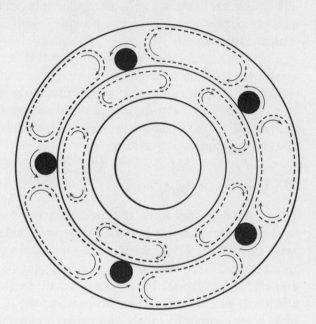

Figure 44. Diagram to illustrate von Weizsäcker's hypothesis of concentric rings of clockwise eddies and intercalated counterclockwise ('roller bearing') eddies (white) in a solar nebula

the counter eddies. At this stage the sun was surrounded by concentric zones of large turbulent eddies of gas and dust particles each rotating forward. They were held in fixed circular orbits by centrifugal force, but mutual attraction among the eddies within a single zone was unopposed and gradually drew them together to form a protoplanet much larger and more diffuse than the present planet. To account for the satellites it was assumed that the larger protoplanets developed zones of turbulent eddies, repeating on a smaller scale the pattern by which the planets were formed.

In 1951 G. P. Kuiper [97] elaborated this general concept with theoretical and mathematical treatment. He assumed that our solar system originated from a gaseous nebula that had a cosmic composition, i.e. a predominance of hydrogen and helium gases with much lesser amounts of the heavier elements and of atomic particles of many kinds. At this stage the nebula was cold. Mutual attraction of all its particles caused it to shrink and to become more dense at the centre and progressively less dense toward the periphery. For some reason not specified, it began slowly to rotate. As it shrank its angular momentum increased and centrifugal force in the equatorial plane gradually transformed the nebula into a thin lens. But, unlike Laplace, Kuiper thinks centrifugal force and internal gravity came into balance at all depths within the nebula so that by the time it had shrunk to the diameter of Pluto it had become stable and rotated as a unit, each particle revolving in a circular course about its centre. But in accordance with Kepler's third law the period of revolution varied with distance from the centre, the inner part of the nebula turning much faster than the outer. The difference in angular velocity thus caused vast turbulent eddies to form, in a sense comparable to the cyclonic 'highs' and 'lows' that race from west to east in the earth's troposphere. But, in contrast to von Weizsäcker, he reasons that turbulent eddies were not generated in concentric zones but that large eddies could form anywhere in the cloud, and that both large and small eddies formed and reformed until a few finally gained enough density to create a gravitative field and then grew at the expense of other eddies. Thus the nebula finally broke up into several large, rotating gaseous masses, one for each of the planets. In this event the forward rotation of the planets poses a problem. It must be noted that they differ one from another in their periods of rotation. Mercury keeps one side toward the sun so that its period of revolution and rotation are the same, i.e. about 88 days. Venus, as determined by the recent probe by satellite *Mariner II*, likewise keeps one face toward the sun or possibly shows a very slow retrograde rotation. Its period is therefore about 225 days. Earth's period of rotation is nearly 24 hours; that of Mars is about $24\frac{1}{2}$ hours; that of Jupiter and Saturn about 10 hours. If during the growing stages of a young planet it was travelling in a circular orbit and gathering up planetesimals travelling in circular orbits, it should develop retrograde rotation; but Whipple [168] explains that if it were spiralling either in or out through a field of solid particles moving in circular orbits it should develop forward rotation. The forward rotation of the planets appears to be one of the moot problems requiring adequate explanation.

To account for the satellite systems it is assumed that each proto-planet was much larger than its present descendant, both because it was still very diffuse and because it then contained a large mass of gases that were subsequently lost; and that in contracting it developed turbulent eddies that condensed into satellites, thus repeating on a smaller scale the process by which the planets were formed.

After the planets were freed, the central part of the nebula continued to shrink and evolved into the sun. Although the nebula was cold at the beginning, adiabatic shrinkage generated heat until eventually the sun reached the temperature at which thermonuclear reactions began. Then a new force came into play. As the sun approached its present furious temperature the radiant energy pouring out from it literally blew away into space a large part of the gases of the protoplanets. Since this force decreases exponentially with distance it was most effective for the nearest planets and hardly affected the remote ones. As a result Mercury, Venus, Earth and Mars (see figure 11) lost most of their gaseous constituents and condensed into solid bodies. Meanwhile, the outer planets, composed from the first almost entirely of lighter gases, were little affected and may have grown by capturing some of the gases blown away from the minor planets.

The dust cloud hypothesis offers a logical explanation for many features of the solar system; for example, the spacing of the planets, their nearly circular orbits, their rotation in a common plane, the organization of the larger satellite systems, and the high temperature of the sun. The impressive differences between the minor and the major planets also find a logical explanation. The great angular momentum of Jupiter is not an obstacle to this hypothesis as it is to those previously discussed; its angular velocity was inherited from the parent nebula.

Nevertheless a number of features remain for which supplementary explanations must be sought. The asteroids, for example, are too small to represent condensations from minor eddies in the nebula, and fluctuations in the light reflected from Eros, one of the largest and nearest of them, suggests that it is not round but is a tumbling chunk of rock of quite unequal dimensions. These are two of the reasons for believing that the asteroids are fragments of a planet that originally formed between Mars and Jupiter and was later disrupted by tidal strains as it repeatedly passed Jupiter. A third reason is that the meteors probably represent fragments of asteroids that passed near enough to Jupiter to be scattered in highly elliptical orbits throughout the solar system; and the mineralogy of the meteorites indicates that they crystallized under great pressure and relatively high temperature. In short, they are fragments of a celestial body of considerable size.

Some of the satellites also present special problems. The retrograde satellites presumably belonged originally to other planets and have been captured. Our moon is unique in being relatively large as compared with the planet about which it revolves and some astronomers have believed that it was produced by fission of the primordial earth and has been gradually receding into a larger orbit ever since.

In summary, it must be confessed that, in the words of Sir Harold Spencer Jones,

The problem of formulating a satisfactory theory of the solar system cannot be regarded as yet solved, though important advances have been made in recent years. The theories that involved the close approach of another star to the sun, or an actual collision, have been abandoned and it seems reasonably certain that an explanation has to be sought in the evolution of an extended system containing gas and solid particles. . . . The theory developed by Kuiper, though not entirely free from objection, appears at present to provide the most satisfactory explanation of the main features of the solar system and may with some modifications prove capable of leading to a theory that can be generally accepted [89].

Chapter 8

Formative Stages of the Earth

IF OUR reasoning in the preceding chapter is valid, the protoplanet that was to become the earth separated from the primaeval nebula as a rotating mass of gases and dust particles – a mass greatly exceeding the size of the present earth, not only because it was still diffuse but also because it included a large volume of gases that were subsequently lost. It is now our purpose to explore the steps by which this nebulous globe was transformed into the solid earth.

As a point of departure we need to know the approximate chemical composition of the protoplanet at its birth. Since the time was some four and a half thousand million years ago and subsequent changes in the earth have been profound, this might seem to be a forlorn hope. Actually we can infer some fundamental chemical relations with considerable confidence. Since the parent nebula was made of atomic particles driven away from the stars, the relative abundance of its chemical elements should agree with that in the stars, that is, with the cosmic abundance of the elements (table 6). Estimates of the cosmic abundance rest on two lines of evidence. First, the light coming to us from the stars, and from the sun, bears a coded message that identifies the chemical elements that are present. The spectroscope makes the identification quite certain. The way in which light reveals the composition of the sun and the stars may seem clear if we think first of an analogous phenomenon – sound. Sound is created by vibrations in the atmosphere and the pitch of the tone is determined by the wavelength, the longest vibrations producing the deepest tones and the shortest, the highest tones. A pure musical tone may be produced by vibrations of a single wave-length, but many sounds involve a distinctive complex of vibrations. Our ears are very sensitive to differences in the wave-length. Thus we can distinguish a bass viol from a flute or a bell by sound alone. Even when a full orchestra is playing, a trained musician can identify the several musical instruments whether they are playing in solo or in unison. Much more subtle distinctions are possible as when we recognize the voice of a friend over the telephone or of a favourite entertainer on radio. We can identify a thousand things about us by sound alone – the whistle of a train, the guttural blast of an ocean liner, the wail of a fire siren, the tinkling of a cow-bell, the song of a bird, the cry of a child, the voice of a friend

Light is fundamentally different from sound but in many ways the behaviour of light and sound waves are analogous. A beam of light is a stream of ultramicroscopic units of electromagnetic energy but it travels with a wavy motion, and the colour of the light depends on the wave-length, just as the pitch of sound depends on the wave-length. In the familiar light spectrum (as seen in a rainbow) the wave-length ranges from about 4,000 Ångströms in the violet to 7,000 Å in the red.* Our eyes are sensitive to large differences in the wave-length so that we readily distinguish the primary colours, but differences of a few Ångströms are too subtle for the human eye, and we turn to the spectroscope, an instrument designed to sort out the rays of different wave-lengths. In passing through a prism the light rays are refracted, and since the angle of refraction varies inversely with the wave-length, a narrow band of light is spread into a broad belt of coloured light – the spectrum. In the spectroscope this can be spread across a scale showing the wave-lengths in Ångström units and can be photographed for critical study.

When any chemical substance is heated to an incandescent gaseous condition it emits a limited number of light rays whose wave-lengths depend on the structure of its atoms. This produces a bright line spectrum. And since each chemical element has a unique atomic structure it produces a unique bright line spectrum. In controlled laboratory experiments the distinctive spectrum of each of the chemical elements has been determined and by matching these against the spectrum of a star, however remote, we can identify the elements that are present. And by techniques too technical to explain here it is also possible from spectroscopic analysis to determine the relative abundance of the elements present. At the temperature of the sun and the stars even the heavy metals are in a gaseous condition, and can be identified.

For the elements that are solid at lower temperatures the meteo-

* An Ångström is a unit of distance equal to 1/100,000,000 centimetre, and is represented by the symbol Å.

rites give us a check on the relative proportions of the non-gaseous elements. Using both methods, the spectroscope and the average composition of meteorites, several specialists have studied the composition of the sun and of a number of stars and have estimated the cosmic abundance of the elements. Table 6 gives the estimates for a few of the elements that are of particular importance for the early history of the earth. While they do not agree in detail all such estimates indicate that hydrogen and helium vastly exceed all the other elements.

TABLE 6

Cosmic abundance of the elements

Element	Ratio by Unsold	Ratio by Brown
Hydrogen (H)	5,100·0	35,000·0
Helium (He)	1,000·0	3,500·0
Oxygen (O)	28·0	22·0
Iron (Fe)	2·7	18·0
Nitrogen (N)	2·1	16·0
Magnesium (Mg)	1·7	0·8
Carbon (C)	1·0	8·0
Silica (Si)	1·0	1·0
Neon (Ne)		0·9–24
Sulphur (S)	0·43	0·35
Aluminum (Al)	0·10	0·08
Sodium (Na)	0·10	0·05
Calcium (Ca)		0·07
Argon (A)		0·0013–0·22

This table includes ten of the elements that are most important in the cosmic history of the earth. The abundance of silica (Si) is chosen as unity.

We are indebted to Urey [157] for a penetrating study of the consequences of such a composition during the formative stages of the earth. As the nebulous protoplanet slowly condensed, the atoms must have combined to form chemical compounds in accordance with thermodynamic principles that are generally well known. Although Dr Urey's analysis is too involved and too technical to be adequately reviewed here, the following conclusions appear to be safe.

1. The oxygen combined actively with silicon, aluminum, magnesium, iron, calcium and potassium to form complex silicates. It also combined with hydrogen to form water. *In the presence of a great excess of hydrogen no free oxygen could have persisted.*

2. Hydrogen united with nitrogen to form ammonia (NH_3), and with carbon to form methane (CH_4). Except for free hydrogen and helium these were the chief gases of the primaeval atmosphere.

3. The fate of iron depended on the temperature. Below about 25°C the iron oxides, Fe_2O_3 and Fe_3O_4, could form and would be stable. Iron sulphide (FeS) could also form. But if the temperature rose above 227°C, the oxides would be unstable and above 327°C the sulphide would be unstable. Above these limits metallic iron was the stable form.

4. The molecules of silicates and iron probably appeared as dust-like solid particles. To aid in their coagulation into larger masses Dr Urey suggests that water and liquid ammonia may have moistened them so that they stuck together like wet snowflakes as they were drawn together to form the solid earth.

5. The solid body of the growing planet must have consisted largely of silicates and iron; its atmosphere consisted of hydrogen, helium, ammonia and methane. (The major planets still consist largely of such gases.)

6. At its birth our protoplanet was vastly larger than the earth because it was still a diffuse nebula, but especially because it was largely made of the gases hydrogen and helium that were subsequently lost into space. Harrison Brown's table of cosmic abundances, cited by Urey [157], indicates that hydrogen is about seven hundred times as abundant as all the rest of the elements combined, and that if we except hydrogen, helium is about seventy times as abundant as all the rest combined. On the basis of such figures Kuiper [97] has estimated that at its birth the protoplanet may have had a mass about 1,200 times that of the present earth.

Having accumulated in the voids of space between the stars the parent nebula of the solar system must have been cold at first like the dark dust clouds that are now visible among the stars. As it grew in mass a gravitative field gradually developed, it began to contract, and adiabatic compression inevitably caused the temperature to rise. At the stage when the earth protoplanet separated from the rest, its temperature may still have been fairly low – perhaps within the range of the surface temperature of the present earth – but as it continued to contract adiabatic compression caused its temperature to continue to rise and Dr Urey calculates that it may eventually have reached a point between 2,000 and 3,000°C. Meanwhile the vast central part of the parent nebula that was eventually to become the

sun became much hotter and eventually reached a temperature at
which thermonuclear reaction occurred and it began to pour out
radiant energy as the sun does at present. The effect of the rising
temperature on the protoplanets near the sun was profound. None
of them was large enough to hold either hydrogen or helium, both of
which began to leak away into space; and as the sun approached its
present temperature its radiant energy literally blew these light gases
away just as it now does the tails of comets. Thus the minor planets
were greatly reduced in size, lost most of their gases and were reduced to solid earth-like bodies. But the radiant energy of the sun
decreased exponentially with distance and scarcely affected the
planets from Jupiter outward. Furthermore Jupiter and Saturn were
so large that in spite of their internal heat they could retain both
hydrogen and helium. They may, indeed, have captured much of the
gases blown away from the inner planets and have grown larger.

Evolution of the Earth's Atmosphere

How then can we account for the earth's present atmosphere so different from that of all the other planets ? First of all, the inert gases,
neon and argon, must have been present in approximately cosmic
ratios. Estimates of their cosmic abundance have varied rather
widely, but even if we accept the minimum estimates they should be
among the most abundant gases in our atmosphere since they do not
combine with other elements and could not be locked up in non-
volatile compounds, and since their escape velocity is comparable to
that of oxygen and nitrogen. On the contrary, they are among the
rarest components of our present atmosphere. To account for their
enormous depletion we must assume that at some early stage in the
earth's growth most of the primaeval atmosphere was lost and the
present gases were conserved because they were locked up in non-
volatile compounds in the solids of the earth whence they have subsequently been freed and sweated out to create a new atmosphere.
This could have happened if the temperature at the surface was
raised to near 3,000°C, for at this level the escape velocity of the
gases would have been reduced to a point at which they could all
leak away as hydrogen and helium now do.

Urey has analysed the conditions in which the chief constituents
of our present atmosphere – oxygen, hydrogen, nitrogen and carbon
– may have been conserved in non-volatile combinations to be

sweated out of the interior to restore our present atmosphere. Oxygen, for example, was built into the silicates and iron oxides; both oxygen and hydrogen were conserved as water, and some of it may have combined with the silicates and some may have been adsorbed on the accumulating solid particles to be deeply buried in the growing solid earth and some of it was probably retained as water; hydrogen and nitrogen were probably both conserved as ammonium chloride (NH_4Cl); nitrogen was also held as metallic nitrides (especially titanium nitride (TiN)); carbon was present in the residue of methane (CH_4) and was conserved as metallic carbides (especially iron carbide (FeC)) and as graphite. Then as heat was generated within the solid earth by radioactivity these gases were gradually freed and sweated out to the surface in volcanic emanations, fumaroles, and hot springs.

Changing temperature conditions played an important role in determining the stability of these compounds. During the earliest stage of the protoplanet the temperature was still probably rather low, but as the gaseous mass shrank, adiabatic compression caused the temperature to rise to a maximum which Urey calculates to have been between 2,000 and 3,000°C. It was at this time that most of the primaeval atmosphere was lost. Then the surface temperature fell again since the solid earth did not suffer contraction. However, the interior heated up because of radioactivity, and the gases locked up in the non-volatile solids began to be freed.

As the atmosphere was restored to its present mass, important changes in its composition took place. In its upper reaches water is dissociated by the incoming radiation from the sun and the hydrogen escaped from the earth while the oxygen is retained. In this way free oxygen has been continually added to the atmosphere throughout geologic time. For an excellent but somewhat technical account of the addition of oxygen see Berkner and Marshall [12]. The residue of ammonia from the primaeval atmosphere, as well as that sweated out of the interior, was then attacked by free oxygen to form water and free nitrogen ($4NH_3 + 3O_2 = 4N + 6H_2O$). Metallic nitrides were broken down into metallic oxides and free nitrogen (which at surface temperatures is virtually inert and continues to accumulate). Residual methane reacted with oxygen to form water and carbon dioxide ($CH_4 + 2O_2 = CO_2 + 2H_2O$). Graphite was oxidized to CO_2. Carbon dioxide should be much more abundant in the atmosphere than it is except for the fact that it reacts so readily with the silicates to form carbonates ($Ca(CO_3)_2$, $NaCO_3$, $Mg(CO_3)_2$, etc.). In this connection water has played an important role in constantly eroding the rocky surface and exposing fresh silicates to the atmosphere. Water is one of the chief volatiles brought to the surface by volcanic activity, and it has been added much more rapidly than it has been dissociated. As a result water has steadily increased throughout geologic time.

The appearance of plants, more than a billion years ago, introduced a new factor. They feed upon CO_2 and water to form the tissue, cellulose ($C_6H_{10}O_5$), and as they decay most of the hydrogen and oxygen are distilled away leaving a residue of carbon. Accumulations of plant tissue have thus become beds of coal or graphite and tiny particles deposited with the mud form the pigment of the black shales and slates. Since the beginning of Paleozoic time a very large amount of carbon has been stored in the sedimentary rocks while water and oxygen have been returned to the atmosphere.

Growth of the Oceans

In the preceding section the concept was developed that most of the primaeval atmosphere leaked away into space during an early stage of high temperature and was subsequently replaced by gases sweated out of the interior. Since water would be vaporized at the postulated temperature, surface water must at the same time have largely disappeared, and the oceans like the atmosphere were, in large part, subsequently derived from the interior of the earth. But was this accomplished rapidly and during the formative stages, or has seawater increased throughout geologic time? The answer has far-reaching implications.

In a magnificent essay entitled *Geologic History of Sea Water*, Rubey [133] has made a strong case for the belief that both the atmosphere and the oceans have been largely derived from the interior of the earth and that the oceans have grown in volume throughout geologic time.

Rubey considers first the sedimentary record. The ratios among the common rock-forming oxides in the ancient sediments can be accounted for as the result of weathering of the igneous rocks from which they were derived. But the more volatile materials, especially H_2O, CO_2, chlorine, nitrogen, and sulphur, that are buried in the sediments, or are present in the atmosphere and hydrosphere, are far too abundant to have been derived in this way. Either they have been inherited from a vast primaeval atmosphere or they have been sweated out of the interior of the earth. Carbon may be used to determine the choice between these two alternatives. Rubey calculates that the amount of carbon buried in the sedimentary rocks as carbonates and as organic carbon (graphite, coal, petroleum, the pigment of black shales, etc.) is about six hundred times as great as that now present in the atmosphere and in the hydrosphere and in living things. If this buried carbon were freed to the atmosphere it would take the form of carbon dioxide (CO_2), and Rubey shows that if as little as one per cent of the buried carbon were thus suddenly added to the atmosphere and the hydrosphere it would cause the extinction of many forms of animal life (see also chapter 6, page 102). In view of the fossil record it appears evident therefore that at least for the last five hundred to six hundred million years (during which most of the buried carbon was being extracted) carbon dioxide in the atmosphere and the oceans did not greatly exceed the proportions now present. On the other hand, carbon dioxide is being used up in the weathering of the crust at such a rate that if more were not being supplied to counterbalance the loss the present supply would be depleted within a few million years so that carbonate sediments would cease to form and brucite ($Mg(OH)_2$) would become a common marine deposit; and since no significant deposits of brucite are known even in the ancient sediments it seems evident that the amount of CO_2 in the atmosphere and in the oceans has remained relatively constant throughout much of geologic time. This implies a gradual and continuous supply to make up for that used up in weathering and buried in the sedimentary rocks.

If this is true, it must apply also to the other volatiles such as H_2O, chlorine, nitrogen, and sulphur. Only a small percentage of the water is withdrawn and locked up in the sediments, however, and Rubey concludes that the amount of sea-water has steadily increased and the oceans have grown larger – probably deeper – throughout geologic time.

Rubey next examines the probable source of these volatiles that exceed the quantity supplied merely by the weathering of the crustal rocks. It is well known that they are copiously supplied by volcanoes and by fumaroles and hot springs arising from intrusive magmas in the crust. As such magmas cool and crystallize, the volatiles tend thus to rise and escape to the surface. Of course this source would fail after a few million years if new magmas were not continually brought up from deep within the mantle, but the geologic record shows clearly that vast bodies of magma have, indeed, approached the surface from time to time throughout the geologic past. Rubey postulates that local fusion within the outer several hundred miles of the mantle has been the source of such rising magmas. Even since his study was made, evidence has been growing rapidly that large-scale convection currents in the mantle are continually bringing fresh material from great depths in the mantle up to the crust and that these are probably the major cause of diastrophism that has caused mountains to rise and has renewed the continents to counterbalance the effects of reduction by erosion. This problem is discussed further in chapter 11.

If it be granted that the hydrosphere has grown throughout the geologic past the corollary follows that the ocean basins have grown larger. Have they grown in area or have they grown deeper? They could only have increased in area if parts of the continents have foundered to oceanic depths. Until recent decades the foundering of large continental areas was considered possible, but geophysical investigations of the ocean floor now make this seem highly improbable. The continental platforms are clearly vast plates of granitic rocks twenty to forty miles in thickness having specific gravity appreciably lighter than the basaltic rocks that floor the ocean basins. It is for this reason that the continents float high on the mantle like vast icebergs of granite. Seismic studies prove that no large bodies of such light rocks underlie the ocean basins. The obvious inference is that the ocean basins have increased in depth rather than in area and the granitic plates that form the continents have grown thicker so that they float high enough to keep pace with the increasing volume of seawater.

Permanence of Continents and Oceans

The character of the sedimentary deposits on the continents clearly indicate that no more than trivial areas, mostly marginal, have ever been parts of the deep ocean floor. At the same time seismic studies of the floor beneath the ocean basins clearly indicate that no appreciable areas have ever been underlain by rocks of continental types. The clear implication is that the continental areas have always been continental and the ocean basins always ocean basins. This does not prove, or necessarily imply, that the continents have always occupied the positions they now hold. The question of continental drift is a major problem which is treated in chapter 11. It may be pertinent to speculate here, however, how the continents came into being and why the light granitic rocks rising from the depths were concentrated in the continental areas which comprise less than one fourth the area of the earth's surface. Why were they not uniformly spread over the surface like cream over the surface of a vessel of milk?

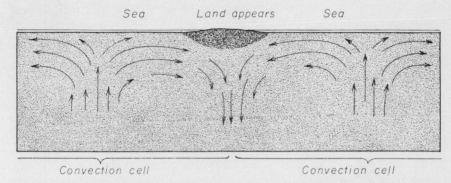

Sea   *Land appears*   *Sea*

Convection cell   *Convection cell*

Figure 45. Vertical section to represent the upper part of two convection cells in the mantle and the accumulation of granitic material (darker shading) between them

This is one of the great mysteries of the earth and although it has always been a challenge to geologists it has remained a moot question. The concept of convection currents in the mantle, developed during recent decades, now offers the first hope for a rational answer. Discussion of the evidence for convection currents is reserved for chapter 11, but the implication of the concept for our present problem may be suggested here.

According to this concept the mantle rock above some locally over-heated region at great depth expands and slowly flows upward where it spreads laterally, is slightly cooled, and descends again just as liquid does in a vessel over a local flame. This creates a convection cell (figure 45) in which the current rises to the surface, or near the surface, and then flows laterally to cooler areas before descending. It is well known from the studies of large bodies of intrusive rocks in the crust that differentiation of the constituent minerals has generally occurred so that a magma of average composition may separate into fractions of markedly different composition, parts of which crystallize as granitic rocks and other parts as gabbroic rocks. It seems altogether probable that as convection currents rise some such differentiation must take place and if so the more acidic increment, being lighter, would tend to remain at the top, just as slag accumulates above the molten iron in a smelter. If so, the lateral flow over the top of the convection cell would tend to drag it to the mar-

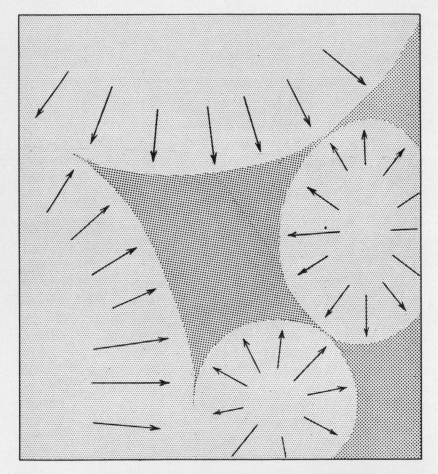

Figure 46. Idealized diagram to represent four convection cells in plan view with granitic material (darker shading) concentrated in the spaces between them

gins of the cell where it would accumulate while the denser material settled again into the depths. Here it would form granitic rocks. Before such differentiation had occurred the entire earth may have been covered by a universal, shallow sea, but as the granitic masses grew thicker by addition at the bottom they, being lighter than the rest, would tend to rise (as icebergs do) above the rest of the mantle until they emerged from the sea to form the first land areas – the nuclei of the continents. And so long as the convection currents persisted they would tend to grow higher and spread by lateral accretion. The convection cells were probably hundreds or even some thousands of miles across and in plan may have been circular or elongated or irregular in shape depending on the shape of the hottest regions at depths. Figure 46 suggests in highly diagrammatic form the accumulation of granitic rocks in the areas between several great convection cells.

It may be granted that this interpretation is still highly speculative, but it is attractive because it is the only rational explanation yet conceived for the origin and growth of the continents. It is now receiving intensive study by geophysicists and will be considered further in chapter 11.

Chapter 9

Earth's Ever-changing Face

There rolls the deep where grew the tree,
Oh Earth what changes has thou seen !
There where the long street roars, hath been
The stillness of the central sea.

TENNYSON

THE ANCIENT psalmists sang of the 'eternal hills', and so long as the earth was believed to be only a few thousand years old it was generally believed that its surface had changed but little since the creation. Nothing could be further from the truth. Great mountain systems have arisen time and again only to be planed down within a few million years by the relentless forces of erosion, and the land surface has varied widely as vast shallow seas at times spread far inland flooding the lowlands, and again retreated into the ocean basins. Continents now separated have at times been connected by land bridges and others now connected have at times been separated by the sea. Changes in the height and extent of the land surface have been endless.

The Forces of Erosion

When exposed to the weather rocks are not quite stable. Limestone is carried away in solution, especially in warm humid regions where sinkholes, underground caverns and hidden rivers bear witness to solution by underground water.

Chemical weathering is most active under a warm moist climate, especially where the relief is sufficient to permit downward circulation of rainwater through the pores and crevices in the rocks. Here the water carries CO_2 and organic acids produced by the decay of plant tissues. These weak acids attack the feldspars and ferromagnesian minerals of all igneous rocks, causing them to weaken and eventually decay into clay minerals, meanwhile releasing part of the silica which, along with the carbonates, is carried away in solution. The quartz crystals, being relatively stable, are freed to form sand grains. Thus chemical decay maintains the veneer of soil overlying a weathered zone of weakened and crumbling rock that may range in thickness to more than one hundred feet.

In colder regions at high altitude, or high latitude, mechanical disintegration is commonly more active than chemical decay. This is caused chiefly by alternate freezing and thawing. Water seeps down into the rocks along cracks and crevices and even penetrates minute pores and, when freezing, it expands enough to exert bursting pressure. This widens and deepens existing fractures, allowing more water to flow in when melting occurs. Alternate freezing and thawing thus reduces the surface to gravel and loose rock fragments. On rocky cliffs the ice may eventually pry off large masses of rock which go tumbling or sliding down the slopes.

Loose particles freed by weathering tend to creep down the slopes under the influence of gravity and are washed down by surface run-off during rains. Eventually they reach the streams where the fine material is carried away in suspension and the sand and gravel goes leaping and rolling along the bottom. Where the current is rapid the bottom load abrades the channel like a sand blast and the stream becomes a flexible rasp. Where relief is high, cutting is chiefly downward and valleys tend to be deep and narrow. But here, also, mass wastage is most active as loose material creeps down the steep slopes. When a valley is deepened to near base-level (e.g. sea level or some local obstruction) the stream can no longer deepen its channel and tends to meander, undercutting its banks first on one side and then the other. Thus streams widen their valleys and slowly migrate laterally until the divides between are virtually planed away. An elevated region passes through stages in its development that have been figuratively termed youth, maturity, and old age. In the first stage, after uplift, drainage is not well organized, valleys are deep and narrow but tributaries are not fully developed, and divides between streams retain much of the old uplifted surface. In maturity the regional relief attains a maximum as valleys reach their full depth and tributaries are deeply incised in the major divides between the master streams. Old age comes on as the main streams are at grade and are widening their valleys while tributaries gradually reduce the divides between until the entire region becomes almost a plane, not far above sea level (a peneplane). Obviously erosion is slowest during old age when the streams flow sluggishly and are able to carry only mud and silt.

Ice is an important agent of erosion on lofty mountains and in the polar regions where snow accumulates to form glaciers that creep down the valleys or spread over the surface with a slow but inexorable motion. The rock debris frozen into the base of the ice scours and deepens and widens the valleys; and where the ice flows as a sheet, as in Greenland and Antarctica, it scours away all the soil and transports it along as though it were a gigantic bulldozer, meanwhile polishing and scoring the floor over which it rides (plate 35).

The moraines that accumulate below the ends of valley glaciers and about the margins of ice sheets are readily recognizable, whether modern or ancient. Fine and coarse materials are carried along together without sorting; chemical weathering is almost absent but abrasion on the bottom produces finely divided particles of fresh rock. The coarse fragments are abraded on the lower side where they ride on the bottom, are flattened (or soled), and are striated by dragging on the floor. From time to time many of them rotate so that more than one side is abraded, and the orientation changes so that younger striations cross the older ones.

When the material thus transported finally comes to rest it is unsorted as to size, with striated and soled boulders imbedded in an unstratified mass of ground up rock powder (rock flour). This is glacial till. Meanwhile the floor over which the ice has moved is polished and grooved in a distinctive way. The surface features of the till left directly by the melting ice are also distinctive, with swells and swales like the uneven deposits pushed together by a giant bulldozer. The meltwater flowing off the ice generally carries a heavy load of the finer material which it gradually drops to form graded valley trains down the valleys and around the margins of great ice sheets. It may cover the surface beyond the marginal till with a wide debris apron of stratified 'outwash'. A vast ice sheet such as those covering Greenland and Antarctica moves laterally with little regard for the underlying topography and may carry boulders of distinctive types of rock far from their source and across divides as streams could not do. And should the ice melt far back or disappear, normal erosion gradually winnows out and carries away the finer material leaving isolated boulders of foreign hard rock scattered over the surface as 'erratics'. All such deposits derived from glaciers, whether till or outwash, are embraced in the term 'glacial drift'. We shall return to this subject in chapter 10.

Although soil erosion and gullying are well known and locally impressive, the erosion over a broad landscape is too gradual to be perceived; but every roily stream in flood should remind us that the land is being carried away. The Mississippi River, for example, transports to the Gulf of Mexico an annual load of some five hundred million tons of mud and fine sand [52]. Since it takes about eleven cubic feet of granite to weigh a ton, this load of sediment is the equivalent in weight of 5,500 million cubic feet of granite. At this rate, since the beginning of the Christian Era the Mississippi would have delivered to the sea the equivalent of eleven million million cubic feet or about seventy-four cubic miles of granite. Most of this load comes, of course, from the tributaries heading in the high country of the Rockies where erosion is much more rapid than it is on plains. In the next section we shall examine evidence of the length of time required to reduce a bold mountain system to a lowland by the forces of erosion.

Growth and Decay of Mountains

The history of a great mountain system is long and complex. Uplift is too slow to be perceptible within a human lifetime. Even within historic time no appreciable change has been recognized in the height of any mountains (except volcanoes). But since the beginning of the Pleistocene Epoch (i.e. within the last million years or less) several of the young mountains have been elevated by a mile or more. Evidence from three continents may be cited. In the Kashmir Valley, high in the Himalayas, lake beds bearing mid-Pleistocene plant fossils have been found at an elevation of ten thousand feet. Among these is a tropical fig and a species of laurel, both of which still live in India but are limited to subtropical climate at an elevation of less than six thousand feet. From this Puri [128] infers that regional uplift of at least four thousand feet has occurred since mid-Pleistocene time. On the high plateau of the central Andes (the Altiplanici) similar lake beds have yielded plant fossils of late Pliocene age. They are now at an elevation of about twelve thousand feet, but Berry states that they are types of plants that could not have grown above six thousand feet, and he infers that the high plateau was lifted by more than a mile during Pleistocene time. Finally, Axelrod and

Ting [2] have studied fossil pollen from lake beds on the High Sierra, near Mt Whitney, and from similar lake beds in Owens Valley far below (plate 24). The pollen represents plants that occupied the region in mid-Pleistocene time but could not have grown at an altitude of more than six thousand feet. From this it is concluded that the Sierra Nevada Range in this area has been uplifted by some six thousand feet since the plants were growing.

Phases of Mountain History

It is significant that all the great systems of folded mountains have developed according to a common plan. The Rocky Mountains of North America (plate 27) afford an almost ideal illustration of this plan because they are still young, their major structures are not too complex and are still grandly displayed, and the regional history has been comprehensively studied.

The first phase of their long and complex history was one of pre-paration preceding the actual orogeny. This involved the formation of the Rocky Mountain geosyncline, a vast trough in the earth's crust several hundred miles wide and some two thousand miles long. It began to take form early in Jurassic time and before the close of that period the sea had crept far inland along its axis from both north and south (figure 47). It continued to subside until near the close of the Cretaceous Period, and by that time the pre-Jurassic floor lay from three to five miles below sea level along its axis and the trough was occupied by a vast inland sea that divided the continent into two land masses (plate 28). Meanwhile, however, sediment eroded from the adjacent land had been transported into the trough, filling it almost as fast as it sank so that the sea remained relatively shallow. Indeed, at times large parts of it were filled above sea level. This enormous fill was gradually consolidated into layered sedimentary rocks that would later rise into mountain folds. This, the geosyn-clinal phase, lasted for about a hundred million years.

The second phase was one of intense deformation as the floor of the geosyncline buckled up into great arches and the sedimentary rocks were folded and crushed and faulted by forces coming from the west. Along the eastern side of the geosyncline (plate 27), in Colorado and Wyoming, each range became a relatively simple open arch in which the old granite floor was brought far above sea level with a towering cover of sedimentary rocks (e.g. the Laramie and

Front ranges, the Bighorns, and the Black Hills) and these ranges were separated by broad structural basins (e.g. Powder River Basin, Bighorn Basin, Laramie Basin, Wind River Basin, and Wasatch

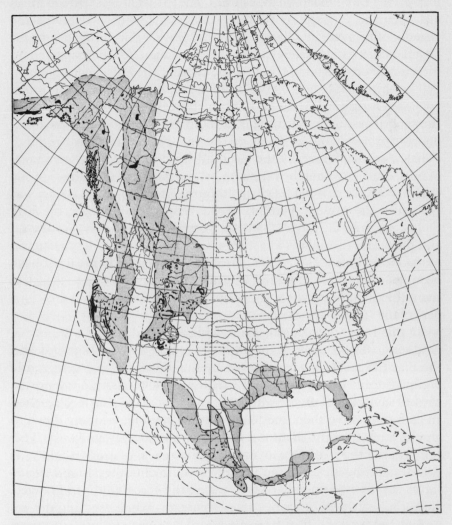

Figure 47. Paleogeographic map of North America in Late Jurassic time when a large seaway covered much of the subsiding Rocky Mountain geosyncline. Black indicates present outcrops of Late Jurassic rocks. From Schuchert [140]

Basin). Farther west, however, the major folds were overturned toward the east and broken by enormous low angle faults along which great slices of the sedimentary rocks thousands of feet thick

143

were shoved one upon another to form a great mountain complex. On the Lewis fault which lies along the front of the Rockies in northern Montana an enormous plate of Precambrian sedimentary formations more than two miles thick was thrust at least fifteen miles out over the Cretaceous rocks of the plains. These relations are grandly displayed in Glacier National Park. This orogenic phase began late in Cretaceous time and continued for perhaps ten to fifteen million years dying out by the close of the Paleocene epoch.

The third phase was one of relative stability and long continued erosion. During Paleocene and Eocene time the material eroded from the ranges gradually filled the intermont basins and spread as a vast debris apron far out in front of the mountains to form the High Plains. Although much of the basin fill was later removed, remnants of horizontal beds perched high up on the flanks of the ranges prove that it was once as much as eleven thousand feet thick and its top was graded to the present summits of the ranges. Meanwhile, by early Oligocene time the range had been worn down to the level of the fill and the entire region was a vast plain broken only by widely scattered monadnocks (plate 25). At this time the continental divide must have been less than three thousand feet above sea level. It had taken less than thirty million years to reduce the original mountains to a peneplane (plates 22, 25).

By this time sluggish streams flowing east had spread a veneer of sediment over the summits of the front ranges and the Bighorns and the Black Hills. This was followed by the fourth phase – very gentle regional uplift in the form of a broad arch with its crest along the present continental divide where the old peneplaned surface reached an elevation of ten thousand to eleven thousand feet sloping down to an elevation of eight thousand feet or less both east and west. This rejuvenated the streams and started a new cycle of erosion. Now, as the streams cut through the veneer of sediments they found themselves superposed upon hard rock where they crossed the old ranges. Here they cut deep narrow gorges (plate 23) while they rapidly removed the weak fill of the basins and developed the present broad flat surfaces between the ranges (plate 26). The major structures of the Rockies thus date from the orogeny at the end of the Mesozoic, but the present relief is due to regional uplift and differential erosion during the latter half of the Cenozoic era.

The final phase of the history of the Rockies is yet to come, for they will eventually be reduced again to a stable lowland. This final phase we know from older mountains in other regions whose roots remain where the relief is slight. Many such ranges are known in the ancient shields of the continents which once were scenes of great disturbance but for more than six hundred million years have been stable regions of slight relief.

The history of the Andes of South America roughly parallels that of the Rockies. Each system developed out of a Mesozoic geosyncline; the orogenic phase which produced the major structures occurred about the end of the Mesozoic Era; both were peneplaned by mid-Cenozoic time, and both were gently upwarped to their present elevation since that time.

Of course no two great mountain systems are alike in detail. The forces of deformation come from independent sources and the shape and arrangement of local ranges are influenced by older structures and rock masses in the crust below. The amount of igneous activity also varies with regional conditions far below the surface. In the Rockies, for example, volcanoes were only locally active during the final uplift and all are long since extinct, but in the Andes a chain of majestic volcanoes crowns the system with peaks rising above twenty thousand feet and several of them are still active.

The Alps and the Himalayas are young mountains probably still in the orogenic phase which has been long and extremely complex. Nevertheless all this great mountain complex arose out of a very broad geosyncline that during Mesozoic time embraced all of southern Europe and extended eastward through the Himalayan region. This, the great Tethyan geosyncline, was covered by the Tethyan sea in which a great thickness of Mesozoic and early Cenozoic sedimentary rocks was deposited. In Jurassic time compression from the south caused two or three great arches to rise out of the sea. Although this marks the beginning of the Alpine structures, the region as a whole remained submerged during most of Cretaceous time. Then came further compression from the south and some uplift. The first decided uplift and thrust faulting occurred in Eocene time. Marine water returned between the rising arches and persisted widely until about the middle of the Oligocene epoch when the first great paroxysm of Alpine orogeny caused recumbent folds to rise as mountain arcs out of the sea and to ride northward to pile up as a series of great nappes. Further uplift and deformation occurred in the Pliocene, and the final regional uplift brought the Alps to their present height during Pleistocene time.

145

The history thus sketched is, in general, like that of the Carpathians and the Himalayas. In the southern great range of the Himalayas, fossiliferous marine beds of Eocene age now occur at an elevation of twenty thousand feet bearing witness to the tremendous uplift of the region during the last forty million years. All these mountains are undergoing intensive erosion but whether the orogenic phase is over no one can tell.

Since all the great mountain systems have developed according to the master plan described above, they must be the product of some basic and far-reaching force within the earth: This we shall examine in chapter 11.

Igneous Activity

Volcanoes are too well known to need description, but they vary widely in shape and in the kinds of material they eject. In general those that rise from the ocean floor pour out basic lavas reflecting the nature of the crust beneath; but on the continents the lavas are more varied and generally more acidic (rich in silica). The shape of the cones and the violence of eruption is largely determined by the composition of the rising magma. The more acidic lava is generally highly charged with gases which upon the sudden release of pressure expand with great violence so that the lava is ejected in a frothy condition. As it is exploded into the air and chilled, the bubbles burst into tiny glassy fragments to form 'volcanic ash'. Larger fragments appear like cinders, and large blobs of lava become more or less rounded in flight before solidifying, and fall back as volcanic 'bombs' each of which, like a loaf of bread, has a crust of more compact material and a vesicular interior.

If the lava is highly fluid and not highly charged with gases, it streams out without much violence and flows far out from the vent to form a broad cone with gentle slopes. Kilauea on the Island of Hawaii is a fine example. This is characteristic of the more basic lavas.

Acidic lavas are generally more viscous and more highly charged with gases and reach the surface with explosive violence, forming steep cones of ash and 'cinders'. Lavas of intermediate composition erupt with less violence and generally build cones of a combination of cinders and lava flows.

The rise of lava is intermittent and, after a period of active eruption lasting for months, or even years, a volcano becomes dormant when the pressure below has been relieved. It may remain inactive for hundreds or even thousands of years, while pressure builds up below, and then suddenly burst into violent eruption. Such was the history of Vesuvius, for example. For many centuries before the Christian Era it had lain dormant, villages had grown up about it, and its fertile slopes were covered with vineyards. In the year AD 63 began a succession of earthquakes that continued intermittently for sixteen years and then, on 24 August, AD 79, a violent eruption occurred. Poison gases and falling ash and cinders overwhelmed and buried the cities of Pompeii and Herculaneum. Since that date there have been several lesser eruptions but during much of the time visitors have dared to climb its slope and peer into the crater.

Nearly all existing volcanoes are old by human standards but one, Paracutin, has been under constant observation since its birth. This vicinity, some two hundred miles west of Mexico City, was shaken by earthquakes for several days in February 1943, culminating in some two hundred quakes during the single day of 19 February. On the next day a farmer working in his field observed a cloud of gas and dust rising from a crevice that had opened in the ground. During the night the eruption began and by morning it had formed a cinder cone about thirty feet high from which ash and large chunks of rock were being hurled into the air and a cloud of vapour and ash arose high above it. Within a month the cone was more than five hundred feet high and by the end of the first year it was one thousand feet high. Finally liquid lava burst out far down on its flanks and flowed out to a distance of several miles, finally engulfing and destroying the village of San Juan Parangaricutiro some six miles away. Meanwhile a pall of volcanic dust settled over a wide area of the surrounding country crushing the roofs of houses and killing the vegetation, including forest trees. After about nine years the activity died down and there has been little change since.

The outburst of lava about the flanks of a volcanic cone is a common phenomenon. By the time the cone has reached a height of hundreds of feet the hydrostatic pressure within the conduit becomes so great as to burst the unconsolidated cinder cone and allow the lava to spill out below the top. Thus many volcanic cones show alternating layers of steeply dipping ash and cinders and of lava.

In some volcanic fields volcanoes several miles apart behave quite differently. On the island of Hawaii, for example, the volcano Kilauea emits highly fluid lava which wells up quietly and from time

147

to time has flowed far out to build a very low broad cone. For many years it has been possible to maintain an observation laboratory on its summit even during eruptions. In contrast, Mauna Loa, less than twenty-five miles away, has erupted intermittently but with great violence and has built a beautiful symmetrical cone that rises to a height of about thirteen thousand feet above sea level. Clearly the conduits of the two volcanoes are independent and come from different magma chambers. Furthermore, studies of many of the older and deeply eroded volcanoes in other parts of the world show that the lava ejected at different stages in their history has varied in composition. These facts confirm the belief that during the course of time the magma in a great magma chamber differentiates into different fractions, as cream separates from milk, the more acidic fraction tending to float above the more basic part. Thus if two conduits arise from different parts of the magma chamber, as in the case of the Hawaiian volcanoes, they bring different kinds of lava to the surface; or after one fraction of the differentiated magma has been drawn off another type may follow.

The vast lava flows (figure 16) that built the great basalt plateaus described in chapter 4 appear to have issued from a complex of fissures instead of restricted conduits, and have shown almost no explosive activity; the highly fluid lava spread like water seeking its own level and forming lakes of molten rock many miles across yet only a few feet deep.

Iceland represents a more complex association of basalt flows and volcanoes. It is the summit of an immense pile of extrusive igneous rocks built up from the sea floor and most of the flows have been gentle, but a violent eruption of the volcano Skaptarjokul in 1783 is said to have killed one-fifth of the population of the island.

Volcanoes are associated with zones of active deformation in the crust. At present they form a 'ring of fire' around the Pacific. They follow the crest of the Andes in South America and the Sierra Madre Occidentale in Mexico. Recently extinct cones rise majestically above the Cascade Range from California to Washington, both dormant and active ones follow the Aleutian Arc of Alaska, they crown the Japanese island chain, the Philippines, and the East Indies. Another great chain of volcanoes runs eastward from the Mediterranean. Others lie along the great Rift Valley of eastern Africa. All are in regions of recent crustal unrest; none occur in the great shields or on the stable platforms of the continents.

148

But volcanoes were not always distributed thus. During parts of the Paleozoic era when the North Atlantic was rimmed with growing mountains it had its 'ring of fire'. A large field of volcanoes was active in northern Wales in Ordovician time, and another was present in southern England during the Devonian Period. New England and the Maritime Provinces of Canada saw great volcanic activity at times from the Ordovician Period to late in the Paleozoic Era. Lava flows were widespread in Newfoundland during the Ordovician Period (plate 30) and volcanoes were active east of the Appalachian geosyncline as far south as Tennessee. Finally, during Triassic time extensive lava flows spilled over subsiding structural basins from Nova Scotia to Virginia. But when crustal deformation died out, igneous activity ceased, and for the last 180 million years eastern North America has seen no volcanic activity. In western Europe, likewise, igneous activity ceased with the demise of the Variscan Alps late in the Paleozoic Era. (The denuded stumps of volcanoes in the central plateau of France are of late Cenozoic age and were associated with the building of the Alps.)

In Precambrian time the shield areas of each of the continents were the scene of colossal igneous activity, but they have been quiet and free of such activity for the last six hundred million years or more. The growth of mountains has commonly been accompanied by massive intrusions of igneous rocks and intensive metamorphism of the deeply buried rocks of all kinds. Indeed, volcanoes are generally the surface manifestation of the deep intrusions below. In short, igneous activity and crustal deformation are associated manifestations of forces originating deep within the earth – forces that have developed at diverse times and in different parts of the earth in an ever-changing pattern.

Ebb and Flow of the Ancient Seas

Each of the continents has experienced a series of partial but widespread submergences when shallow seas crept slowly in over the lowlands and then retreated again. North America will be chosen for illustration not only because it is most familiar to the author but particularly because the lifelong researches of Charles Schuchert have made its paleogeographic history better known than that of any other continent. Two of the several great cycles of submergence will serve to illustrate the phenomenon.

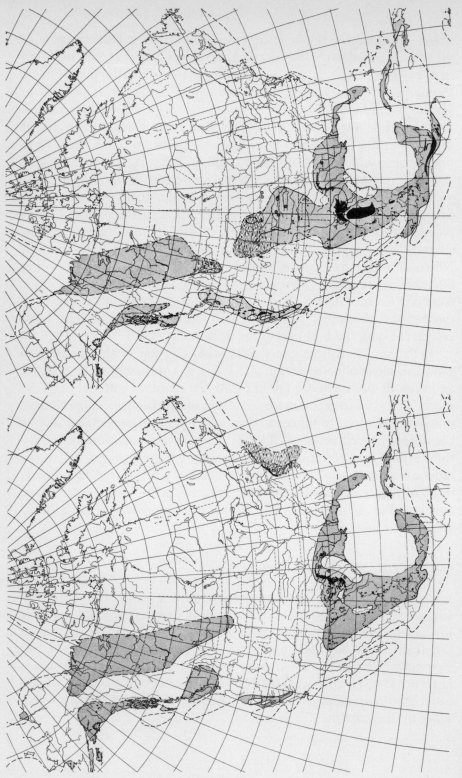

Figures 48, 49. Two stages in the advance of the seas in North America during Early Cretaceous time. After Schuchert

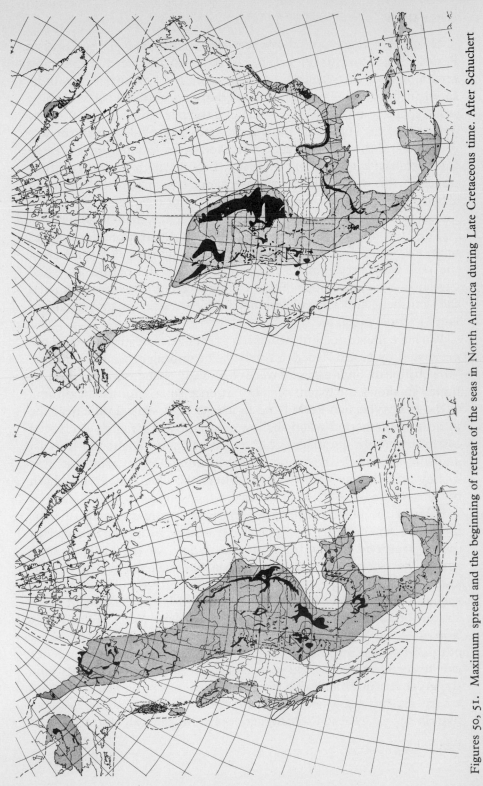

Figures 50, 51. Maximum spread and the beginning of retreat of the seas in North America during Late Cretaceous time. After Schuchert

North America stood above sea level at the end of the Jurassic Period, but slow subsidence began early in Cretaceous time and several marine embayments soon occupied the lowest parts, as indicated in figure 48. With gradually changing outlines these shallow seas expanded until past the middle of the period when about thirty per cent of the continent was submerged. Then the movement was reversed and the seas gradually retreated again leaving the continent fully exposed at the end of the period. Figures 48 to 51 illustrate four stages in this great cycle of submergence which covered a span of almost seventy million years. The evidence for these seaways is to be found, of course, in the marine deposits spread over their floors.

The Devonian cycle will serve as a second illustration. Four stages in an ever-changing scene are illustrated in figures 52 to 55. At first the seas were very limited and at the end of the period they had vanished, but for millions of years in between, great seaways crossed the continent and virtually reduced North America to a group of large islands.

We have illustrated but two of ten great cycles of submergence experienced by North America since the beginning of Cambrian time. The outline of lands and seas were constantly changing. For example, figure 56 shows the extent of submergence soon after the beginning of the Pennsylvanian Period and figure 57 represents a time near the middle of the period when shallow seas and vast swamps alternated east of the 100th meridian and the coal fields of Oklahoma, Illinois, and the Appalachian region were forming. How prescient was Tennyson when he wrote, 'There where the long street roars, hath been the stillness of the central sea'.

Each of the other continents experienced similar cycles of submergence separated by emergence. In Europe as in North America they correspond in number with the periods of the geologic time scale. This is generally true also in Asia wherever the geology is well known (i.e. in European Russia, in India, and in China). Africa is exceptional in having been more stable and largely emergent since Precambrian time, so that marine sedimentary rocks are virtually limited to the Atlas mountain region in the north and to Cape Colony at the far south. But in both these regions the times of submergence can be correlated in general with those described above. In Australia the great central shield, like most of Africa, has remained stable and emergent, but the eastern part of the continent and the western margin record cycles of submergence that, in general, match those of

North America and Europe. South America has a record paralleling that of North America.

The record of the ebb and flow of marine waters upon the continents poses three fundamental problems that are still the subject of serious study and considerable controversy. The first is: were submergences essentially synchronous in the several continents, or did the continents rise and sink independently? In the large view they seem clearly to have been synchronous. This is indicated by the fact that fossiliferous marine formations in regions as remote as Russia, China, Japan, India, and South America can be correlated readily with the systems established in Europe and North America. Even in far-off Australia the several parts of a very thick Devonian sequence can be correlated in detail with the Devonian units of Europe and North America. The Ordovician formations of Australia likewise include faunal zones that are well known in Europe and America. In some regions the cycles of submergence are less complete and emergences were longer than in others but, by and large, they fall into a common framework.

The second question is this: were the changes due to eustatic rise and fall of sea level or did each continent rise and sink independently? The fact that submergences were largely synchronous suggests the first alternative. But rise and fall of sea level could only be explained by changes in the capacity of the ocean basins or in the volume of marine water. As explained in chapter 7, there is strong evidence that the oceans have steadily increased in volume throughout geologic time, but most of the increase must have come before the beginning of Cambrian time. Evidence was cited also that the area of the oceans has not changed materially. Rise and fall of sea level could therefore be due only to alternate deepening and uplift of some large areas of the floor of the ocean basins. Even if eustatic changes in sea level have occurred it is not necessary to assume that all the continents should have been affected to the same degree. The continents float in isostatic balance on the denser rock of the mantle and each has its own distinctive complex of rock masses. Each shows clear evidence of warping and of the rise of mountain systems that are largely independent of the great cycles of submergence and emergence. Whenever these movements are out of phase with the rise and fall of sea level, exceptions to the general pattern of flooding would naturally occur.

The third and most fundamental question is: what colossal and

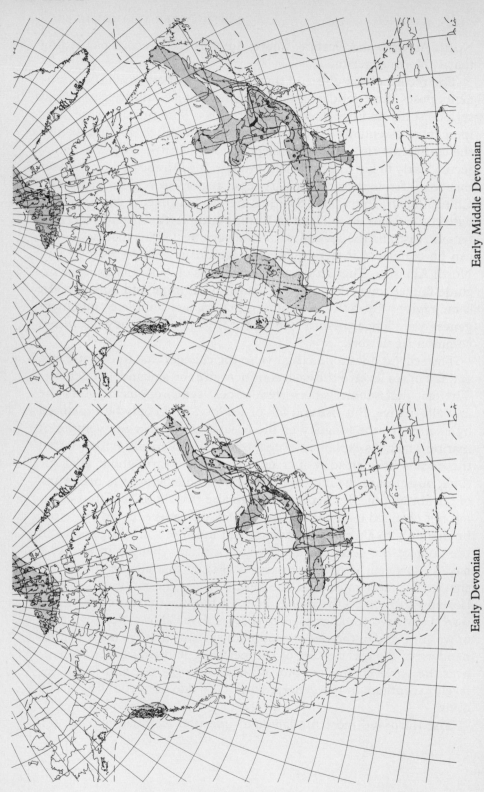

Early Middle Devonian

Early Devonian

Figures 52, 53.   Early Devonian and early Middle Devonian seaways in North America. After Schuchert

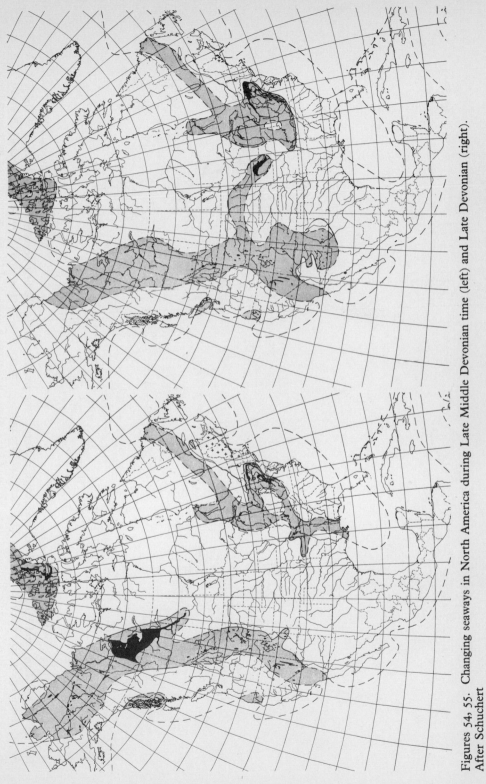

Figures 54, 55. Changing seaways in North America during Late Middle Devonian time (left) and Late Devonian (right). After Schuchert

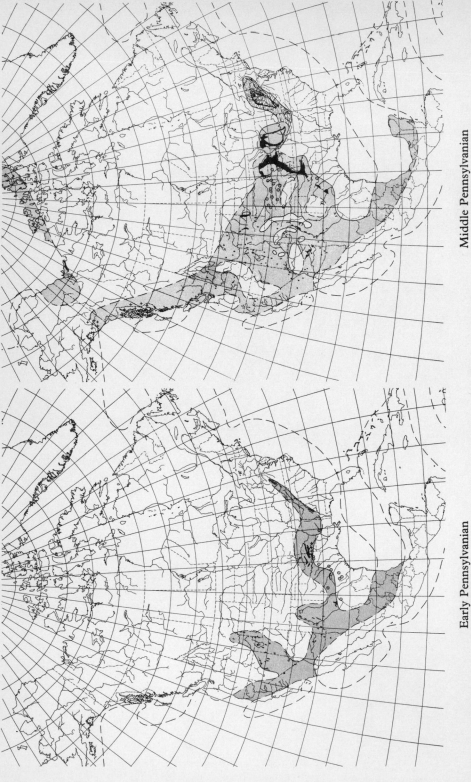

Middle Pennsylvanian

Early Pennsylvanian

Figures 56, 57. Early and Mid-Pennsylvanian seaways in North America. Horizontal shading denotes swampy lowland in the Appalachian region. East of the 100th meridian the areas here indicated as sea were alternately shallow sea and swampy lowland as the sea oscillated back and forth many times. Much of the coal of Oklahoma, Kansas, and Illinois accumulated in the swamps of this time pervading forces are at work within the earth to cause such endless changes in the relations of land and sea? This problem is reserved for chapter 11. There we shall examine also another aspect of the earth's ever-changing face — the possibility that the continents have not always been where they are now but have drifted like vast icebergs while floating on the mantle beneath.

Chapter 10

Climates of the Past

Climatic Factors

THE INFLUENCE of latitude, of topography, and of ocean currents on climate are well known. In general the mean temperature falls with increasing latitude because the sun's rays fall more and more obliquely as we approach the poles. Thus a given amount of warmth is spread over increasingly large areas (figure 58). Combined with this factor, the inclination of the earth's axis of rotation explains why winter and summer seasons alternate and are in opposite phase in the northern and southern hemispheres. Temperature also falls with increasing altitude because that of the atmosphere decreases upward. Thus the snow line falls to sea level in the subarctic zone and lofty mountains rise above it even at the equator.

Even within a single belt of latitude other factors introduce local and regional variations in temperature and rainfall. Western Europe, for example, enjoys a mild climate but lies opposite the inhospitable barrens of Labrador, and northern Norway faces the ice cap of southern Greenland. The reasons for these contrasts is not far to seek. The Gulf current crosses the North Atlantic bringing warmth from the tropics to western Europe while the Labrador current flowing southward from the polar seas bathes the east coast of Canada.

Large bodies of water moderate the climate because the latent heat of melting and of evaporation of water greatly exceeds that of the land. For this reason oceanic islands and coastal borders generally enjoy more equable climate than continental interiors. Thus, for example, the temperature at Seattle, Washington, normally ranges between 37°F and 75°F; and that of Boston is between 0°F and 90°F, whereas in the plains of Alberta, Saskatchewan, and the Dakotas it occasionally falls to −50° in winter and in summer frequently rises above 100°F. And because the oceans supply abundant

158

moisture to the atmosphere both coastal cities enjoy plentiful rainfall whereas the central plains are semi-arid. Obviously a great inland sea such as that of mid-Cretaceous time (plate 28) must have had a profound effect on the climate of most of North America.

Figure 58. Diagrams to illustrate the influence of latitude on temperature and the change of seasons resulting from the inclination of the earth's axis. The groups of three lines at the right represent equal bundles of light and heat coming from the sun. Where they strike the earth near the equator the heat is concentrated in the smallest possible area; and with increasing latitude the same unit of heat is spread over progressively larger areas. Furthermore, as they arrive at lower angles in the polar regions a larger part of the energy is reflected away from the earth. Since the northern hemisphere is inclined toward the sun in summer it receives more heat than the southern hemisphere and in winter the relations are reversed

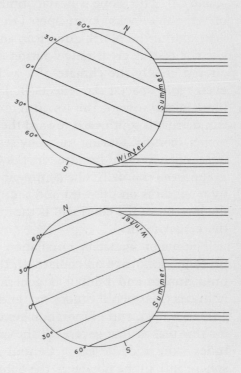

Every lofty mountain illustrates the climatic effect of altitude. The great volcano, Kilimanjaro, rising to a height of 19,317 feet in east Africa is permanently snow capped though it is within 3° of the equator, while in western Africa the Congo Basin in the same latitude is a teeming tropical jungle. The climatic effects are greatest where lofty mountain ranges lie athwart prevailing wind belts, for in ascending the windward slope the atmosphere is cooled and most of its moisture is dropped as rain or snow, and in descending over the leeward slope where it is warmed again rapid evaporation takes place. For this reason most mountain ranges have abundant moisture on one slope and an arid 'rain shadow' on the opposite side. This is strikingly illustrated in tropical South America where the trade winds crossing the Amazon Basin and the eastern slope of the Andes maintain a lush tropical rainforest, and in descending on to the coastal lowland west of the crest of the range have created intense desert conditions. The relations are reversed in California and Nevada which lie in the temperate zone where the prevailing 'westerlies' blow eastward up the long western slope of the Sierra Nevada range (plate 24). This slope is heavily timbered but the abrupt eastern face of the range looks down upon Death Valley, the hottest and most arid spot in the North American continent. It must be evident that the rise of this great range during the Pleistocene epoch must have altered greatly the climate of a wide region. The Himalayas cause even more spectacular effects in India where the monsoon winds blow inland toward the torrid interior of the continent during the summer, and southward toward the warm Indian Ocean during the winter months. During the rainy season the rainfall amounts locally to as much as eight hundred inches, and during the dry season there is almost no rainfall. The continent of Eurasia is largely hemmed in by mountains on the west and south and south-east, and as a result the interior of the continent is the largest area of desert wasteland in the modern world.

The major planetary circulation of the atmosphere also exerts a profound influence on climate. In the tropics ascending air currents predominate and rainfall is generally abundant, but in the horse latitudes (between latitudes 20° and 30°) the descending air (figure 39) is warmed, and evaporation generally exceeds precipitation. It is for this reason that several of the great deserts lie in the horse latitudes – the wide desert of Central Australia in the southern hemisphere and, in the northern, the Sahara desert of Africa, the Sonoran desert of Mexico and the Mojave desert of southern California.

Evidence of Past Climate

In view of the endless changes in the topography and the configuration of the continents discussed in the preceding chapter, we could infer that both local and regional climatic changes have been common throughout the geologic past. Impressive evidence of such changes is revealed both in the nature of the sedimentary rocks and in their entombed fossils.

In the modern world each kind of animal and plant is well adapted to a particular environment and we have every reason to believe that this was true in the past. Few creatures that thrive in the humid tropics could survive in the semi-arid plains of the temperate zone and none adapted to the temperate zone can live either in the tropics or the frigid zone. Land plants are particularly sensitive to both moisture and temperature and for this reason there is almost nothing in common between the flora of the Gulf coastal plain of Louisiana, the semi-arid grassy plains of Nebraska, the mixed hardwood forests of the Great Lakes region, the spruce and tamarack forests of southern Canada, and the moss barrens about Hudson Bay. Even the marine shellfish are nearly all restricted to distinct provinces determined by the temperature of the ocean water. In a comprehensive analysis of the shell-bearing invertebrate animals of the shelf sea bordering eastern North America, Dall and Harris [31] recognized five faunal provinces with the following populations:

	Species
The coast of Greenland	180
The Gulf of Maine	277
The shelf off the Carolina coast	305
The shelf off the west coast of Florida	681
The shelf along the east coast of Panama	517
Total	1,960

However, these faunas actually include only 1,772 distinct species. This means that less than two hundred species cross from one province into the next in spite of the fact that shallow sea connects them all. Temperature differences alone serve as a barrier restricting nearly every species to the province to which it is adapted.

Evidence of warm climate. In view of this, when at times in the geologic past we find species and genera ranging far to the north and south, we can only assume that climatic zones were then much less sharply differentiated than they are now, or that warm ocean currents were involved. Such conditions have obtained again and again when the continents were low and were extensively submerged beneath great inland seas. In middle Devonian time, for example (plate 29), the large brachiopod, *Stringocephalus*, ranged from European Russia by way of the Arctic shelf sea into the Cordilleran seaway of Western North America. Its fossil shells occur abundantly along the ramparts of the Mackenzie River, which is near the Arctic circle, and have been found as far south as Utah and Nevada. A little later in the period the very distinctive *Theodocia* fauna followed the same path from Russia into Nevada and New Mexico. And during the preceding Silurian period two highly distinctive coral genera, *Goniophyllum* and *Calceola* travelled by the arctic route from western Europe into Iowa and as far south as Tennessee. In mid-Silurian time, also, coral reefs were formed of chain corals, honeycomb corals and horn corals in Tennessee, Indiana, New York, and along the west side of Hudson Bay and in northern Greenland. These are but a few examples of many that might be cited as evidence that the climatic zones have at many times in the past been less well defined than at present.

Land animals are even more sensitive than marine animals to climatic controls. The restriction of the musk-ox and the reindeer to the frigid zone is as impressive as the restriction of elephants, hippopotami and rhinoceroses to subtropical regions. In dealing with extinct species, even those with living relatives, caution is of course needed since exceptional adaptations have sometimes been made. During the Pleistocene epoch, for instance, a species of elephant and one of rhinoceros lived in the snow fields of the Arctic. Unlike their modern relatives which are almost hairless, the woolly Mammoth and the woolly rhino were protected by a thick coat of woolly hair. A diversified fauna is obviously more likely to be trustworthy than one or two species.

But in another way land animals can bear witness to warm climate, however ancient they are and however distantly related to living forms. The dinosaurs, for example, are long since extinct and have no close living relatives; but they were reptiles, and all modern reptiles are cold blooded and become torpid and helpless when the temperature drops to near freezing. Snakes, small lizards and small land turtles survive in the temperate zone by crawling into holes and hibernating, but large reptiles (alligators, crocodiles, large lizards, large tortoises, and great snakes such as the anaconda and boa constrictor) cannot find such refuge and all are confined to regions without frost. Unless, therefore, the many kinds of dinosaurs had developed warm blood (which seems highly improbable) they could not have lived where freezing occurred. Yet in late Jurassic time large dinosaurs ranged as far north as Montana in North America and were at home in Mongolia. In Cretaceous time dinosaurs of many kinds (plate 31) were common in Alberta, and in Mongolia. Still more surprising was the recent discovery of a trail of footprints of the large dinosaur, *Iguanodon*, on a bed of sandstone of Cretaceous age in west Spitzbergen, half way between the northern tip of Norway and the north pole [27]. This dinosaur was common in western Europe, and many skeletons have been found in Belgium.

On the basis of the distribution of dinosaurs we must infer that in late Jurassic and Cretaceous time the climate in North America and far to the north in Europe, as well as in Mongolia, was much warmer than it is today. For this there is even more evidence. On Disco Island (figure 59) near the middle of the west coast of Greenland, Cretaceous beds have yielded abundant fossil plants among which are species of figs, breadfruit, cinnamon, laurel and tree ferns. These

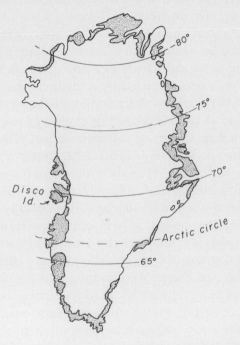

Figure 59. Map showing the position of Disco Island

belong to existing genera that are characteristic of the tropics or of warm temperate regions; yet the fossils are within the arctic circle and close beside the Greenland ice cap far beyond the range of any modern trees. Abundant corals in the late Jurassic rocks of England and Germany confirm the belief that the climate in Europe was then warmer than at present.

For the last sixty million years fossil plants are especially useful indices of climate since most of the genera and many species of forest trees now living were already present in Eocene time. From a study of fossil plants of many localities in western North America, Chaney [26] showed that in Eocene time the flora that now characterizes the warm moist lowlands of the Gulf coastal plain ranged widely over the western part of the continent, even as far north as Alaska. During Miocene and Pliocene epochs it retreated southward and was finally restricted to its present range just before the onset of the Pleistocene ice age. The inference is clear that a secular change in climate had occurred and that during the early part of the 'Age of Mammals' the north polar region probably was not ice bound as it is now.

More recent studies of fossil plants throughout the western states by Axelrod [3] and by Axelrod and Ting [2] have added much detail to the climatic record and have shown how regional changes in climate reflect the orogenic history. Because plants are so sensitive to temperature and moisture the timber on a mountain slope is strati- fied into zones each characterized by a distinct type of vegetation. A typical succession in the temperate zone would be mixed hardwood trees on the lower slopes succeeded by a zone of pine and aspen and that in turn by a zone of spruce and fir and finally by dwarfed plants of the alpine meadows above the timber line. When traced into higher latitudes each zone descends to progressively lower levels, but in any particular region the vertical range of each zone is well marked. Thus by a study of fossil plants from twenty localities widely distributed from the basins of western Nevada across the High Sierra Nevada (plate 24) and into the lowlands of west-central Cali- fornia, Axelrod showed that in late Miocene and early Pliocene time the present site of the Sierra Nevada mountains was a broad plateau at an elevation of about three thousand feet while the basins of wes- tern Nevada were only about one thousand feet lower. Moreover, the climate across the entire region was more uniform and much milder than at present and the rainfall over western Nevada was more plentiful than it is now. Axelrod and Ting have recently studied pollen from lake beds of late Pliocene age near the summit of the High Sierra and from Owens Valley which lies just east of the range and some six thousand feet lower. The similarity of the plant assem- blages indicates that the climate was similar in both places. From this and other plant evidence these authors conclude that the first major uplift of the Sierra Nevada came about the middle of Pleisto- cene time and amounted to only about three thousand feet, and that this uplift was followed late in Pleistocene time by a final uplift of another six thousand feet. It was similar evidence, cited in chapter 9, that has led to the conclusion that great uplift occurred also in both the Himalayas and the Andes late in Pleistocene time. Thus fossil plants provide at once a record of past climate and dates of major uplift of growing mountains.

Quite independent of the biologic evidence, the sedimentary rocks in many places tell a story of climatic conditions surprisingly unlike the present. The Permian System in Utah, for instance, includes ancient dune sands ranging in thickness up to several hundred feet spread over an enormous area. The distinctive cross-stratification in this mass of sandstone is so obvious that the aboriginal Indians of Utah called them, in their own language, 'frozen dunes' (plate 32). To be sure, dunes form in many places along sandy shores and, therefore, are not confined to deserts, but for the Permian dunes their wide distribution suggests a desert and there is striking confirming evidence in the vast salt deposits laid down in an inland sea from Kansas to west Texas. Early in middle Permian time extensive salt beds were laid down in Kansas and when the dwindling sea had retreated into a great structural basin in west Texas and south-eastern New Mexico, late in Permian time, one of the three major salt deposits of the world was formed. In the Permian Basin of west Texas saline deposits, mainly salt ($NaCl$) and anhydrite ($CaSO_4$) attain a thickness of over four thousand feet. Udden [156] studied a well core of about 1,100 feet of banded anhydrite in which pairs of layers, like the growth rings in trees, almost certainly mark annual deposits (plate 33) and from his study of the salt basin Udden concluded that for a period of some three hundred thousand years this region must have been about as arid as Death Valley while millions of cubic miles of sea water flowing into the basin from the south was evaporated. It may be noted in passing that all three of the greatest salt deposits in the world were formed during Permian time. Beside that of west Texas and New Mexico there is the famous salt basin about Stassfurt, Germany, and the greatest of all about Solikamsk in the Permian Basin west of the Urals. Of course, this does not indicate that all the lands were arid at this time, but it may be emphasized that the Permian Period was a time of exceptionally widespread continental emergence and of lofty mountains and that other climatic extremes, notably glaciation, occurred during this period.

All this contrasts to a striking degree with the immediately preceding period, the Upper Carboniferous or Pennsylvanian Period (figure 57) when the vast coal beds of Europe and eastern North America were laid down. Here we have a record of vast swampy lowlands where lush vegetation accumulated under standing water and primitive reptiles and large amphibians indicate climate without frost. Similar coal beds were formed at the same time in western Europe and over a large part of North China and southern Manchuria.

Glacial climates. The most spectacular of all climatic extremes recorded in the rocks is glaciation. At several times in the geologic past enormous areas now far from the frigid zone have been covered with sheets of glacier ice like those of modern Antarctica and Greenland. Although the evidence is unmistakable, the causes of glaciation are still not satisfactorily known. They may be complex and may even be due, in part at least, to variation in solar radiation. Fortunately the last great period of glaciation is so recent that its record is clear. We may begin, therefore, with the story of Pleistocene glaciation.

Not more than twenty thousand years ago vast ice sheets similar to those still present in Greenland and Antarctica covered virtually all of Canada and extended as far south as the Ohio and Missouri rivers in the United States, its southern margin lying where summer temperature frequently exceeds 100°F (plate 34). At that time a scene in Kansas or Illinois must have resembled that in plate 36. The moving ice scraped off the soil and mantle polishing and striating the bedrock surface. Meanwhile the boulders frozen in the base of the ice were abraded on the lower side until they were flattened or 'soled' and were scratched by the floor over which they were dragged. Plate 35 shows such a surface left by the ice sheet in southern Connecticut and one of the glacial boulders left lying upon it when the ice melted away.

Where the relief was higher the ice near its margin flowed down valleys as rivers of ice as it does now in much of eastern Greenland (plate 36). Where the ice melts away as fast as it advances the debris carried with it is left in the form of terminal moraines. This material, thrust forward as if by a great bulldozer, is entirely unstratified and consists of unsorted silt and sand and gravel in which striated boulders are embedded. The meltwater flowing away carries a heavy load of the finer sediment that silts up the valley below with stratified drift.

Where the relief is slight a marginal moraine forms along the edge of the ice sheet whenever melting equals ice flow and the ice front is stationary for a time, and the meltwater may form a wide outwash plain beyond it. Such marginal moraines still loop across the north central states in great festoons recording the outline of lobes of the ice sheet. Long Island is formed by such a moraine about one hundred miles long and twenty-five miles wide.

As the ice melted back, proglacial lakes commonly formed along its margins where the meltwater was dammed by the moraines, and in such lakes distinctively laminated or varved clays accumulated in which summer and winter layers, like the growth rings in trees, record the years. The layering results from the fact that most of the melting occurs during the summer during which a layer of silt is spread over the lake floor; then during the winter when melting is reduced and the lakes freeze over only the fine material held in suspension settles out to form a thin layer of clay. The silt layer is lighter in colour and the clay layer is darker (plate 38).

In Europe the Pleistocene ice sheet centred over Scandinavia, whence the ice pushed southward across the floors of the Baltic and the North Sea to cover the plains of northern Germany and most of the British Isles. Another great ice sheet at the same time covered parts of Siberia.

In New England the ice overrode the Green Mountains and all but the highest peaks of the Adirondacks, and in central Canada it probably exceeded ten thousand feet in thickness, as it still does in Greenland and Antarctica. In the north central United States streams that had previously flowed north were blocked and the meltwater was diverted along the ice front until it overflowed to the south remaking the drainage pattern so that the Ohio and Missouri rivers now mark approximately the southern limits of the ice sheet.

The weight of this vast sheet of ice depressed the crust of the earth beneath it, and as the ice slowly melted away the sea for a time spread inward over the lower parts of New England and up the St Lawrence Valley and into Lake Champlain. For a brief time this Champlain Sea entered the Hudson Valley separating all of New England from the mainland. During the further retreat of the ice front large shallow lakes formed about its southern borders and along their shores beaches were formed that are still clearly recognizable. Of course they were originally horizontal since they were formed at water level. Many of these have been mapped and all are now found to rise progressively when traced northward, proving that since the ice disappeared the land has been recovering from its depression. This data has been assembled by Flint [53] as summarized in figure 60. From this it is evident that the maximum depression had occurred in the region of Hudson Bay. Evidence of post-glacial recovery is abundant in a wide peripheral belt but little evidence has been found in the unsettled barrens of central Canada. Within a distance of about one hundred miles to the north-north-west of west-central Vermont the marine beaches rise from one hundred to seven hundred feet above present sea level, and the beach of old Lake

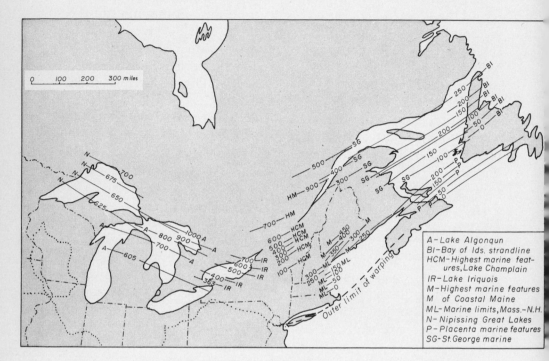

Figure 60. Deformation in eastern North America resulting from the weight of the ice sheet. The elevation of post-glacial strand lines is indicated in feet above present sea level. The lines are isobases. Adapted from Richard F. Flint, from *Glacial and Pleistocene Geology*

Agassiz rises from 605 feet to one thousand feet in an equal distance across present Lake Huron. Farrand [49] has estimated that subsidence under the centre of the ice cap may have been as great as three thousand feet. Mere compression of the rocks beneath could not conceivably account for such subsidence; some of the rock below must have been displaced, and since the crustal rocks are not appreciably deformed it must have been the underlying mantle that flowed from under the depressed area and has since been flowing back.

Because of the absence of tide gauges or historical records in the

Hudson Bay region it is not known whether uplift is still continuing, but Gutenberg [59] has calculated that the centre of the depressed area should still rise by about 250 metres (825 feet) before recovery is complete. Historical records in Fennoscandia give clear evidence of current uplift in that region. Many tide gauges in operation since 1918 have shown that the southern shores of the Baltic and North seas are still rising and that, at the north end of the Gulf of Bothnia, current uplift amounts to nearly one metre per one hundred years

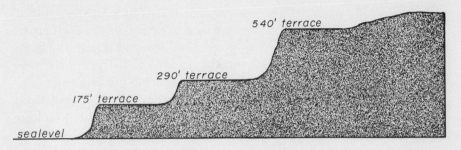

Figure 61. Diagram to show relations of the uplifted marine terraces in the Pelly Bay area of Northwest Territories north of Hudson Bay. Data from *Radiocarbon*, Vol. 4, 1962, p. 37 [155]

[53], and Niskanen [116] has estimated that within the next eight thousand years the Gulf of Bothnia will be reduced to a small lake cut off from the sea.

By an intriguing new technique the actual rate of post-glacial uplift has been determined for the region about Pelly Bay in the Northwest Territories to the north of Hudson Bay [155]. Three uplifted marine terraces in that region (figure 61) mark pauses in the uplift during which the sea cut a terrace and left it covered with beach sand in which shells of animals living at the time are buried. The shells have been dated by radiocarbon and thus it is known that the 540 foot terrace was cut about 8,370 years ago, the 293 foot terrace about 7,880 years ago, and the 175 foot terrace about 7,160 years ago. Thus we know that in the 490 years between the cutting of the two upper terraces the region rose 227 feet, for an average of about five inches per year. In the 720 years between the cutting of the two lower terraces the uplift amounted to 118 feet or an average of 2·15 inches per year, and in the 7,160 years since the last terrace was cut the average uplift has been only one-third of an inch per year. These figures indicate that about the time of the final disappearance of the ice, uplift was relatively rapid and that the rate has declined progressively as the crust floated up toward equilibrium.

The glacial drift widely spread over northern Europe was an enigma to the geologists of the eighteenth century. Shortly before the end of that century some of the Swiss geologists, familiar with the Alpine glaciers, correctly interpreted the erratic boulders and roches moutonnées (glacially polished hillocks) in the foothills north of the Alps and stated that at some time in the past the glaciers had descended far below their present limits. One of the leaders of this school was Charpentier. But when the drift was found to extend far out over the plains of north Germany and to be present in the British Isles and Scandinavia, numerous geologists believed that it had been dropped from icebergs that floated down from the Arctic when the lowlands were submerged beneath the sea. During the first half of the nineteenth century it was widely believed that the drift had been spread across Europe by vast waves and currents during the Deluge described in the Scriptures and it was commonly called Diluvium.

One of the first to believe that it was the result of continental glaciation was the Swiss civil engineer Venetz, who published this view in 1829. He soon had a disciple in the young Swiss zoologist, Louis Agassiz. Agassiz had been sceptical until he joined Venetz on a field trip and saw the evidence, but in 1837 he presented the idea of an 'ice age' before the Helvetic Society picturing a time when a vast ice sheet extended from the North Pole to the Alps and to central Asia [53]. This marked the beginning of the concept of a Pleistocene ice age.

Similar glacial drift had been recognized in New England and soon several American geologists were endorsing Agassiz's 'theory'. In 1840 Agassiz came to America and joined the Harvard faculty and threw his influence behind the glacial theory, but opposition to it persisted as late as 1899. Even after continental glaciation became an accepted fact it was believed to be the result of a single period of refrigeration and it remained for R. D. Salisbury, working in the upper Mississippi Valley, to show that we had had not one but several glacial episodes separated by interglacial intervals when the ice disappeared and the climate over North America was as warm as it is today [23]. This he discovered when localities were studied in which two distinct sheets of glacial till were directly superposed and were separated by a weathered zone, old soil, a layer of loess, or stratified drift containing fossil plants and animals (figure 62).

Eventually four major glacial stages were recognized in America and an equal number in Europe, and it is now known that they correspond in time in both continents. Many dates during the last glacial age and in post-glacial time have now been determined by radiocarbon. For the older glacial ages and the three interglacial ages indirect and less precise dates have been estimated and the Pleistocene chronology as now recognized is summarized in figure 63.

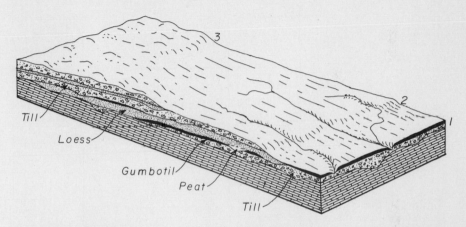

Figure 62. Diagram to show evidences of glacial and interglacial ages. In the regions of accumulation the ice during each glacial age scoured away all loose material; but in the marginal zone where it was thinned by melting, it commonly was overloaded and overrode soil and older till sheets without disturbing them. Gumbotil is a leached soil zone formed on a till sheet as a result of long weathering. Loess is a deposit of wind-blown dust

There is good evidence that the second interglacial age was long and that the climate in southern Canada then became warmer than it is now. Many radiocarbon dates establish a rather precise chronology of events since the Tazewell ice advance, and it is clear that the continental ice sheets disappeared about eleven thousand years ago [53]. This date is also confirmed from a study of numerous sediment cores from the floor of the North Atlantic, in which the foraminifera indicate a distinct warming trend following that date [46].

One of the puzzling features of the Pleistocene glaciation is that the large continental ice sheets were confined to the northern hemisphere. Nevertheless the snowline was depressed all over the world and valley glaciers occurred in many mountains where none now exist and existing mountain icefields were more extensive than at present. This indicates that the temperature was depressed the world over.

The deposits left by the Pleistocene glaciers are unmistakable and give us good criteria for recognizing more ancient ice ages. The un-

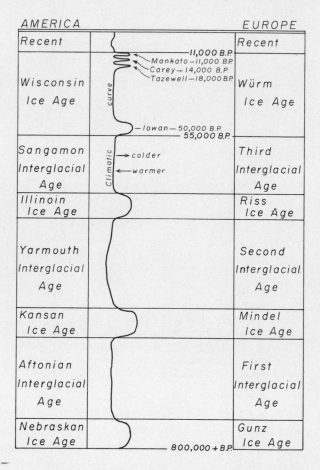

Figure 63. Pleistocene chronology. The space allotted to the several ages is not to uniform scale, and the climatic curve is without scale and is only intended to be suggestive. Dates within the Wisconsin ice age are based on radiocarbon ratios and are approximately accurate

sorted till with its striated and soled boulders, the polished and grooved floor over which the ice moved, the varved (seasonally banded) clays deposited in periglacial lakes, and erratic boulders derived from distant sources all attest to the work of flowing ice. Recent study of the marine deposits surrounding Antarctica also give a clear understanding of the deposits formed where icebergs float to sea and drop the enclosed rock debris to form glaciomarine deposits. Only the depth of the water can limit the thickness to which such material may accumulate, and it has most of the characteristics of till, being unsorted, with large boulders imbedded in fine material, some of them striated. It differs from till only in that it may include marine fossils.

As indicated in figure 63, the time since the last ice advance is shorter than either of the interglacial ages. About five million square miles of glacier ice still persist in Antarctica and Greenland, and it is estimated that a decline of only 5° in the mean annual world temperature would bring a return of the great ice sheets as they were during the last ice advance [53]. Whether the temperature will continue to rise to the geologic norm until the polar ice caps disappear or whether we are still in an interglacial age after which the ice caps will return, is an open question. Meanwhile the sword of Damocles hangs over us. If the ice sheets should return to the limits they had only a few thousand years ago, mass migrations would occur on a scale without precedent in human history, for the densely populated regions of Europe and the United States, to say nothing of all Canada, would be uninhabitable; and if the present ice caps of Antarctica and Greenland should melt away, sea level will rise by about one hundred feet, flooding all the great seaports of the world!

Among the ice ages of the distant past that of the Permian Period is perhaps the most remarkable (figure 64). At that time each of the southern continents had enormous ice sheets. Nearly all of Africa south of latitude 20°S was ice covered. There were three or four centres of accumulation from which the ice spread. The greatest of these appears to have been in the Transvaal which was then a plateau from which the ice spread at least seven hundred miles to the south-west. Here the Dwyka tillite rests on a glacially polished and striated floor of older rocks (plate 39). In the northern part of the region where it rests on a glaciated floor the tillite ranges up to about one hundred feet in thickness, but farther south, in southern Karoo, where it has no glaciated floor and ranges up to some two thousand feet in thickness the tillite was probably dropped from floating ice.

In Australia a vast ice sheet moved northward across Victoria and New South Wales leaving five distinct sheets of tillite interbedded in a section of about two thousand feet of Permian strata. It is clear that glacial and interglacial ages alternated here as they did in the northern hemisphere during Pleistocene time. In the Canning Basin of western Australia [162] the Grant formation of Early Permian age includes thick glacio-marine beds similar to those now forming about Antarctica and similar deposits in all four of the Permian Basins of

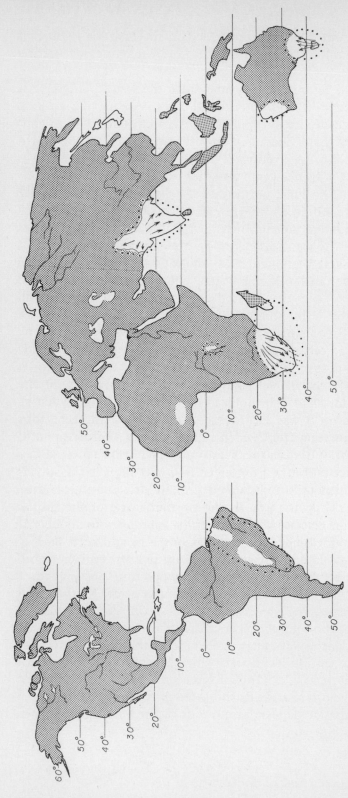

Figure 64. World map showing the distribution of Early Permian glaciation. Dotted lines encircle the glaciated regions and unshaded areas indicate the known extent of the ice sheets. The arrows indicate the direction of ice movement where determined. In India the ice radiated both north and south from a centre of accumulation in the region of the modern Arivalle highlands. In South Africa the ice flowed some seven hundred miles south-west from a centre of accumulation in the northern Transvaal. Another centre of accumulation lay between the present coast of Africa and southern Madagascar. A smaller area of glaciation lies in eastern Congo, its northern limit lying on the present equator. In Tasmania and south-east Australia the ice moved northward. The direction of movement in western Australia and large ice fields of Paraguay, Uruguay, and Brazil in South America is not known. The ice field in northern Brazil reached to the present equator

western Australia include scattered Lower Permian fossils or are immediately succeeded by early mid-Permian marine limestone [153]. Tasmania was also partly ice covered at this time. In South America glaciation was widespread in Argentina and south-eastern Brazil, even up to the present equator.

The only glaciation of this age known in the northern hemisphere occurred in India where the Talchir tillite is widespread and bears evidence that the ice was moving both north and south from a highland in the region of the modern Arivalle mountains. In the Salt Range at the southern margin of the Himalayas this impressive tillite is overlain directly by early middle Permian limestone.

We now have considerable evidence that the Permian glaciation occurred late in Early Permian time or very early in mid-Permian time and that it was a relatively short episode in the long Permian Period; also that in some areas glacial and interglacial ages alternated as they did during Pleistocene time. By mid-Permian time the climate was warm again in Africa where reptiles in great variety roamed over regions previously covered by ice. In Australia, also, the marine faunas above the glacial deposits are large and varied and seem to indicate warm waters.

The most remarkable feature of the Permian glaciation was its distribution. It led to the theory, still under debate, that the southern land masses are parts of a great continent that in Permian time occupied the south polar region and have since drifted apart. We shall return to the theory of continental drift in the next chapter.

More local glaciation during Lower Carboniferous time has been reported in eastern Australia and in Argentina.

Widespread glaciation occurred at least twice during the Cryptozoic Eon, once near the middle and once near its close. In south-east Australia a thick sequence of rocks underlying the Cambrian System includes at least three extensive tillites of which the greatest is the Sturtian tillite which in New South Wales is as much as six hundred feet thick. Extensive tillites are also present in the Precambrian of South Africa [40]. The Griquatown tillite of the northern part of Cape Colony is of late Precambrian date and may be contemporaneous with the Numees tillite of western Cape Colony and others in Katanga.

The Chuos tillite of Southwest Africa is believed to be much older. It has been recognized over an area of some twenty thousand square miles and has the characteristics of a great glacial moraine.

India also had extensive glaciers in Precambrian time and in the Yangtze Valley of China scattered exposures of Precambrian tillite indicate an ice sheet at least eight hundred miles across.

In North America the Gowganda tillite (plate 40) in the Huronian 'system' includes striated boulders as much as ten feet in diameter and in at least two places can be seen resting on a grooved and polished floor. It proves that in relatively late Cryptozoic time an ice field at least one thousand miles across from west to east lay over southern Canada north of the present Great Lakes.

In summary, it is clear that widespread glaciation has occurred in many parts of the world at several times in the geologic past, that each has been of relatively short duration alternating with much longer spans of mild climate, and that glaciation was as common during the early part of earth history as in later time.

Without citing the very extensive evidence it may be stated, in summary, that the present is an exceptional stage in earth history when the continents are high and almost completely emergent, when we are just emerging from a time of widespread glaciation, when the polar regions are ice-bound, and when about ten per cent of the land surface is desert. The Permian was a comparable time when the continents became widely emergent, deserts were widespread, vast salt deposits were formed, and the world experienced perhaps its most widespread glaciation. On the contrary, during much of the long Paleozoic Era, as well as during the Mesozoic Era, the continents were generally lower, extensive epeiric (inland) seas flooded across the lower parts and such evidence as we have indicates that the climate was more equable and milder than at present, and that probably there were no polar ice caps. The emergence of the continents, the growth of lofty mountain ranges, and restriction of marine waters appear to have exaggerated climatic zones and regional climatic extremes.

Chapter 11

The Driving Force Within

THE ENERGY required to lift mountains out of the sea and hold them miles high is beyond comprehension. Yet there they are! Sea shells may be collected in the white peaks of the Alps, in the top of the snow-capped Canadian Rockies (plate 41), and at an elevation of twenty thousand feet in the high Himalayas. Whatever the cause, there is evidence on every hand that the earth's crust has been deformed, time and again, in ways that stagger the imagination. What can be the source of such elemental forces?

Before the present century the earth was believed to be molten except for a relatively thin 'crust' of solid rock. Its internal heat was thought to be residual from a primaeval molten stage. On these assumptions it seemed obvious that the loss of heat has caused the interior to shrink and the crust to wrinkle like the skin of a shrivelled apple. This was long the accepted origin of mountain folds. We now know better.

The discovery of radioactivity about the turn of the century proved this simple hypothesis to rest on false premises. Instead of cooling, the interior of the earth may actually be growing hotter and expanding. Furthermore, the crust is not a primaeval surface layer; it has grown throughout geologic time by the rise of lighter fractions of the mantle rock that have come to the surface, as slag rises above the metal in a furnace.

While developing the Planetesimal hypothesis early in this century, Chamberlin advanced a new theory of diastrophism [24]. He assumed that, from a small nucleus, the earth has grown by the in-fall of planetesimals that accumulated as a loose, porous mass resembling a bed of cinders. After deep burial this material was believed to be crushed and compacted by the weight of further additions at the surface so that the interior continually shrank. Chamberlin believed, however, that the body of the earth was sufficiently rigid to resist deformation for many millions of years and that when the stress had grown to the breaking point the oceanic segments settled to fit the smaller interior. This deepened the ocean basins drawing the water off the continents and exposing them completely to erosion (figure 65). Meanwhile, the wedging by the subsidence of the ocean basins squeezed the continental segments and caused mountains to rise along their borders. Chamberlin believed that after a few million years of crustal deformation the stresses were relieved and a long

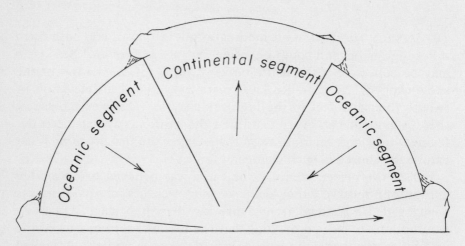

Figure 65. Diagram to illustrate Chamberlin's hypothesis of a shrinking earth in which oceanic segments subsided in adjusting to the shrinking interior

period of stability ensued during which sea level gradually rose and shallow seas spread widely over the lower parts of the continents where sediments accumulated to record a new chapter of earth's history. Chamberlin invoked two factors to account for the rise of sea level. First, he argued that all the sediment eroded from the continents and transported to the oceans displaced an equal volume of water. Second he suspected that the summits of the continental segments standing so far above the ocean basins were not quite rigid enough to be stable and tended to spread, like glacier ice, toward the ocean basins. To explain why the oceanic segments, rather than the continental segments subsided, he had to assume that for some unknown reason they were made of heavier material.

With these assumptions it seemed probable that at times of worldwide diastrophism and crustal readjustment, erosion prevailed over the continents and no stratigraphic record was formed on the lands.

Thus geologic history was neatly divided into chapters, the periods of recorded time being separated by world-wide breaks in the record. This led to his famous dictum, 'Diastrophism is the ultimate basis for correlation.' It was a beautiful theory, and for a time was widely accepted but, like its predecessor, it proved to be invalid because it rested on false premises. The Planetesimal hypothesis was later found to be invalid and, as we now know, diastrophism has not been periodic. Mountains have grown repeatedly while the continents were widely flooded and orogeny has not generally coincided with the breaks between periods [141; 55].

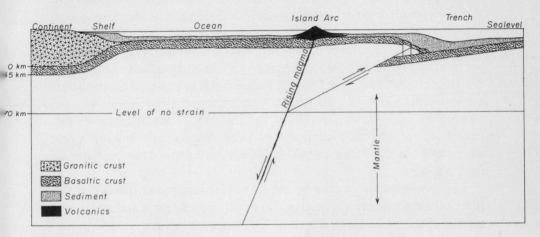

Figure 66. Idealized cross-section through an island arc, after Wilson, 1959, figure 1 [170]

J. Tuzo Wilson has returned to the theory of a shrinking interior to account for island arcs and arcuate mountain systems near the continental margins, but he attributes the shrinkage to transfer of material from the depths to form the crust. He believes that the crust adjusts to the smaller radius by thrusting under the continental regions as indicated in figure 66, and he argues that a planar fault (or zone of faults) dipping under the continents would intersect the surface of a spherical earth in an arc facing the sea. He believes that the rising magmas are generated in the zone between a depth of seventy and seven hundred kilometres and that this zone is shrinking and under tension, whereas the zone above seventy kilometres is under compression. According to this concept the thrust faults end at a depth of seventy kilometres where they intercept normal faults in

179

the deeper zone. These normal faults then afford an avenue for the escape of magmas to the surface along the axis of the island arc. This hypothesis affords a logical explanation for the oceanic trenches in front of the arcs and for the volcanic activity in the arcs. Nevertheless it appears weak on at least two counts. In the first place the crust is extremely thin in comparison with the size of the earth. On the scale used in our figure 11 it would be thinner than the surface line. Over the broad ocean floors it is not more than five miles thick and even if it were all derived from the zone between a depth of seventy and seven hundred kilometres the amount of shrinkage in that zone would appear to be small. Furthermore this thin rind would have to be very rigid if it is to concentrate the deformation at the continental margins. We should expect it to buckle and break at relatively short intervals over the ocean floors. In the second place if this is the method of adjustment to a shrinking interior, it is difficult to account for the distribution of the island arcs, which are almost continuous, for example, along the western border of the Pacific Ocean, but are lacking on its eastern side. They are lacking in the Atlantic Ocean except in the relatively small area of the Caribbean region, and none are present in the vast expanse of the oceans south of the continental land masses.

These weaknesses would be avoided, if instead of shrinkage of the interior we attribute the active forces to convection currents in the mantle discussed below. Much of Dr Wilson's structural interpretation of the island arcs would apply as well to this hypothesis.

Convection Currents in the Mantle

The theory of convection currents in the mantle is relatively new and cannot be accepted as finally proved, but it fits so many of our problems that it has fired the imagination of geologists and geophysicists the world over, and recent discoveries have given it growing support. Proposed by the Dutch geologist, Veneg-Meinez, in 1948 [163], it is based on the belief that local or regional areas of excessive heat deep within the earth cause the mantle rock to expand and move upward by solid flow. Approaching the surface it spreads laterally under the crust, loses heat, and thus becomes dense enough to settle slowly back into the depths and be reheated. Thus a vast convection cell is formed above a hot region in which the current flows as it does in a shallow vessel of fluid over a flame (figure 67).

Veneg-Meinez knew, of course, that the mantle rock is dense and rigid and cannot move as a fluid, but in many parts of the world old rocks, once deformed deep within growing mountains, show unmistakable evidence of solid flow (plate 42). Ice is truly a rock, as is granite, and we know that, while brittle and hard, glaciers flow down slopes as rivers of solid ice. The exact means by which they flow has

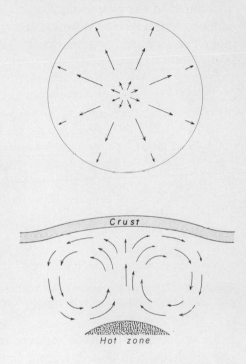

Figure 67. Diagram to represent a convection cell in the mantle. Above, a plan view showing direction of flow near the top; below, a vertical section

been the subject of recent study and it now seems evident that the movement takes place at the molecular level. Granted that rock flowage has occurred in many places of intense deformation, it was believed until recently that frictional resistance would prevent large-scale movement in the mantle. Veneg-Meinez has forced us to take a new look at the evidence.

Evidence of Convection Currents

In the preceding chapter we discussed the subsidence of the crust under the continental ice sheets of Pleistocene time. It is inconceivable that compression of the underlying rocks by the weight of the ice could permit subsidence of such magnitude; an enormous volume of rock must have been displaced. And since the crustal rocks were not appreciably deformed, the movement must have been in the mantle below, which flowed aside under the weight of the ice and has been slowly returning since the ice disappeared.

The history of any of the great mountain systems tells a similar story. The Rocky Mountains provide a typical illustration. As recounted in the preceding chapter, the first stage involved the subsidence of the Rocky Mountain geosyncline. During a period of perhaps one hundred million years this great trough, several hundred

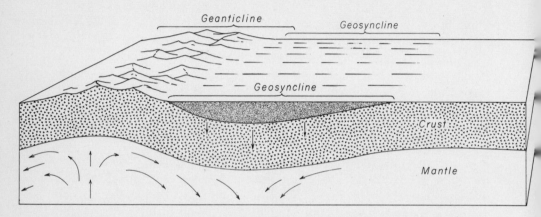

Figure 68. Diagram to indicate the relation of the Rocky Mountain geosyncline and the Mesocordilleran geanticline to convection currents in the mantle

miles wide and some two thousand miles long, slowly subsided until the pre-Mesozoic floor lay from three to five miles below sea level along its axis. But as it sank the Mesocordilleran geanticline was slowly rising and undergoing erosion. Meanwhile the eroded sediment was being transported into the geosyncline filling it almost as fast as it sank. The Jurassic and Cretaceous strata thus formed are now uplifted and exposed and, although partly eroded away, their original volume can be estimated with considerable accuracy from the regional structure. Gilluly [56] has estimated the volume of the Upper Cretaceous beds alone at about 750 million cubic miles. This gives a minimum measure of the amount of material displaced as the geosyncline subsided. But this is only one face of the coin. At least ninety per cent of the fill came from the Mesocordilleran geanticline the area of which is fairly well known since it was bordered on both sides by seaways (plate 28). Thus Gilluly was able to calculate that the volume of rock eroded to make the fill in the geosyncline would equal a layer averaging nearly five miles thick over the entire uplift. It probably was never this high for the texture of the deposits in the geosyncline clearly shows that the uplift was continuous or inter-mittent throughout the subsidence of the geosyncline. In short, movement in the two great structures was reciprocal, the geanticline rising about as fast as the geosyncline sank. A plausible explanation is indicated in figure 68.

Evidence of presently active convection in the mantle has come from the recent study of the Mid-Pacific Rise [110]. This is an enor-mous bulge in the earth's crust several hundred miles wide and some eight thousand miles long running generally north–south. The sou-thern part lies in the Pacific basin paralleling the west coast of South America, but farther north it passes under Mexico and the high Cordillera of North America, its western flank being exposed along the coast of Canada as far north as Alaska (figure 69).

In the South Pacific its crest rises as much as three miles above the general level of the ocean floor. Seismic studies indicate that the crust is abnormally thin along its crest, and temperature probes at more than one hundred stations show that in a belt about one hundred miles wide along its crest the heat flow ranges from two to eight times the norm for the ocean floors. Here then is a vast bulge in the crust, an arch where it has been thinned and below which the rocks are abnormally hot. Menard [110] considers this to be the summit of an enormous, elongate convection cell that is bringing excess heat up from the depths.

Spectacular discoveries of a different kind have been made farther north. On its west flank, off the coast of the United States and Mexico, the ocean floor is broken by a series of sub-parallel rifts that separate enormous rectangular blocks of the crust [129]. The faults were discovered by sonic depth recorders where vertical movement has left one side higher than the other. Mendocino fault, for example, has a great south-facing scarp from six thousand to nine thousand feet high. Horizontal movement of amazing magnitude has recently been measured by an ingenious technique. In 1952 Ronald Mason, trailing a magnetometer behind a research vessel observed unexpec-ted variations in the magnetic attraction of the ocean floor. This led to the discovery that in the region traversed by the great rifts the excessive magnetism exists in bands that in general run north and south, crossing the faults. A large-scale magnetic survey of the region was then carried out by means of airborne magnetometers flown in east–west traverses in parallel courses some miles apart.

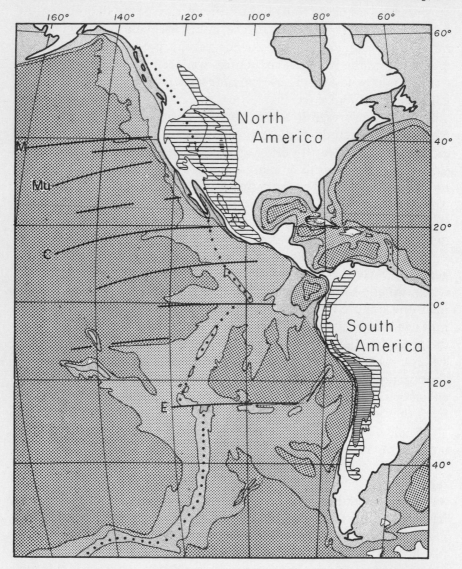

Figure 69. Map showing relations of the East Pacific Rise, after Menard. The darkest shading indicates ocean floor more than 13,200 feet deep; intermediate shading 9,900 to 13,200 feet deep; lightest shading less than 9,900 feet deep. The dotted line follows the crest of the rise. On the continents the lighter horizontal shading indicates elevation between 3,300 and 9,900 feet and the darker shading above 9,900 feet. C, Clarion fault; E, Easter fault; G, Galapagos fault; M, Mendocino fault; Mu, Murray fault; P, Pioneer fault

After deducting the normal earth magnetism from the measured attraction the data for each traverse was then recorded in the form of a curve in which the height is proportional to the magnetic attraction. Portions of four such curves are reproduced in figure 70, the upper two in the block north of the Mendocino fault and the lower two in the block south of the fault.

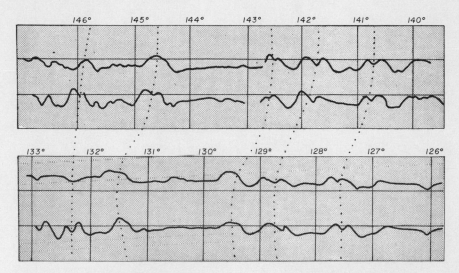

Figure 70. Matching magnetic profiles. The upper panel shows parts of two parallel east–west profiles in the block north of the Mendocino fault; the lower panel shows corresponding profiles south of the fault. The height of the curves indicates the degree of magnetic intensity. The upper profiles were moved about 14° to the west before a match was made. After Raff [129]

From many such curves it was possible to prepare a magnetic map of the area (figure 71) which reveals a series of bands of excess magnetism (shaded) alternating with bands of deficient magnetism. The reason for this is unknown. At each of the great faults the magnetic bands are broken and offset. The small portion of the map reproduced in figure 71, for example, is crossed by the Murray fault. The drag of the bands to the right on the south side of the fault and to the left on the north side clearly indicates that the block south of the fault has moved west with respect to the block on the north side. By cutting the map along the fault line and sliding the upper part to the left until the pattern on opposite sides match gives a measure of the amount of horizontal displacement. The profiles can be used in a similar manner as shown in figure 70. Here the two curves in the

185

block north of the Mendocino fault are superposed over two in the block south of the fault and the dotted lines pass through corresponding points on all four profiles. It may be noted that the upper panel is almost 14° or about six hundred miles farther west than the lower panel. In this way Raff [129] found that the block north of the Pioneer

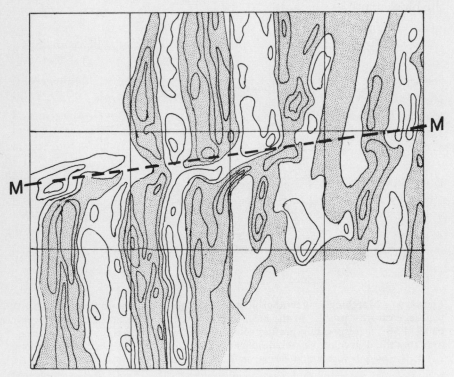

Figure 71. A map of the magnetic field near the Murray fault (M—M). The shaded bands show excess magnetism and the unshaded bands magnetic deficiency. Contours indicate the amount of magnetic anomaly. After Raff [129]

fault has moved about 130 miles west with respect to the block on the south side and that the block north of the Mendocino fault has moved still farther west by about six hundred miles. Since the movement caused no appreciable deformation within the blocks it seems evident that they were not thrust westward but were dragged or slid down the western slope of the Rise, riding on the flowing mantle.

Application of the Theory of Convection Currents

In chapter 8 we suggested the possible role of convection currents in the origin of the continents. If the granitic crust was separated from the mantle, like slag in a furnace, why did it not form a continuous layer over the earth as cream covers a vessel of milk ? What special mechanism could have concentrated it within less than a third of the earth's surface ?

A few geologists, notably Hilgenberg [77] and Carey [21], believe it actually did form a continuous layer when the earth was young and much smaller than it is now, and that subsequent expansion of the interior caused it to pull apart to form the continents and leave the ocean basins between. They cite as evidence the way in which the continents could be fitted together like pieces of a jig-saw puzzle to neatly cover a small earth. But since the continents now occupy only about thirty per cent of the earth's surface, this hypothesis would require an expansion by several fold in the volume of the earth since the crust was formed, and no physical basis for such an enormous expansion has been conceived [34; 10]. Of course, this does not prove that such expansion did not occur, even though it would violate known physical principles, but it does throw a heavy burden of proof on proponents of the idea. A further consideration seems to offer more positive disproof.

This is the evidence that the continents have grown larger during geologic time by lateral accretion. Age determinations based on radioactive minerals at many places in North America have been assembled by Wilson [171] and by Engel [44]. As indicated in figure 19, the oldest rocks occupy a large area in the middle of the Canadian Shield where the dates exceed 2,500 million years. Largely surrounding this nucleus is a wide zone in which the ages range between one thousand million and 2,500 million years, and in the peripheral regions the ages are generally less than six hundred million years. Wilson states that in similar fashion all the shields so far investigated are similarly zoned. If this be valid, the present size and shape of the continents affords no evidence of a primaeval fit about a much smaller earth, and they compound the difficulty of accounting for the postulated amount of expansion. The pulling apart of a primaeval granitic crust could not account for growth of the continents by lateral accretion.

Convection currents in the mantle offer a much more promising explanation of the concentration of the granitic rocks and of continental growth.

The contrasting features of the western margins of North and South America may be even more significant. The Pacific Rise roughly parallels the coast of South America but lies well out in the ocean basin. If it follows the crest of a great convection cell the lateral flow on its eastern flank should tend to drag the ocean floor under the edge of the continent. Two striking features indicate that this is taking place. The first is a nearly continuous string of deep oceanic trenches that lies close against the continental margin from

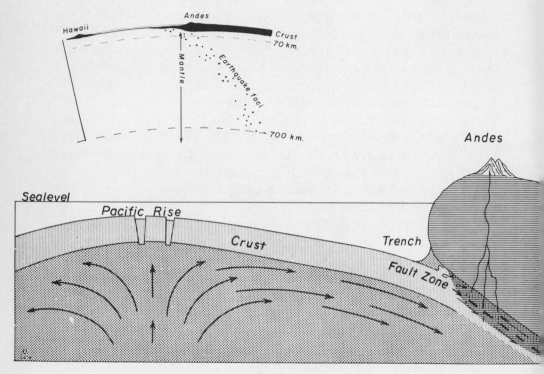

Figure 72. At top an idealized section from Hawaii to South America showing the locus of deep earthquake foci under the Andean region, from Wilson, figure 5 [171]
Below an idealized section showing the inferred relation of the Pacific Rise to the Oceanic trench, the zone of deep earthquakes, and the Andes

Patagonia to southern Mexico (figure 34). The second is an intensive belt of earthquakes that underlies the edge of the continent. The quakes, of course, are caused by rupture in the crust. The depth of focus of many of these earthquakes has been determined and thus it is known that a belt of faulting dips eastward under the continental margin (figure 72). Drag of the ocean floor under the continent could explain both the trenches and the earthquakes. Gutenberg

[59] has marshalled similar evidence indicating that the ocean floor at the western margin of the Pacific is being thrust under the Japanese Island Arc. Here the Kurile trench lies close in front of Hokkaido Island which is the locus of volcanic activity and many earthquakes. The depth of focus of the earthquakes near shore is shallow and most of those farther inland are progressively deeper (figure 73)

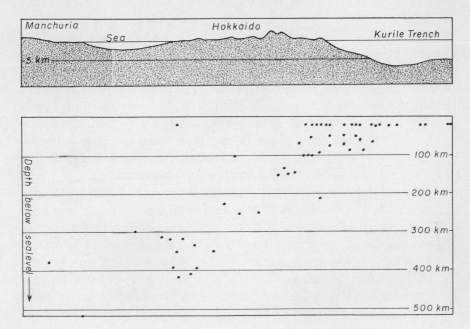

Figure 73. Vertical section across the Japanese island arc, after Gutenberg [59]. In the upper panel the vertical scale is exaggerated but in the lower panel it is not. Each dot in the lower panel marks the focus of an earthquake

indicating that a major zone of thrusting plunges under the island arc.

The contrast in the structure of the western margins of South America and North America is striking. Where the Rise passes inland under Mexico the oceanic trenches end and from there northward great rectangular blocks of the ocean floor have moved westward away from the continental margin. They appear to have been dragged or to have slid down the western flank of the Rise.

Where the Rise underlies the great Cordilleran highlands the mountains rise above the level of the plains of the continental interior about as high as the crest of the Rise in the south Pacific stands

189

above the ocean floor. Its crest coincided in position with the Meso-cordilleran geanticline that was actively rising throughout Jurassic and Cretaceous time (plate 28). The Rocky Mountains were formed to the east of it about the end of the Cretaceous period and their structure shows clearly that they were produced by colossal forces directed eastward. From central Utah to the Canadian border a belt of large low angle thrust faults caused great slices of sedimentary deposits to shingle up into a mountain complex. East of this thrust zone the structure changes progressively, first to great arches broken by thrust faults along their eastern flanks, then to more symmetrical arches, and finally to the Bighorns and the Black Hills that buckled up as simple arches out in the plains. The source of this eastward thrust has long been an enigma. Subcrustal flow in the mantle away from the crest of the Rise offers a simple explanation (figure 69).

During the formation of the Rocky Mountains the Rise occupied the position of the modern Basin and Range Province, the Colorado Plateau, and the Columbia Basalt Plateau. This remained a highland with external drainage until Miocene time when the Basin and Range Province and the Columbia Plateau region began to subside and were riven by many large north–south normal faults as though the crest of a broad arch was collapsing. The Basin and Range Province now lies about a mile below the summits of the Sierra Nevada on the west and the Colorado Plateau and the Wasatch range on the east. Farther north subsidence was largely balanced by the outpouring of basic lavas that formed the Columbia Plateau. It seems probable that the arch was held up by the rising convection current and that as the upward movement declined after the Rockies were formed, isostatic adjustments caused the arch to collapse by down faulting.

Recent study of the mid-Atlantic Ridge (figure 29) has added further evidence of convection currents in the mantle. This broad ridge has long been known but its real nature has come to light only during the last two decades, largely through the work of Ewing and Heezen and their colleagues of the Lamont Oceanographic Laboratories. Many traverses with sonic depth recorders have proved it to be a broad bulge rising to mountainous heights along its crest and following the middle of the Atlantic floor from the Arctic to the Antarctic regions. In places its crest is within six thousand feet of sea level whereas the broad basins on opposite sides range in depth from fifteen thousand to eighteen thousand feet. The greatest surprise came with the discovery of an enormous rift valley along its crest. Profiles across it show this valley to be a fault trough like the rift valleys of East Africa. In short, it is bounded by faults that have permitted the crest of the arch to subside. It is also the locus of a great belt of shallow focus earthquakes. This implies that the crest of the mid-Atlantic Ridge is under tension. Heezen [71] offers the explanation that the arch follows the summit of an enormous elongated convection cell from which the currents flowing east and west

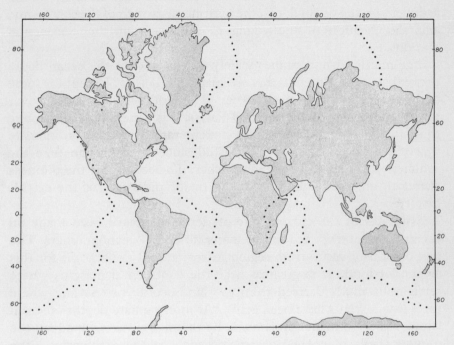

Figure 74. Map showing the distribution of mid-oceanic ridges of the world, after Heezen

are pulling the ocean floor apart. Still more remarkable is the discovery that each of the ocean basins has a comparable mid-ocean ridge (figure 74). Thus, whatever their cause may be, such arches in the ocean floors are a worldwide phenomenon. In a few regions a mid-ocean ridge converges toward the shore and passes under a continent. The extension of the Mid-Pacific Rise under the western part of North America was described above and the mid-ocean ridge in the Indian Ocean seems to reach Africa in the vicinity of the Red Sea and to become confluent with the great Rift Valleys of East Africa.

From such considerations Dietz [35] has advanced the daring hypothesis, also shared by Heezen [71], that the ocean floors are drifting laterally and sliding under the margins of the continents. Thus he believes the old sediment layers of the ocean floors have been skimmed off and, along with the thick accumulations at the continental shelves, have, from time to time, been tucked under the margins of the continents where they are heated and metamorphosed into new granite. Thus he would account for the thinness of the sediment on the ocean floors, the peripheral growth of the continents, and the location of the young mountains near the continental margins.

The many seismic studies widely scattered over the ocean floors prove that the sediment layers are surprisingly thin. Except for some of the oceanic trenches the thickness is generally less than a mile over the Atlantic basin and in the mid-Pacific it is generally less than one thousand feet. Estimates of the current rate of deposition indicate that if the ocean basins have existed since Precambrian time the sediment layer should be much thicker. To account for the thinness therefore appears to be one of the major problems of the earth's history.

Estimates of the current rate of deposition have been made on several lines of evidence and by many different oceanographers. The rate obviously varies from region to region and the reasons for this are understood. It is greatest near the continental margins where terriginous muds derived from the lands come to rest and where turbidity currents have been active. At intermediate depths far from land a major contribution is made by the organic oozes made of the minute shells of pelagic organisms such as the globigerines, the coccoliths, and radiolaria. The rate is slowest in mid-ocean and at depths of more than fifteen thousand feet where red clay is the dominant sediment. Even though the estimated rates differ from place to place and some of them may be inexact they are all of the same order of magnitude.

Bramlette and Bradley [16], basing their estimate on four Piggott cores from the western Atlantic Basin, concluded that the average rate of deposition during post-glacial time has been about one cm in five hundred years. Schott [139] had previously estimated that in the southern Atlantic the rate has averaged about one cm in eight hundred years. In both these regions organic oozes are a major component of the sediment. Broecker, Turekian, and Heezen [18] studied core No. A-180-74 from the eastern flank of the mid-Atlantic ridge and found that during the last eleven thousand years the rate of deposition has averaged one cm in about 450 years, but that in the deeper part of the core the rate had exceeded the average, ranging from 240 to 300 years per cm. Ericson *et al.* [46] have estimated that the normal rate of deposition in the mid-Atlantic has varied from one to ten cm per one thousand years, but that in areas reached by turbidity currents it has been as high as thirty to sixty cm per thousand years. In summary, a conservative estimate for the North Atlantic basin where globigerina ooze is an important component of the sediment, would be one cm of deposit in five hundred years. At this rate a little less than 40,000 feet of sediment should have accumulated since the beginning of Cambrian time and if this rate had persisted since early Precambrian time the thickness should be about 208,000 feet. Of course compaction would have greatly reduced this thickness and we shall return to its consideration below.

For the red clay in deep water far from land perhaps the most significant observations were made on a core taken by the US Navy during Operation Highjump at a locality about 1,200 miles northwest of Lima, Peru, in the Pacific Ocean where the water is about 11,880 feet deep. The core was 194 cm long, and as reported by Hough [79] it consists of alternating layers of red clay and of globigerina ooze. Radiogenic age determinations were made by W. D. Urry at twenty-eight depth levels in the core. The lowest of these indicated that the bottom of the core is about 800,000 years old. If this date is valid, the average rate of deposition has been one cm in about four thousand years. However, the dates at successive depths in the core indicate a rate of one cm in 440 years near the surface and one cm in 6,033 years between the time 338,000 and 700,000 years ago. In part, at least, compaction accounts for the slower rate in the older layers. But if for the present we accept an average rate of one cm in four thousand years, then in one million years about 8·2 feet of sediment should have accumulated, and since the beginning of Cambrian time it should have totalled about 4,920 feet, and since early Precambrian time about 26,220 feet or almost as much as the entire thickness of the suboceanic crust.

In a very thoughtful study Hamilton [64] has tried to reconcile such estimates with the actual thickness of the sedimentary layer which seismic evidence proves to be generally less than a mile. When first laid down the globigerine and coccolith shells of organic oozes are empty and the red clay is almost a watery soup. In the course of time and under the load of later deposits it appears probable that the shells will be crushed and partly recrystallized into compact limestone, and the water will be squeezed out of the clay and the clay minerals pressed together and perhaps rebuilt into a more compact form. Such changes Hamilton calculates would reduce the original thickness by perhaps fifty per cent. Furthermore erosion of the lands is now abnormally rapid as compared with much of the geologic past when the lands were generally lower and large parts of the present continents were covered by shallow seas. Moreover, the organisms which form organic oozes did not evolve until about the middle of the Mesozoic Era and probably had no counterparts in the older oceans. And, finally, if the continents have grown larger by lateral accretion, the Precambrian lands may have been much less extensive than they are at present. In view of these considerations Hamilton is inclined to think that the existing sediment layer can account for continuous deposition throughout geologic time.

The most significant counter argument may be based on three cored wells drilled by the Mohole Project in the Pacific floor in 1961 at a locality about 150 miles west of the coast of Mexico where the water is almost twelve thousand feet deep. All previous investigations were based on piston cores less than about eighty feet long only a few of which reached to the Pleistocene–Pliocene boundary. The Mohole cores, on the contrary, reached a depth of 560 feet and probably went to the base of the Miocene. Fossils from near the bottom prove Miocene age [131], and the underlying basalt has been dated on the basis of the potassium–argon ratio as about thirty-two million years old [93]. This indicates that the basalt is a submarine lava flow and the probability seems great that older sediments lie below it. But if we accept the age of the lowest sediment penetrated as thirty-two million years, then the average rate of accumulation at this locality has been one cm in about 1,880 years. At this rate the deposit formed since early Cambrian time should be about 10,640 feet; and if continuous since early Precambrian time, it should be one hundred times 560 feet or 56,000 feet. This is about ten miles or twice the thickness of the sub-oceanic crust. And since most of the sediment in these cores is several millions of years old we should expect that it has already suffered much of the compaction of which it is capable. The information about the Mohole cores was not available when Hamilton's study was made and it throws grave doubts on his conclusion that the sediment layer beneath the oceans represents all of geologic time.

The continental shelf along the west side of the Atlantic is underlain by a vast wedge of Cretaceous and younger sediments. At its landward margin their feathered edges rest unconformably on metamorphics but they have thickened to more than 9,880 feet at Cape Hatteras. If the continental margin has been stable since the beginning of Cambrian time, a vastly greater wedge of Paleozoic and early Mesozoic formations should lie buried in the ocean floor, but seismic studies indicate that no such deposits exist. If they were tucked under the continent and added to the metamorphics during the Appalachian Revolution, as Dietz believes, their absence is understandable. No other explanation seems plausible.

If the Mohole Project is carried to completion and brings up cores clear down to the mantle, we can hope that included fossils will prove whether Mesozoic and Paleozoic deposits are present. This will throw light on one of the great unsolved mysteries about the earth and its history, and is one of the reasons why geologists and geophysicists are so deeply interested in the Mohole Project.

Convection in the mantle offers the only known rational explanation for the history of the great mountain systems. That of the Rocky Mountain system was set forth in chapter 10. Why was the crust first slowly depressed for a hundred million years to form a great geosyncline? Why was the geosyncline then crushed and uplifted into mountains during a relatively shorter period of intense orogeny? Why should the region then remain stable while the mountains were slowly eroded away, and finally rise gently as a broad arch without further crushing and then remain stable and slightly positive? Many geologists now believe that convection currents could be the answer to all these questions. One of the pioneers in such thinking is Hess [76]. He postulated that where the current is descending it pulls the overlying crust down, thus forming a geosyncline at the margin of a convection cell or between two cells. So long as the flow is active the floor of the geosyncline continues to sink. Meanwhile the trough is filled with weak sedimentary deposits of relatively light specific gravity and the granitic crust is depressed to form a great bulge extending some miles deep into the mantle. This bulge Hess termed a tectogene. Eventually it is weakened by the heat of the surrounding mantle. Squeezed by the converging mantle current, it is

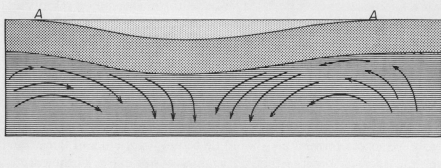

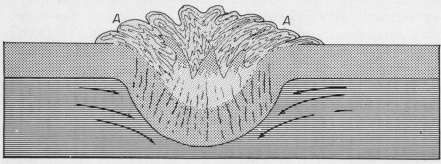

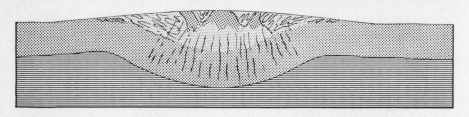

Figure 75. Diagrams to illustrate three stages in the evolution of a tectogene. At the top an early stage when a geosyncline is being pulled down by the descending convection currents. In the centre a later stage when the crust beneath the geosyncline has been weakened by the heat in depth and has yielded to the drag of the converging convection currents. The sedimentary fill of the geosyncline is thereby crushed and elevated into mountain folds while a great bulge of the granitic crust is pushed down into the mantle. During this, the orogenic phase, the rock deep within the tectogene is strongly metamorphosed and some of it is melted and rises as granitic intrusions into the heart of the mountains. At the bottom a late stage after the mountains have been planed away by erosion and the convection currents have died out. Now the great bulge of relatively light material has floated up into isostatic balance

then crushed and thickened and the sedimentary fill of the geosyncline is crushed and uplifted into mountains. Eventually the return flow of relatively cooled mantle rock into the depths restores the heat balance and the movement dies out. Then the orogenic phase comes to a close. But as the mountains are eroded away a great welt of granitic crust is left projecting down into the mantle and, being lighter than the mantle rock, it tends to float up until isostatic balance is restored. Thus the region rises gently as a broad arch without crushing. Even this leaves the crust thickened by a welt of 'scar tissue', to borrow a happy simile from Deutsch, and thereafter the region, once disturbed, becomes more stable than it was originally and remains slightly positive. This is the nature of all the great continental shields which have been welded together by ancient mountain making.

This history suggests that a convection cell is a transient, even though long enduring, feature of the earth. The circulation eventually reduces the temperature of the deep hot spot that produced it and then the movement dies out. Meanwhile excessive heat builds up in other places and new convection cells are generated. Thus mountains have grown now in one part of the world and later on in other regions.

This brings us to another profound problem: what has caused shallow seas to spread over large parts of the continents and then retreat, time and again, throughout the geologic past? And have the continents moved independently or has sea level risen and fallen? If the changes are due to eustatic (equal standing) rise and fall of sea level, then our major subdivisions of the geologic record have a natural, even though imperfect, basis; but if the changes are the result of independent movement in the several continents, it is essentially artificial and might have been quite different if it had been based on some other continent instead of Europe. Geologists have tended to fall into two schools of thought on this problem, one favouring eustatic changes of sea level and the other independent rise and fall of the several continents. During several decades following Chamberlin's proposal of his theory of the causes of diastrophism belief in eustatic changes of sea level was dominant, and widespread orogeny was commonly believed to be the cause of major breaks in the record. This view was carried to extremes by Stille [150; 151] who proposed to name the breaks between systems and even between series of rocks after local mountains. Such ideas were first challenged by Shepard [141] and were effectively laid to rest by Gilluly [56]. Probably no one now believes that orogeny is limited to or even concentrated at the ends of periods and epochs of geologic time. It is well known that local or regional deformation has occurred within each of the continents, commonly within the midst of a geologic period. As Gilluly emphasized, for example, the enormous uplift of the Mesocordilleran geanticline occurred throughout Cretaceous time while North America was experiencing one of its greatest submergences. If eustatic changes of sea level have occurred, they clearly are not dependent on orogeny, which is essentially local in its nature. If there is a natural basis for subdivision of the geologic record, it is imperfect and must rest on some other factor.

Nevertheless study of paleogeography and of the stratigraphic record strongly support the view that major changes of sea level have occurred at times in the past. During the Cretaceous Period, for example, when a vast interior sea occupied the Rocky Mountain geosyncline, the Atlantic and the Gulf and western margins of the continent were also submerged beneath shelf seas and the shoreline was far inland from its present position. While some thirty per cent of North America was thus flooded extensive shallow seas covered parts of South America, much of Europe, large parts of Asia and part of Australia, only Africa remaining fully above sea level. Then within a relatively short time early in the Cenozoic Era the inland seas retreated almost to their present position, and for the last sixty million years or so all the continents have remained high and exposed to erosion, only the Baltic Sea and Hudson Bay remaining as vestiges of the epeiric seas that had been extensive during much of geologic time. Moreover, faunal zones can be correlated from one continent to the next in the Cretaceous deposits proving that submergence was contemporaneous in many parts of the world. In so far as local or regional warping took place within the continental plates the movement was locally out of phase with eustatic changes in sea level so that submergence began earlier, or lasted longer in some regions than in others. But except for the very earliest and the latest of the marine Cretaceous formations, faunal zones in one continent can be correlated with synchronous deposits in many other parts of the world. There can be no gainsaying the fact that the Cretaceous Period was a time of widespread continental submergence and that about the end of the period the seas retreated within a relatively short time to about their present distribution leaving all the continents high and widely emergent as they have remained until the present.

It can hardly be a coincidence, moreover, that at the time of emergence a very large area of the mid-Pacific sea floor began to sink and has been subsiding ever since. This is now known as a result of extensive oceanographic research during the last two decades in that region. Several of the guyots, for example, have shallow-water marine Cretaceous fossils on their summits which now lie at a depth of more than a mile below sea level [61] and deep drilling on the atolls of Bikini and Eniwetok show that they have grown up from a truncated volcanic base by the skeletons of very shallow water organisms such as those now living on the atolls. And since these limy deposits range in age from Eocene to Recent it is clear that the base has subsided slowly and progressively since early Cenozoic time. On the basis of such evidence Menard has concluded that several million square miles of the mid-Pacific sea floor have subsided by a mile or more since Cretaceous time [111]. Movement of such magnitude could only be the result of convection in the mantle below.

The end of the Paleozoic Era was another time when the continents all stood emergent as at present and deserts were widespread as they are now. During the Carboniferous period swampy lowlands and extensive inland seas existed in every continent except Africa. Both were much restricted during Permian time, and at its close the continents were all fully emergent. These two times, the end of the Paleozoic Era and the end of the Mesozoic, were marked by the greatest biologic changes since the beginning of Cambrian time.

Ten major cycles of submergence are now widely recognized, one for each of the periods in the Paleozoic and one for each of the Mesozoic periods. The emergences between the periods were less profound than those separating the eras and the faunal changes were not as great, and in places adjacent systems of rocks are not separated by a conspicuous hiatus. Yet the maximum submergences fell within the recognized periods and continuous marine deposition from one to the next are at most regional and generally are quite local. In these places regional warping may have been out of phase with the rise and fall of sea level. But if it be granted that the end of the Paleozoic and Mesozoic Eras were marked by simultaneous emergence of all the continents, it would seem to imply eustatic fall of sea level; and if this be granted, it is difficult to deny that lesser emergences between the periods were produced in the same manner.

It must be admitted that the spread of the seas was not equal in the several continents during any period and that they appeared earlier in some regions and retreated sooner or later in others. This is not surprising on any basis for it is well known that independent movements take place within the continents, and, as in the case of the Cretaceous history of North America, mountains may be rising while the sea is advancing. Unfortunately the geologic history of large parts of the world is still not adequately known. When the paleogeography of each of the continents is as well known as that of North America it should provide a more critical test of the theory of eustatic changes of sea level.

Meanwhile the theory of convection in the mantle suggests a probable mechanism for such changes. If a convection cell develops under a continent, the movements are likely to be regional and reciprocal, one area rising while another sinks. This was clearly the situation in North America during Cretaceous time. For this reason orogeny is not a satisfactory basis for subdivision of the geologic record. If convection cells are entirely under the ocean basins, the movements are equally likely to balance out as one region subsides while another is rising. But if a cell underlies a continental margin, the adjacent ocean basin should subside as the land is uplifted; and if convection cells underlie the middle of all the oceans, so that from the mid-ocean ridges the ocean floor tends to spread and crowd under the margins of the adjacent continents, then the ocean basins may be enlarged while at the same time the continents are elevated. At the same time the continents may be forced to drift into regions between the most active convection cells.

Paleomagnetism. Within the last two decades a powerful new tool has been brought to bear on the problem of continental drift. This is the study of the residual magnetism left in the rocks since their formation. The basic concept is that ferro-magnesian mineral particles have a dipole axis similar to that of a compass needle and in the presence of the earth's magnetic field they tend to orient themselves like so many compass needles. This happens as a crystal is forming in a cooling magma, or when a sedimentary particle settles freely in standing water to be incorporated in a sedimentary deposit, the dipole axis being aligned with the lines of force in the earth's magnetic field. Two components of their orientation are important. The first is the horizontal declination of the dipole axes which should point to the earth's magnetic poles at the time of the formation of the rock masses, whether in a magma or in a sedimentary deposit. The second is the inclination of the dipole axes. This follows from the fact that the lines of force are approximately parallel to the earth's surface in low latitudes but dip more and more steeply at higher latitudes and plunge vertically down at the magnetic poles (figure 20).

Techniques have now been developed to determine the average orientation of the dipole axes of such particles in a rock mass and such measurements have been made at many places. The results are not all consistent and their interpretation is less simple than indicated above. The techniques used and the difficulties to be overcome have been treated recently in a monumental treatise on paleomagnetism by Irving [82]. To mention two of the problems, for example, compaction of a mass of sediment after the particles have settled may reduce the inclination of the dipole axes, or intense deformation may alter their direction. Under certain conditions of heat the original magnetism may be destroyed.

With local exceptions, however, the average orientation of the residual magnetism in recent deposits and in rocks formed during the latter half of Cenozoic time accord well with modern world geography, the dipole axes pointing toward the earth's present magnetic poles. When applied to the older rocks, however, the results are surprising. A group of measurements in the Permian rocks of Europe, for example, indicated that the north magnetic pole in Permian time was in the western Pacific east of Japan and the south pole midway between the tips of South America and Africa. When such observations were first made it was widely believed that the magnetic poles have wandered during geologic time. And since the orientation of the magnetic axis is controlled by the spin of the earth about its metallic core this involved the supposition that the earth as a whole has rotated on its axis.

It was soon discovered, however, that measurements taken in different continents do not agree. Those in the Permian rocks of North America, for example, point to a north magnetic pole in China somewhat west of Peking and a south pole on the west coast of Argentina. Deutsch [34] and, later, Irving [82] have pointed out that such divergences between continents could only be reconciled by the assumption that one or both continents have drifted and rotated into a new position since Permian time. Thus two theories, polar wander-

ing and continental drift, have been invoked to account for the
information gained from paleomagnetism. The choice between these
alternatives has a critical bearing on the restoration of past world
geography.

In a recent reconstruction of Permian world geography, for example, Bain [5] used paleomagnetic data indicating that the north
pole was in the Pacific Ocean at latitude $7\frac{1}{2}°$S and longitude 165°W.
His world map (figure 76) thus places the equator almost at right

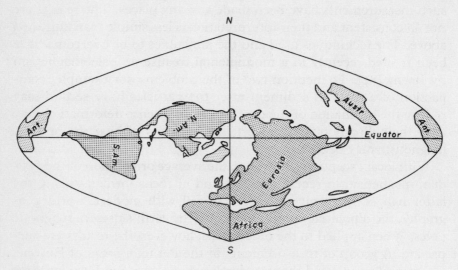

Figure 76. Bain's interpretation of world geography in Permian time.
After Bain [5]

angles to its present position with Antarctica on the equator and
South Africa at the south pole. A completely different interpretation
was made by Van Hilten in 1964 [160]. Using paleomagnetic data
summarized by Cox and Doell in 1960 for both North America and
Europe [29] he drew isoclines running through places of equal

Figures 77, 78, 79.   Paleomagnetic maps by Van Hilten for Permian, Triassic,
and Permian periods, respectively, showing isoclines of magnetic inclination and
positions of the magnetic poles as indicated by the several continents. Af, polar
positions indicated by Africa; As, polar positions indicated by Asia; Au, polar
positions indicated by Australia; Eu, polar positions indicated by Europe;
Gr, north polar position indicated by Greenland; NA, polar positions indicated
by North America; SA, polar positions indicated by South America

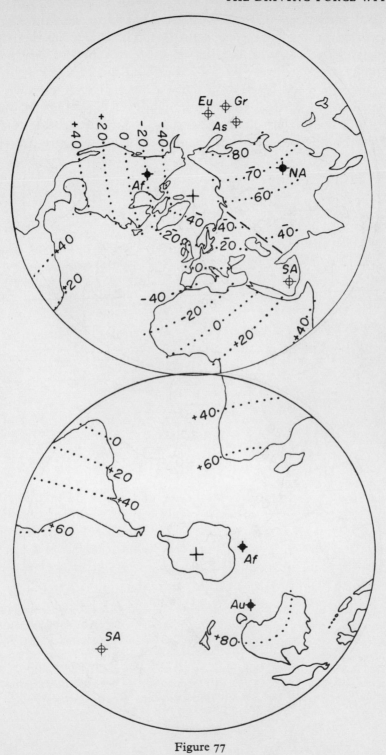

Figure 77

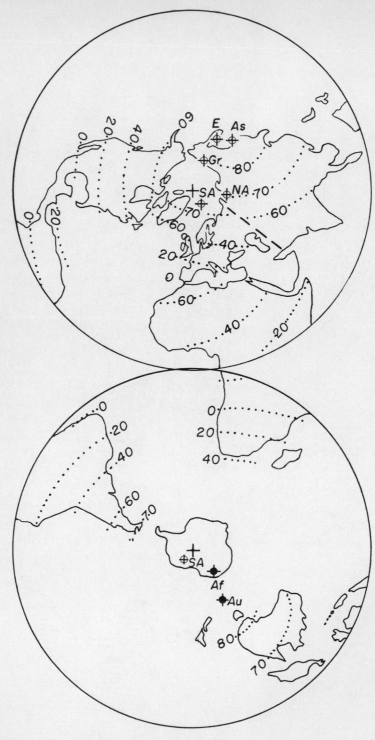

Figure 78

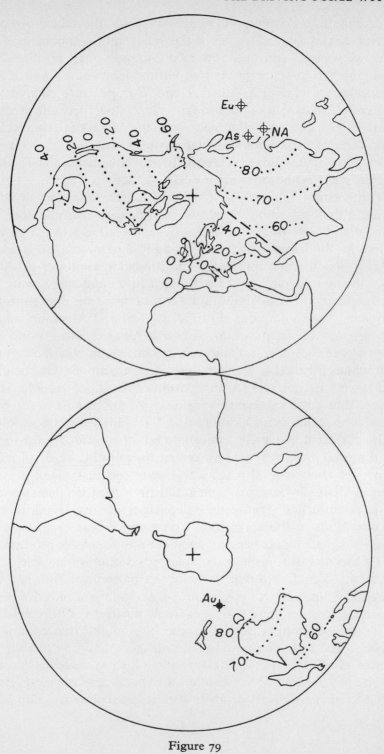

Figure 79

paleomagnetic inclination. In a unit land mass these lines are parts of great circles and on a sphere the horizontal component of the dipole axes would converge toward a common polar position. The result is shown in figure 77. As Van Hilten points out, if one or both the continents of North America and Europe were rotated in a counterclockwise sense and brought closer together, the isoclines could be brought into alignment and the horizontal components would converge at a common polar position. And he points out that if one continent has moved it is equally probable that each has moved and thus there is no evidence for polar wandering. Van Hilten's map for Triassic time is based on data from North America and Africa and again the orientation in the two continents is contradictory, but if Greenland were rotated in a clockwise direction and Africa were rotated in the same sense and brought northward, or if North America were brought southward and rotated in a counter-clockwise direction the isoclines could be brought into close agreement. The map for Carboniferous time (figure 79) is based on data from four continents, North America, Europe, Africa, and Australia, and all show divergent polar positions. If North America and Europe were drawn closer together, it would require but slight rotation to bring the isoclines for these continents into close alignment. On the other hand the orientation and the inclination of the dipole axes in Africa indicate that both continents were near the south pole in Carboniferous time. Such considerations led Van Hilten to conclude that continental drift is clearly indicated, but they afford no evidence that the poles have moved. In a recent, penetrating study of paleomagnetism Deutsch [34] reaches the same conclusion and presents strong evidence favouring continental drift rather than polar wandering. A monumental treatise on paleomagnetism by Irving in 1964 [82] also leads to the conclusion that since Precambrian time the earth's magnetic dipole has remained close to its axis of rotation and that continental drift rather than polar wandering is indicated.

It must be confessed that the study of paleomagnetism is a very young discipline and that many more observations are needed before a consistent picture of past changes in the positions of the continents can be attained, but it can no longer be doubted that continental drift has occurred. The findings of paleogeography meanwhile can be checked against other and independent lines of evidence, particularly the past distribution of animals and plants and physical criteria of climate such as glacial deposits and desert sediments. This is not a simple matter, however, since these criteria all involve basic assumptions that may not apply without local or regional exceptions.

The distribution of most kinds of animals and plants, for example, is controlled by climatic zones which at present are rather sharply defined. Cold-blooded land animals become torpid and helpless when the temperature falls to the freezing point. Small reptiles and amphibians take refuge in holes or caverns underground and hibernate and thus manage to survive, but large reptiles could not find such refuge. Thus the crocodiles and alligators, large snakes such as the boa constrictors, large turtles, and large lizards are all confined to tropical or subtropical regions, and we may safely assume that the dinosaurs and other large reptiles and large amphibians of the past were similarly restricted. Most of the tropical vegetation cannot survive where winter temperature drops to the freezing point. The mixed hardwood forests of the temperate zone do not thrive in the tropics and in higher latitudes are replaced by dominantly evergreen forests, while in higher latitudes where the mean summer temperature is near the freezing point only the arctic tundra survives. Reef-forming corals are confined to the tropics and sub-tropical regions where the minimum temperature is about 71°F, and in general the molluscan faunas in the sea differ markedly from one temperature zone to the next. Dall and Harris [31] found, for example, that on the continental shelf of eastern North America 180 species of shell-bearing invertebrates live along the coast of Greenland, 277 in the Gulf of Maine, 305 off the Carolina coast, 681 on the shelf west of Florida, and 517 off the coast of Panama. These figures total 1,960; but actually the species involved number 1,772. This means that only about two hundred species range from one of these faunal provinces into the next. In short the faunal provinces are almost entirely distinct in spite of the fact that all are freely connected by shallow open water. Temperature differences appear obviously to be the only barrier restricting the distribution of the marine invertebrates.

In view of such facts the fossil animals and plants found in the rocks of a given past age should be a good criterion of the latitude of the land mass in which they are found at the time when they were living. But caution is needed on several counts. At present, for example, both polar regions are ice capped and the climatic zones are strongly differentiated, but there is much geologic evidence that the present is an exceptional stage in earth's history and that during much of the past the poles were not ice-bound and the world climate was more equable and climatic zones were less sharply differentiated than at present. Under such conditions organisms now confined to low latitudes may have spread much farther north and south.

Furthermore, ocean currents may greatly affect the climate of a region. At present the Gulf current carries warmth to western Europe even as far as the northern tip of Norway while at the same time an Arctic current flows southward from Greenland bathing the eastern coast of North America as far south as Cape Cod. Thus the most densely populated part of Europe lies in the same latitude as the barrens of Labrador and central Canada, and northern Norway with its lush evergreen forests faces the southern half of the Greenland ice sheet. At many times in the past when vast interior seas covered large parts of the continents the climate even in high latitudes was ameliorated and ocean currents may have carried warmth into regions now much colder. In short, the presence of Cretaceous plants such as figs, bread-fruit, cinnamon, and tree ferns beside the Greenland ice cap and far to the north of the present range of such plants might be interpreted to mean that in Cretaceous time Greenland was much farther south than at present, or that world climate was milder than now in Cretaceous time and the climatic zones much less restricted, or that at that time western Greenland was bathed by a warm ocean current flowing north.

The presence of coral reefs in the Silurian rocks in Manitoba and along the west side of Hudson Bay where winter temperature falls as low as 50°F below zero presents the same choices.

In all such cases there is another factor to consider. Living organisms show remarkable ability to adapt to climatic conditions beyond their normal preference. During the Pleistocene ice age, for example, the woolly mammoth and the woolly rhinoceros were at home in Alaska and Siberia more than two thousand miles to the north of the range of other species of elephants and rhinoceroses. If it were not for the frozen carcases that prove these great beasts to have had a heavy coat of wool, their presence in the midst of glacial deposits would be a complete enigma. It seems safe to assume that extreme specializations for climatic tolerance have been made by relatively few species of any biologic group and that a large and varied assemblage will therefore be more trustworthy than a few species.

Coral reefs present a somewhat different problem. Modern hermatypic (reef making) corals have abundant symbiotic algae embedded in their tissues, and the algae give off oxygen that may be critically needed in the crowded conditions that exist in a coral reef. Such algae require sunlight and for this reason are confined to shallow water. This may be a vital factor in controlling the distribution of modern coral reefs. However, other types of corals thrive in water as much as a mile deep and make coral banks in relatively cold water along the continental margin of Europe even as far north as Norway. We have no way of knowing whether the Paleozoic and Mesozoic corals had commensal algae and whether they were thereby limited to shallow water to the same extent as modern reef-making corals. There is, nevertheless, independent evidence that they thrived only in relatively warm water. This is the fact that ancient coral reefs are generally confined to extensive calcareous deposits. Such deposits in modern seas are confined to warm regions for the reason that in such places the sea water is saturated with respect to calcium carbonate whereas colder water is undersaturated. And since chemical laws do not change with time it seems safe to conclude that throughout the ages limy deposits have been concentrated in the warmer regions. But here again the presence of coral reefs in central Canada, and even in far northern Greenland could mean that these regions were once farther south, or that the climatic zones were less restricted than now, or that world climate was milder, or that these places were then bathed by warm ocean currents.

In view of such considerations it is not surprising that biologists have held widely divergent views, some favouring the theory of continental drift and others stoutly opposing it. Bain, for example, attempted to support his interpretation of Permian world geography (figure 76) whereas Stehli [148], Stehli and Helsley [149], and Axelrod [3] have vigorously opposed it. The paleobiologic data are vast, complex, and partly contradictory, and thus far relatively few attempts at critical analysis of it have been made and these deal generally with only a single facet of it. We have only made a beginning in this endeavour and much more research is needed. We can hope that such studies will eventually make a major contribution to the problem of continental drift.

Physical evidences of climate are also important and equally subject to different interpretations. The widespread glacial deposits of late Paleozoic time in Australia, Africa, South America, and India provided the first great impetus for the theory of continental drift. They suggested that these southern land masses lay far to the south of their present position at the time of glaciation. Du Toit was a

leader among many geologists in the southern continents who have
believed that in Permian time the continents were grouped as indicated in figure 80. Paleomagnetism now seems to lend strong support to this belief. Nevertheless study of the Pleistocene glaciation in
the northern hemisphere, which is now so well known, shows that
the problem of glaciation is not simple. The accumulation of great
ice sheets demands low temperature to be sure, especially low mean
summer temperature, but it is also affected by altitude and by the
amount of precipitation. In North America the continental ice sheet

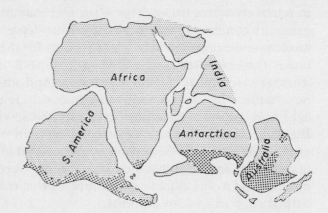

Figure 80. Du Toit's
arrangement of the
southern continents
during late Paleozoic
time. After Du Toit

pushed far to the south over a low plains region and as recently as
twenty thousand years ago its southern margin stood along the Ohio
and Missouri river valleys where summer temperatures now range
as high as 100°F. At the same time the Scandinavian ice sheet
pushed far south over the Baltic Sea and the plains of Germany.
Moreover, the ice sheets developed four different times during the
million years or so of Pleistocene time, and disappeared completely
during the somewhat longer interglacial ages, and there is much biologic evidence that at least during the second interglacial age the
climate was warmer in southern Canada than it is today. If we were
to assume that the growth of the Pleistocene ice sheets were dependent on latitude, we would have to believe that North America and
Europe moved far to the north during the relatively short glacial
ages and retreated far to the south during the interglacial ages.
Movements of such magnitude in relatively brief periods of time
are quite incredible and it seems certain that factors other than
continental migration have been dominant. We still do not adequately

understand what these factors were, but whatever their nature may have been they may have been involved in the Permian glaciation of the southern lands. For example, the impressive Dwyka tillite of South Africa shows that most of Africa south of the present equator was covered by a great ice sheet and that the ice radiated to the south and south-west from the highlands of the Transvaal but pushed out to sea toward the south. Certainly most of Africa was frigid at this time. Nevertheless the thick system of Permian formations that succeed the tillite includes fossil reptiles at many levels and in variety and abundance unequalled in any other part of the world. Such a variety of cold-blooded animals, many of which were relatively large, clearly indicates a climatic environment without freezing winters. If Africa was in high latitude during the glaciation, we must assume that it then moved rapidly to the north by middle Permian time. Otherwise we must believe that the climatic change was due to factors other than latitude.

The distribution of ancient desert deposits such as the great salt deposits, the gypsiferous red-beds, and large masses of wind-blown sand in the Permian System should also bear on the question of latitude. In the modern world deserts are largely concentrated in the horse latitudes that depend on the general planetary circulation of the atmosphere and form one belt between about 20° and 30° north latitude and another in the same situation in south latitude. We can safely assume that these climatic zones have held similar positions in the past though each may have shifted somewhat either north or south and each may have varied in width and intensity. But other factors are also involved. Arid conditions exist in the lee of the great north–south trending mountain systems throughout both torrid and temperate zones. The centre of the largest land masses are also arid. The interior of Asia, for example, is a vast desert region stretching from the Caspian Sea into Mongolia and North China and here salt lakes persist, and great deposits of wind blown dust (loess) and of desert sands have accumulated during late Cenozoic time. The present is an exceptional stage of earth history when arid conditions characterize about ten per cent of the land surface. The Permian was a comparable time of continental emergence, lofty mountains, and widespread deserts. But during much of the past when the continents were extensively covered by shallow epeiric seas arid conditions were much less widespread.

In summary it must be evident that the several lines of evidence bearing on the problem of continental drift are all complicated and that we have only fairly begun to assemble and critically analyse the data. Paleomagnetism has reached a stage where it can no longer be ignored, and it may prove to be the most definitive evidence we have. But even here only a start has been made. We need many more determinations within each continent in formations of equal age to

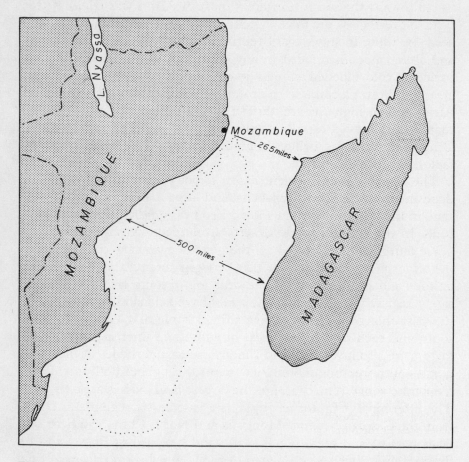

Figure 81. Map showing the relation of Madagascar to the mainland of Africa

see if they give consistent results for a particular land mass, and we need many determinations from successive geological horizons in different continents to see if they will indicate a consistent pattern of migration. In short the problem is soluble but will require much more research and penetrating analysis of the data from several disciplines before a definitive synthesis is achieved. Meanwhile, in the present state of our knowledge it is difficult to avoid the conviction that continental drift has been an important feature of earth's history. Indeed there is concrete evidence of some fragmentation of the present continents. Madagascar, for example, now lies several hundred miles off the coast of east Africa from which it is separated

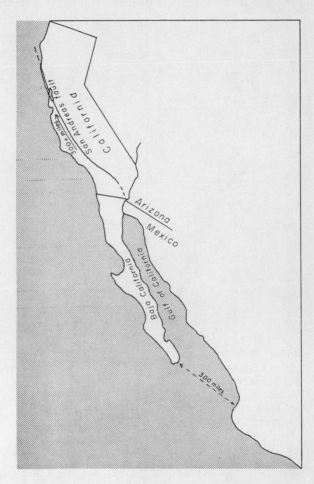

Figure 82. Map indicating that Baja California, has pulled away from the mainland of Mexico as the crustal block west of the San Andreas fault has moved north-westward

by oceanic depths of water (figure 81), but its mammalian fauna shows such affinity with that of the mainland that zoogeographers are convinced that land connection existed as late as early Cenozoic time. Furthermore, during Permian time when South Africa was covered with glacier ice, southern Madagascar was also ice covered, and along the eastern margin of the Union of South Africa the ice was moving inland from a source that is now deep sea. The dotted outline in figure 81 suggests the original position of Madagascar.

It is well known that in California the area west of the San Andreas fault zone has been and is still moving to the north-west, and Crowell [30] has found evidence that since early Cenozoic time it has moved at least three hundred miles. This great rift can be traced almost to

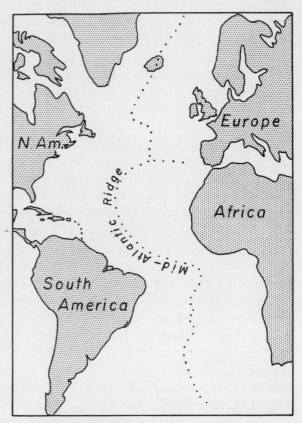

Figure 83. Map of the Atlantic region showing the resemblance of the outline of the continental margins on opposite sides of the ocean

the head of the Gulf of California where it is lost under the delta of the Colorado River (figure 82). At the same time it appears that the peninsula of Baja California has been pulled away from the coast of Mexico leaving the Gulf of California in its wake. Greenland appears also to have drifted away from Canada leaving Davis Strait in its wake. This inference is confirmed by paleomagnetic data. Finally it is difficult to account for the remarkable fit of opposite sides of the Atlantic Ocean on any other basis than continental drift (figure 83).

The question of former connections between continents is still controversial, and for this the biologic evidence should be most significant. Wegener and many other proponents of continental drift have believed that in Permian time India and the southern continents were united in one great land mass which at some later time broke into pieces that drifted apart to form the present continents. They also emphasize that the similar outlines of the continents on opposite sides of the Atlantic suggest that the Americas once lay contiguous to Europe and Africa and later drifted apart leaving the Atlantic Ocean between. Several international symposia have dealt with this problem and a wide variety of biological arguments have been made in its support. The occurrence of the distinctive 'tongue-fern', *Glossopteris*, in the Permian rocks of South America, Australia, Africa, and India, and in these alone, was one of the first and strongest biological arguments in favour of a former land mass called Gonwanaland or Pangea. The possibility exists, however, that even if open oceans separated these land masses but lay in a common wind belt, the spores or small seed of *Glossopteris* may have been transported from one to the other by the wind, perhaps during exceptional storms. The occurrence of a rare genus of aquatic marine reptiles, *Mesosaurus*, in the Permian rocks of Africa and South America has also been cited as evidence of land connection, but it is now known that the African species are distinct from those of South America. Of course if these land masses were actually joined in Permian time identical species should occur in both continents. Certain parasites living in the alimentary tract of genetically related amphibians in both South America and Africa have been cited as evidence of former land connections. If the identifications are valid, and if the host species are now completely isolated, the possibility remains that it was once more widespread or that on some rare occasion an aquatic fowl having ingested the amphibian was driven by storm winds across the Atlantic quickly enough to transplant the parasites from one continent to the other. In this connection the many seamounts that dot the Atlantic basin may at some time in the past have served as island stepping stones by which such a journey by aquatic birds could be made in short stages. In South Africa the only marine formations are in the Devonian and certain resemblances in these faunas and those of South America have been noted, but in this case two alternatives to land connections must be considered. Many shallow water marine organisms pass through a larval stage when they float for days and drift with the currents before settling to the bottom and others may be transported while attached to seaweeds or driftwood. Thus the volcanic islands so widely distributed across the mid-Pacific have many identical species of corals, bryozoans, and shallow water molluscs all the way from Hawaii to Guam. In this case the islands lying in a common belt of ocean currents have served as stepping stones for the migration of benthonic organisms across several thousands of miles of deep ocean. Furthermore, if climatic zones were less diversified than now many species may have migrated around the margins of the Atlantic basin without directly crossing it.

The Paleozoic marine faunas of Europe and North America have much in common at the generic level and at several levels the faunal resemblances are striking, especially between Europe and the Maritime Provinces of Canada. As just one example we may note the presence in the latter of the small freshwater clams of the genera *Anthracomya* and *Carbonicola* that are so characteristic of the coal measures in western Europe and occur also in Nova Scotia. But, as Simpson has emphasized, if two continents now separated were once united, the faunas of that age should be largely identical at the specific level, whereas if migration between land masses was by way of stepping stones, a screening effect would result whereby only certain forms would cross while many would remain isolated. In the present state of our knowledge there is little evidence for direct connection between Europe and North America since the beginning of Cambrian time. Groups of organisms that float in the open ocean, as did the graptolites, have identical species on both sides of the Atlantic, but the benthonic forms which have many genera in common to both continents are nearly all represented by distinct species on opposite sides of the Atlantic.

In summary, the biologic evidence for Paleozoic land connections between the continents is still inconclusive. The evidence for Mesozoic and Cenozoic time makes it quite certain that the present continents have been isolated except for temporary land bridges between North America and Eurasia by way of the Behring Strait, and between North and South America by way of the Isthmus of Panama. But whatever the extent of past continental drift may have been, convection currents in the mantle afford the only rational explanation thus far conceived for such movements.

Chapter 12

Life's Record in the Rocks

*The eyes of trilobites eternal be in stone and seem to stare about in
mild surprise at changes greater than they yet have known.*

T. A. CONRAD

THE HISTORY of life on earth is known from the fossils entombed in
stratified rocks. This is now common knowledge, but before it was
understood the intellectual world was once racked by bitter controversy over their meaning.

Long before the beginning of recorded history such 'curios' in the
rock had attracted the attention of primitive man. One of the ancient
Neanderthalers carried a fossil shell as an amulet to his death at
Saint Leon in the Dordogne Valley in France, undoubtedly attributing to it some magic charm. Some of the Greeks, long before the
beginning of the Christian era, observed such objects and correctly
interpreted them as remains of once living creatures. Herodotus, for
example, during his travels in Egypt about 450 BC observed fossil sea
shells in the Libyan desert and correctly inferred that the Mediterranean Sea had once spread over northern Africa. On the other hand
such objects were regarded with mysticism even by great thinkers
such as Aristotle who, while believing them to be organic remains,
thought that they had grown in the rocks. His ideas of how this
came about are obscure, but one of his pupils, Theophrastus, explained that eggs or seeds buried in accumulating sediments had
grown there after burial. In spite of such fanciful interpretations,
fossils seem to have been generally regarded as remains of once living
creatures until after the Christian Church became a dominant influence in the western world. Thereafter such objects were given
scant attention until the beginning of the Renaissance. Interest was
revived about AD 1500 when the digging of canals in the Cenozoic
marine formations in Italy brought to attention abundant well-
preserved shells so obviously similar to those to be seen on the

217

modern beaches that their significance could hardly be missed (plate 43). Leonardo da Vinci, who besides being a great artist had been trained as an engineer, took special interest in these discoveries and argued forcefully that the fossils were ancient shells of animals that had once lived where now found and had turned to stone along with the enclosing sediments. While many supported this view, others took issue with this simple explanation. Under the ruling dogma of the time, the earth was believed to be only six thousand years old and to have been created fully formed. This left little room for extinct creatures or for changes in the position of land and sea. Thus a controversy began over the nature of fossils that raged over Europe for the next two hundred years and led to persecution and ridicule of those who accepted their organic origin.

Some of the alternative explanations were entirely mystical, even to the point of attributing fossils to the work of the Devil who had placed them in the rocks to delude men. A remarkable example of such fantasy occurred in Germany as late as 1696 when parts of a skeleton of a mammoth were dug from the Pleistocene deposits near Gotha. They fell into the hands of William Tentzel, a teacher in the local high school, who recognized them as the remains of some prehistoric monster. In the controversy that ensued they were submitted to the faculty of the school of medicine by whom, of all people, they were dismissed as a 'freak of nature'!

Such controversies only served to stimulate public interest, and soon fossil hunters were amassing collections, one of the greatest of these being assembled at the Vatican. It was while this controversy raged that, in 1706, the tooth of a mastodon (plate 44) was dug out of a swamp at Coxsackie, south of Albany, New York. Having excited great local interest it was sent to Governor Dudley of Massachusetts, who wrote to the distinguished cleric, Cotton Mather of Boston, on 10 July as follows [66]:

I suppose all the surgeons in town have seen it, and I am perfectly of the opinion it was a human tooth. I measured it and as it stood upright it was six inches high lacking one eight, and round thirteen inches, lacking one eight, and its weight in the scales was two pounds and four ounces, Troy weight.

I am perfectly of the opinion that the tooth will agree only to a human body, for whom the flood only could prepare a funeral; and without doubt he waded as long as he could keep his head above the clouds, but must at last be confounded with all other creatures and the new sediment after the flood gave him the depth we now find.

It is difficult to realize that these lines were written in pious seriousness and not as a jest, until we recall that Governor Dudley was thinking of *Genesis*, Chapter 6, v. 4: 'There were giants in those days'. This was only a few years after Cotton Mather had been a leader in the ignorant and senseless butcheries of Salem witchcraft.

Yet so great was the influence of established dogma that as late as 1784, six years before he was to become President of the United States, Thomas Jefferson wrote to President Stiles of Yale asking his opinion about the mastodon tooth and additional mammoth remains recently discovered near Albany, to which, after a lengthy discussion, President Stiles concluded: 'Perhaps the sensible rational and ana- tomical Virtuosi will judge those dug up at North-Holston, at Claverack, and elsewhere (of this enormous Description) and the mammoths of Siberia all belong to an Animal Race in the shape of Men, called Giants in the Scriptures,' etc.

An extended account of the controversy over the remains of the mastodon in America and the mammoth in Siberia will be found in John Greene's fascinating book, *The Death of Adam*.

During the sixteenth century it became evident to almost all thoughtful people that fossils are actually the remains of once living creatures. Whereupon various enthusiasts saw in them confirmation of the Scriptures – they were the remains of the animals killed and buried by the Deluge. The extreme to which this idea was carried is immortalized in a small volume by Johan Andrias Scheuchzer pub- lished in 1726 under the title *Homo diluvii testis* [The man who is proof of the Flood]. It contained illustrations and descriptions of articulated skeletons found in lake beds of Oligocene age at Oeningen, Switzerland. They were later restudied by the great French paleonto- logist Cuvier, who found them to be the remains of a giant salaman- der which, with roguish justice, he described and named *Andrias scheuchzeri*!

In the meantime Scheuchzer had described two large vertebrae from older rocks 'as relics of that accursed race that perished with the flood', and his figures were reproduced in the *Copper Bible* of 1731. Cuvier later found these to be vertebrae of Mesozoic reptiles.

When in the latter half of the eighteenth century the Law of Superposition and the Law of Faunal Succession were recognized, such fantasies were laid to rest, for it became evident that a long succession of once living creatures is recorded in the rocks and that the older ones are quite unlike those now living.

Modes of Preservation

Generally only the hard parts of organisms are preserved, but bone and shells and wood are commonly turned to stone, whence they are said to be petrified (L. *petra*, stone +*facere*, to make). This occurs generally in one of three ways. The first mode occurs where ground water seeping through the enclosing sediment carries mineral matter in solution which, in the presence of decaying organic matter, is precipitated in the interstices of the hard parts, thus making them dense and hard, without altering the original structure of the objects. This is the method of permineralization. But commonly the original material of the hard parts is dissolved, molecule at a time, and replaced by some other mineral, commonly silica (SiO_2) and, less commonly, calcite ($CaCO_3$). This may take place in such manner that even the microscopic structures are not obscured. Wood is thus commonly replaced by silica without destroying the cell walls, medullary rays, or growth rings. Here the empty cells are also filled with clear calcite by permineralization (plate 45). In such cases the structure can be studied in thin sections and the plants can be identified as to genus as readily and as certainly as if it were modern wood. Shells are often preserved in the same way. Less commonly woody tissue is replaced by calcite as in the remarkable 'coal balls' found in places in the coal measures. Calcareous shells are in many instances replaced by silica even though the enclosing limestone matrix is unaltered. In such cases the matrix can be dissolved by hydrochloric acid, freeing the fossils (plate 46).

In other cases the original organic deposits are dissolved away leaving cavities in the rock in the form of natural moulds (plate 47) that faithfully preserve the external and internal surface features of a shell. By pressing a plastic material into such moulds, artificial casts of the originals may be secured that show the shape of the shell, its surface ornamentation, and even the internal markings such as scars of muscle attachment. Commonly underground water has filled the moulds to form natural casts or pseudomorphs which faithfully preserve the external form but not the microstructure of the organic remains. Even such perishable things as leaves have in many instances left sharp moulds, or imprints in the rocks (plate 48).

After quick burial which excludes free oxygen, even soft organic tissues are preserved. In this case the volatile constituents are distilled away as carbon dioxide and water, leaving a residue of carbon, a carbon copy of the original. Leaves are often preserved in this way (plate 49) and less commonly the flesh of animals is preserved as a carbon film surrounding the skeleton. Thus we know the size and shape of the fins and tail flukes of some of the ancient reptiles even though they were not supported by bony structures. The shape and extent of the wing membranes in the ancient flying reptiles is known either from imprints or carbon films in the rocks (plate 50).

Footprints and trails (plate 52) form another category of fossils that tell an interesting story since they are the autographs of living animals. Thus we can tell by its tracks whether an animal was quadrupedal or bipedal, and if bipedal, as many of the dinosaurs were, whether it ran like an ostrich or leapt like a kangaroo. We can also know whether an animal moved with its body off the ground, as the mammals do, or sprawled like the living reptiles. Tracks alone give us some of the earliest records of land animals, and in some formations tracks alone prove that animals were once abundant where no skeletal remains have been preserved.

Fossil excrement, known as coprolites, supplement our knowledge of some of the extinct animals since undigested bits of food are preserved to prove their feeding habits. Thus for example we know the kind of vegetation the great ground sloths fed on and the kinds of vegetation the extinct woolly mammoths of Siberia were feeding on when they died.

Finally the ice and frozen ground in Siberia and Alaska have served as a cold storage locker in which animals have been naturally preserved, entire, for many thousands of years. More than fifty frozen carcasses of the woolly mammoth have been found, and radio-carbon dates for several of these run as follows [118]:

Mokovaja specimen	Yenesei Valley	over 32,500 BP
Sanga-Jurjak specimen	Yenesei Valley	over 39,000 BP
Lena River specimen	Lena River delta	over 33,000 BP
Taimyr specimen	Taimyr Peninsula	11,450 ± 250 BP
Beresovka specimen	Beresovka Valley	over 39,000 BP
Gyda specimen	Yakut	33,500 ± 1,000 BP

A woolly rhinoceros from the Elga Valley was similarly dated at over 38,000 BP.

The Beresovka mammoth is particularly interesting and well

known. It was excavated in 1901 and portions of the soft parts were preserved and the skin was brought back to Leningrad and mounted in the zoological museum of the University in the position in which it was found. Its left leg, a hip bone, and three ribs were broken, it had suffered massive internal hemorrhage, and its mouth contained unswallowed food. Evidently it had fallen and died quickly. Its body was covered by a thick coat of brownish woolly hair, as was that of the woolly rhinoceros. If only the skeletons had been preserved, we could never have guessed how these great beasts were able to survive in the ice fields so far north of their living relatives. When dug out of the frozen ground the flesh of the lower hind leg of the Beresovka specimen was 'dark red in colour and looked as fresh as well-frozen beef or horse meat', and some of it was eaten by the dog teams used by the collectors [75].

One of the most remarkable occurrences of fossils recording soft tissues is about Solenhofen, Germany. During Late Jurassic time this was the site of several atolls built by corals and sponges. Fine limy sediment was swept over the reefs to accumulate in the lagoons which were normally occupied by sea water but at low tide were occasionally laid bare as soft mud flats. Animals from the nearby shore at times ventured out on to the atolls and died there. Insects in great numbers, presumably blown seaward during storms, landed on the mud flats. All these remains were covered by a film of limy sediment when the tide returned and were thus protected from the air. Articulated skeletons of vertebrate animals were permineralized and the soft tissues left an imprint after the organic matter had been distilled away. The fine lime mud later solidified into lithographic limestone which for generations was quarried and widely used in the printing of lithographs and etchings. In the extensive quarrying operations the rock was split into slabs of convenient thickness and fossils frequently appeared on the bedding planes. Thus a very large number of fossils was assembled. Among these are many insects, including the earliest known representatives of such modern orders as the Diptera (flies) and the Lepidoptera (moths and butterflies). More remarkable still is the articulated skeleton of the oldest known bird, Archeopteryx, with clear imprints of its feathers (plate 51). A fine articulated skeleton of a small dinosaur is another of the treasures thus discovered. Along with these creatures of the land there are imprints of many marine animals including shrimp-like crustaceans, crinoids, and, of all things, jellyfish.

Another remarkable occurrence of fossil insects is in the Lower Permian rocks near Abiline, Kansas, where more than ten thousand specimens have been collected from a thin ledge of limestone in a pasture field. Here the chitinous wings have escaped destruction and some of them have retained a brownish pigment that records the original colour pattern (plate 53). After being preserved underground for more than 250 million years this pigment fades within a short time if the specimens are exposed to strong light! From this locality some twenty orders of insects have been described, most of them long since extinct, but among them are the oldest known representatives of the Odonata (dragonflies) and the Coleoptera (beetles). Similar deposits, though none so prolific, have been found in other places, notably in Australia and in the Permian basin of the USSR.

A somewhat different and much younger deposit of insects and plant leaves occurs near Florissant in Colorado, USA, where lakes of Oligocene date received repeated falls of fine volcanic ash in which a great variety of insects is preserved.

Probably the most significant of all fossil localities is that in the Burgess slate of mid-Cambrian age in the flanks of Mt Wapta in British Columbia. Here the organic remains have been reduced to a mere lustrous film on the bedding planes. From this single locality (plate 54) Walcott collected seventy genera and 130 species of marine animals nearly all of which lacked hard parts and are otherwise unknown in the entire geologic record. Among these are jellyfish, worms, sponges, and a great variety of arthropods resembling primitive crustaceans and Chelicerata but more primitive than either. The special significance of this occurrence is the perspective it gives us on the early history of life. Except for this one find the only Cambrian fossils are animals that bore limy shells or, like the trilobites, had a heavy carapace of chitin. The Burgess shale fauna shows that the Cambrian seas teemed with a great variety of soft-bodied organisms many of which had complex structures and must have had ancestors ranging far back into Precambrian time. Without these fossils we could only have inferred that such primitive creatures existed in Cambrian time and have guessed what they were like.

We may infer the circumstances under which this unusual deposit was formed. The fine-grained mud, rich in decaying organic matter, must have formed a soft oozy deposit deficient in oxygen and reeking in hydrogen sulphide (H_2S) gas. It was probably a local depression in the sea floor. Occasional storm waves stirred the surrounding bottom and liberated H_2S which poisoned the organisms. The dead then settled or were drifted into this depression where they remained below wave base and were never again disturbed. Because of the poisoned water no scavengers were present to devour them and so they remained whole with limbs and other delicate appendages intact. Such mass destruction of the bottom faunas by the liberation of H_2S gas has been observed in modern seas.

To permit the preservation of organisms two conditions are of major importance. The first is the possession of hard parts – shells, bone, heavy carapaces of chitin, or woody tissue. The preservation of soft tissues described above is quite exceptional. In the overwhelming majority of cases only the hard parts are preserved. Vertebrate skeletons are generally incomplete because the flesh was devoured and the bones were scattered by scavengers before burial. Occasionally, however, an animal mired in a bog or in quicksand, or was drowned and buried by a flood and thus escaped carnivores. In such cases complete, articulated skeletons are preserved. The bogs that formed in the wake of the melting Pleistocene ice sheet were veritable death traps for heavy animals such as the mastodons and mammoths (relatives of the elephants). Hartnagel and Bishop, for example, have recorded finds of 217 of these great beasts in the peat bogs of New York state alone [66]. In the remarkable petrified forests of Arizona and of the Yellowstone only logs and stumps are preserved and the wood is replaced by silica (plate 45). Shells of marine animals are by all odds the most abundant of all fossils.

The second prerequisite for fossilization is quick burial. Leaves of the forest decay about as fast as they fall. In bogs where the vegetation settles under standing water, on the contrary, leaves are abundantly preserved as in the shales associated with coal beds (plate 49). When exposed to the atmosphere even teeth and bones crumble into dust after a few years. During a couple of decades before 1840 literally millions of bison were slaughtered on the plains of the western United States for their hides, their carcasses being left to rot; few traces of these skeletons remain. Even after burial, bone is readily destroyed if exposed to circulating ground water. The dissolved oxygen and carbon dioxide, and especially organic acids derived from decaying organic matter, soon destroy bones and teeth where enough relief exists to permit rapid circulation of ground water. Thus preservation is extremely rare in regions of tropical forests. Vertebrate fossils are most common in old channel sands where they were below the water table, and are rare or absent in contemporaneous deposits above the water table. In semi-arid regions where deposition is rapid and rains are infrequent the chances of preservation are much better.

On the sea floor, shells are partly protected by the sea water, which is largely saturated with respect to calcium carbonate, and they are soon covered with shifting bottom sediment. For this reason marine formations are seldom without fossil shells and in many places they form a large component of the rock.

The Pageant of Life

For more than 150 years the paleontologists of the world have collaborated in discovering and describing the fossils of the geologic column, and since the sequence in time is now known, the main features of the history of life on earth are now well established. The time of appearance and the geologic range of the major groups of life are shown in figure 7.

The pageant of life throughout geologic time is treated in detail by Dr A. S. Romer in volume 4 of this treatise, but for the benefit of those who may not have the complete series of volumes at hand a brief epitome of the record is included here.

The Precambrian rocks of the world have yielded only the most meagre record of life and these are nearly all of the most primitive groups of microscopic plants. Yet when fossils appear in abundance at the base of the Cambrian the major phyla of animals, except the vertebrates, are represented and are so distinct as to afford no direct evidence of their phylogenetic relationships. Certainly their origin lies far back in Precambrian time.

This poses one of the unsolved problems in geology – why did the record of abundant living creatures begin suddenly at the base of the Cambrian? Many theories have been advanced but none is quite convincing. It has been suggested, for example, that the older seas were deficient in calcium carbonate so that animals could not make shells. But this is disproved by two things. First, there are, in places, extensive limy reefs precipitated by calcareous algae. Such seas were probably as rich in calcium carbonate as the modern oceans are. In the second place, the dominant groups of animals that are so well preserved in the Cambrian rocks made their shells of organic material such as chitin. They did not need or use calcium carbonate.

225

A more probable hypothesis is that before Cambrian time the animals were herbivorous and none of them needed shells for protection, but that the development of carnivorous habits about the beginning of Cambrian time placed a great premium on the ability to form a protective armour and natural selection favoured forms that could produce shells. Many forms protected themselves in other ways – by alert movement, by burrowing, or by other means – but at least some members of most of the great phyla rapidly developed armour capable of preservation.

The many soft-bodied creatures discovered by Walcott in the Burgess shale of Middle Cambrian age suggests what the life of late Precambrian time may have been like. Without hard parts these animals were reduced to mere lustrous films of carbon on the bedding planes of black slate. The preservation is extraordinary, for many of them show delicate bristles and ventral appendages and some of them clearly show traces of internal organs such as the alimentary canal. Such preservation was made possible by an unusual combination of circumstances. These creatures were killed by some natural catastrophe and settled in a depression floored by fine black mud where reducing conditions inhibited decay and excluded scavengers, and where they were below wave base so that they were never disturbed. Of course these animals were widespread in the Cambrian seas, even though rarely preserved. Moreover, their discovery was accidental. As Dr Walcott was leading a pack train up a steep mountain trail a horse stumbled over a fallen block of slate and split it open. His trained eye happened to catch the glint from the carbon films of fossils and he stopped to exploit what turned out to be an amazing find. Here the planes of schistosity happened to coincide with the original bedding planes. If the trail had been a short distance at either side where the schistosity crosses the bedding, no fossils could have been seen.

Some of these animals are several inches long and none of them are microscopic. Of course they were not confined to this one locality and there must be other places in the vast and unexplored deposits of black shale in the Cambrian and older rocks where similar fossils await discovery. This is the environment in which soft-bodied animals of the Precambrian are likely to be found.

Several of the great phyla of animals appear in the early Cambrian rocks where they are represented by small and relatively primitive forms, but even these are far from simple and the phyla are already so distinct as to afford no direct evidence of their phylogenetic relations. Their origin must lie far back in Precambrian time. Most of the classes of animals were well differentiated before they appeared in the fossil record, but when the smaller taxa are traced back many of them converge structurally with others in a way to indicate a common origin so that many genetic lines can be represented in the form of a family tree and the time of their origin is known. Thus the course of evolution within the animal kingdom becomes clear at least in its general features and in many cases in great detail. The geologic history and genetic relations of the better known groups are epitomized in figures 84, 85, and 86.

Among the Protozoans, the Radiolaria and Foraminifera are known from the late Cambrian to the present and an elaborate phylogenetic family tree has been worked out for the forams, only a few of the major branches of which are represented in figure 84.

With the probable exception of a single species of burrowing anemonae in the Burgess shale, the phylum Coelenterata did not appear as fossils until about the base of the Middle Ordovician where two major groups of corals, the horn corals (Rugosa) and the honeycombs (Favositidae), appeared. Both evolved rapidly during Silurian and Devonian time and both persisted until the end of the Permian Period when both became extinct. They were joined late in Ordovician time by the chain corals (Halysitidae) that ranged through the Silurian and then died out. The modern stony corals (Scleractinia) can be traced back to middle Triassic time and probably developed out of some of the specialized late Permian Rugosa.

The brachiopods, which were the dominant 'shell-fish' of the Paleozoic era, appeared in considerable abundance at the base of the Cambrian when most of them bore nitrogenous shells and were quite small and simple. Calcareous shells became dominant at the base of the Ordovician and such types thrived in great abundance and

Overleaf: Figures 84 and 85. Diagrams to epitomize the geologic record of the more important groups of animals. The width of a line is intended to suggest the relative importance of a group during its range, but is without scale. For example, nautiloid cephalopods evolved rapidly during Ordovician time, reached their greatest diversity in Silurian time, and then declined gradually until late Paleozoic time, since when they have been relatively few; in contrast the ammonites appeared in Devonian time, increased gradually in variety and numbers as the nautiloids declined, reached their greatest importance during Mesozoic time, and then became extinct, meanwhile suffering near extinction at the end of Permian, Triassic, and Jurassic periods

227

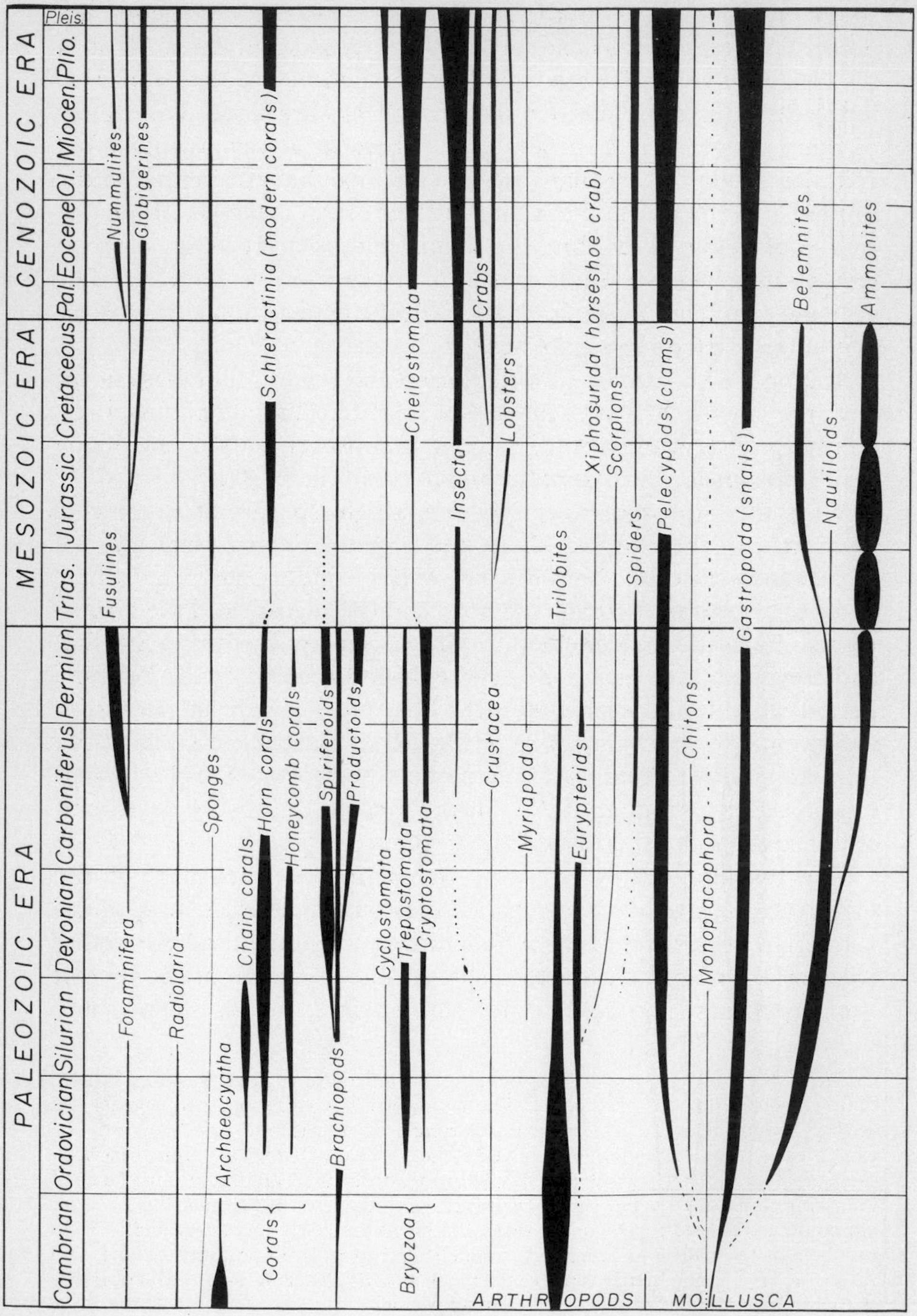
PALEOZOIC ERA
MESOZOIC ERA
CENOZOIC ERA
Cambrian
Ordovician
Silurian
Devonian
Carboniferus
Permian
Trias.
Jurassic
Cretaceous
Pal.
Eocene
Ol.
Miocen.
Plio.
Pleis.
Foraminifera
Fusulines
Nummulites
Globigerines
Radiolaria
Sponges
Archaeocyatha
Corals
Chain corals
Horn corals
Honeycomb corals
Schleractinia (modern corals)
Brachiopods
Spiriferoids
Productoids
Bryozoa
Cyclostomata
Trepostomata
Cryptostomata
Cheilostomata
Insecta
Crustacea
Crabs
Lobsters
Myriapoda
Trilobites
Eurypterids
Xiphosurida (horseshoe crab)
Scorpions
Spiders
ARTHROPODS
Pelecypods (clams)
Chitons
Monoplacophora
Gastropoda (snails)
Belemnites
Nautiloids
Ammonites
MOLLUSCA

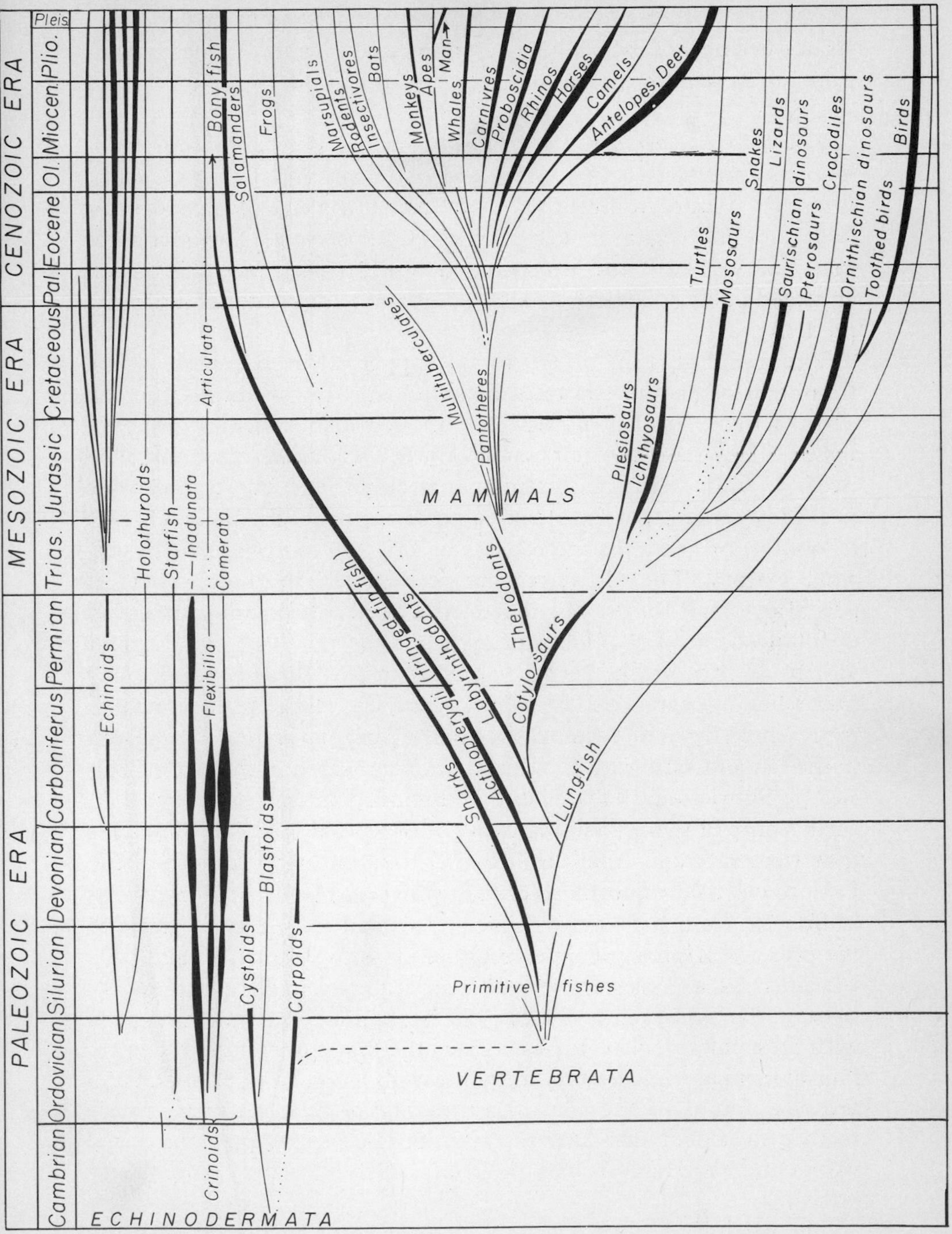
CENOZOIC ERA
MESOZOIC ERA
PALEOZOIC ERA
Pleis.
Plio.
Miocen.
Ol.
Eocene
Pal.
Cretaceous
Jurassic
Trias.
Permian
Carboniferus
Devonian
Silurian
Ordovician
Cambrian
ECHINODERMATA
Echinoids
Holothuroids
Starfish
Inadunata
Camerata
Articulata
Flexibilia
Crinoids
Cystoids
Blastoids
Carpoids
VERTEBRATA
Primitive fishes
Bony fish
Salamanders
Frogs
Sharks
Actinopterygii (fringed-fin fish)
Labyrinthodonts
Lungfish
Cotylosaurs
Therodonts
MAMMALS
Pantotheres
Multituberculates
Marsupials
Rodents
Insectivores
Bats
Monkeys
Apes
Man
Whales
Carnivres
Proboscidia
Rhinos
Horses
Camels
Antelopes, Deer
Plesiosaurs
Ichthyosaurs
Turtles
Mososaurs
Snakes
Lizards
Saurischian dinosaurs
Pterosaurs
Crocodiles
Ornithischian dinosaurs
Toothed birds
Birds

variety to the very end of the Paleozoic Era when all but two lesser strains became extinct. These survivors underwent a modest evolution during Mesozoic time and still exist as a minor group in modern seas.

The bryozoa appeared in the Ordovician Period in four well-defined classes, two of which (Trepostomata and Cryptostomata) were very abundant until their extinction at the end of the Paleozoic Era. Two more conservative classes (Ctenostomata and Cyclostomata) survived to the present and a fifth class (Cheilostomata) appeared in Triassic time and is a dominant and prolific group in the modern seas.

The great phylum of arthropods appeared at the base of the Cambrian when the trilobites included the largest animals on the earth (about eight inches long) and formed the most prolific group of fossils. They reached their acme early in Ordovician time and then declined until their final extinction near the end of the Paleozoic Era. Most, at least, of the other Cambrian arthropods, along with the trilobites, formed a distinct class, the Trilobitomorpha, that is long since extinct. The Crustacea are represented in the Ordovician period by small forms, but remained a rather inconspicuous group until Mesozoic time; lobsters appeared in the Triassic; a great variety of shrimp-like forms appeared in the Jurassic; and crabs made their appearance in the Cretaceous. The class Chaelicerata was represented by small forms related to the Eurypterids and Xyphosura in the Upper Cambrian; the Eurypterida appeared in the Ordovician and by Silurian and Devonian time included the largest animals on earth, some of them attaining a length of several feet, but thereafter they were rare and small until their extinction near the end of the Paleozoic Era; the Scorpions probably diverged from the Eurypterids in Silurian time and have persisted as a small conservative group to the present; Xiphosura appeared as early as the Devonian and have remained as a conservative and genetically isolated group to the present, the living genus *Limulus* (the horse-shoe crab) having existed with little change since Jurassic time; the first spiders and mites are known from a single locality in the Lower Devonian of Scotland and are next found in the coal measures of the Carboniferous where many genera of spiders are preserved, but because of their terrestrial habits and their soft bodies their later history is very imperfectly known.

The phylum Mollusca begins in the Cambrian period with the

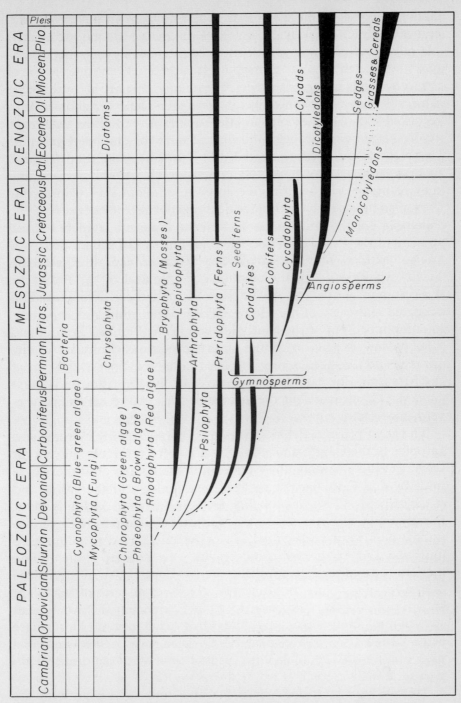

Figure 86. Diagram to epitomize the geological history of the chief groups of plants. The bacteria, fungi, and marine algae should be represented by broader lines if their record were adequately known. The rapid deployment of land plants in Devonian time is noteworthy

class Monoplacophora, which was supposed to be extinct before the end of Silurian time until the recent discovery of a typical genus, *Neopilina*, still living in great depths of the ocean. From this primitive stock the chitons and gastropods diverged in Cambrian time and the Pelecypods in early Ordovician time (*fide* Lee McAlester, 1965). The cephalopods probably diverged from this same stem but are first recorded by small nautiloids in late Cambrian rocks. The nautiloids evolved rapidly in Ordovician time and were the dominant group of cephalopods until near the end of the Paleozoic when they declined to a few survivors much like the modern pearly nautilus. Meanwhile they had given rise to primitive ammonites about the beginning of Devonian time. As the nautiloids declined during the later part of the Paleozoic era the ammonites underwent expansive evolution until the end of the Permian period when all but two of thirteen families became extinct. These survivors underwent an explosive evolution in the early Triassic. Near extinction occurred again at the end of the Triassic and at the end of the Jurassic and their final extinction occurred at the end of the Mesozoic Era. Meanwhile the belemnites had developed out of the nautiloids late in the Permian Period, and after a slow expansion in the Triassic became abundant in the Jurassic and Cretaceous seas and then became extinct at the end of the Mesozoic Era. Squids are known since Jurassic time and octopi since the Cretaceous, but the history of these naked cephalopods is very imperfectly known.

The great phylum Echinodermata is represented by cystoids and carpoids in the Cambrian, both of which were extinct by the end of Devonian time. Meanwhile the blastoids had diverged from the cystoids by mid-Ordovician time and the vertebrates had evolved out of the carpoids. Crinoids probably developed from the cystoids about the beginning of Ordovician time, and during that period three distinct orders were represented, all of which thrived in abundance until the end of the Paleozoic era only to become extinct. The modern order, Flexibilia, probably evolved out of one of the Paleozoic orders just before its extinction. An aberrant stock of starfish is known from the late Cambrian rocks in France, but the first typical starfish are known from Middle Ordovician rocks. The oldest echinoid is known from the late Ordovician rocks of Scotland, and their evolution was gradual until Jurassic time when rapid specialization for new living habits led to the evolution of two new orders to which two more were added in Cretaceous time. The Holothuria are known to have been present as early as Silurian time but because they do not have a calcareous shell their history is very imperfectly known.

The strange Ordovician carpoid, *Enopleura*, appears to be a connecting link between the echinoderms and the most primitive jawless fish. The phylogeny of the vertebrates is known in considerable detail as indicated in figure 85 and needs no explanation here except to call attention to the great dominance of the reptiles in the Mesozoic, the sudden extinction of so many orders at the end of the Cretaceous Period, and the spectacular evolution of the mammals in the Cenozoic.

Finally it may be emphasized that the long history of life has been one of endless change and that the end of the Paleozoic and the end of the Mesozoic eras were times of crisis when many groups of animals became extinct only to be replaced by others that expanded to take their places in the economy of nature. We still have no adequate explanation for such vast and relatively sudden extinctions and probably the causes were complex, but it may be noted that both times of crisis coincided with very extensive continental emergence and climatic extremes.

The remarkable discovery of single-celled plant fossils in the Knife Lake chert near Schreiber, Ontario, proves that plants were in existence as long as 1,600 million years ago. Little is known of the history of plants, however, until they discovered the lands about the beginning of Devonian time. Their evolution had begun in the sea where the surrounding water gave them support and from which nutrients could be absorbed by all parts of their bodies so that no circulatory system was required. To this day the soft-bodied algae have left only the most meagre fossil record. An exception must be made for the calcareous algae which grow in colonies of microscopic filaments and in extracting carbon dioxide from the water cause an encrusting precipitate of calcium carbonate to form about them. Such limy deposits have formed impressive banks and small reefs since far back in Precambrian time, but they preserve only the general shape of the colonies and give us little information about the plant structures.

Such primitive groups of plants as the lichens and mosses may have made their way into moist places on the land far back in time but they are so poorly suited for preservation that they have left virtually no fossil record. The evolution of the higher plants was long delayed for it required two fundamental changes in plant anatomy.

The first was the evolution of a circulatory system to carry moisture up from the ground and distribute it to the foliage. This took the form of tracheids, those long slender cells in which the moisture (sap) is carried upward by capillary attraction. The second requirement was a supporting tissue to hold them up, since they could no longer float. The tracheid cells were adapted to this purpose and became the source of woody tissue. Once this adaptation had been made, shortly before the beginning of Devonian time, plants were able to spread over the lands and their evolution was rapid. By Carboniferous time forests of large trees were world-wide. Most of the Paleozoic plants were spore-bearers, shedding their pollen to be carried by the winds and during the reproductive season the verdant landscapes must have been fairly covered by a 'snowfall' of spores. In some of the lakes and swamps great concentrates of spores accumulated to form the compact waxy variety of coal known as cannel coal.

Among the early land plants ferns were prominent and some of them strikingly resemble modern ferns (plate 49). Many of them in Carboniferous time had attained the size of the largest modern tree ferns.

The most impressive plants of the Paleozoic forests were the great 'scale trees' some of which grew to a height of more than one hundred feet and had trunks as much as six feet in diameter at the base.

The 'seed ferns' (Spermophyta) showed an evolutionary advance of the first importance. In this case the female trees retained their spores in special reproductive organs awaiting the wind to waft the male spores to them for the marriage. The fertilized female spore was then nourished until it had developed into an embryo plant with a supply of food to insure its later growth. The evolution from spore-bearing to seed-bearing plants is comparable to the change from egg laying to viviparous habit on the part of animals and served the same purpose, the egg being retained in the mother's body during the embryonic growth so that the offspring could be more safely launched on its own career.

It was probably from some of the early seed-ferns that the Cordaites evolved into the first trees with solid woody trunks. These trees bore large strap-like leaves. From the Cordaites it required only reduction of the strap-like leaves into needles and the concentration of racemes of small nuts into cones to produce the conifers which are first known from the rocks of middle Upper Carboniferous (Pennsylvanian) age and became increasingly abundant in the Permian period and dominated the forests of Mesozoic time after the scale trees and cordaites and seed ferns had disappeared. The modern maidenhair tree, *Ginko*, is a lone descendant of a tribe of broad-leafed gymnosperm that was common during Mesozoic time.

One of the greatest advances in the evolution of plants was the appearance of the angiosperms, that vast group that includes our modern deciduous trees, the flowering and fruit-bearing trees and the cereals, on which so many of the mammals depend for food. The exact time of their origin is uncertain, for it is probable that they developed in the uplands where fossil plants are rarely preserved. The oldest clear evidence of the angiosperms is in early Cretaceous rocks where the leaves of such familiar trees as sassafras and poplar have been found. During Cretaceous time deciduous forests spread around the world and included many of the familiar modern genera. It probably is no accident that the great upwelling of the mammals had to wait on the spread of the angiosperms.

Bibliography

1　ARMITAGE, A. (1951) *The world of Copernicus*. The New American Library: New York

2　AXELROD, D. I. & TING, W. S. (1961) Early Pleistocene floras from the Chagoopa surface, Southern Sierra Nevada. *Univ. Calif. Publs geol. Sci.* **39**: 119–93

3　—— (1963) Fossil floras suggest stable, not drifting continents. *J. geophys. Res.* **68**: 3257–63 and 1669–71

4　BABCOCK, H. W. (1960) The magnetism of the sun. *Scient. Am.* **202**, No. 2: 53–62

5　BAIN, G. W. (1963) *Climatic zones throughout the ages*. Soc. Econ. Paleont. and Mineralogists, Special Publ. 10, 100–30

6　BALDWIN, R. B. (1949) The craters of the moon. *Scient. Am.* **181**, No. 1: 20–4

7　BANKS, M. R. (1958) *Recent additions to the knowledge of the Permian System in Tasmania*. Int. Geol. Congress, Mexico

8　BASCOM, W. (1961) *A hole in the bottom of the sea*. Doubleday: Garden City, New York

9　BEALS, C. S. (1958) Fossil meteor craters. *Scient. Am.* **199**, No. 1: 33–9

10　BECK, A. E. (1961) Energy requirements of an expanding earth. *J. geophys. Res.* **66**: 1,480–1,485

11　BEISER, A. (1962) *The earth*. Life Nature Library: New York

12　BERKNER, L. V. & MARSHALL, L. C. (1964) The history of growth of oxygen in the earth's atmosphere. In *The origin and evolution of atmospheres and oceans*, P. J. Brancazio and A. G. W. Cameron, Editors. John Wiley: New York

13　BIERMANN, L. F. & LÜST RHEA (1958) The tails of comets. *Scient. Am.* **199**, No. 4: 44–50

14　BLACKETT, P. M. S. (1961) Comparison of ancient climates with ancient latitudes deduced from rock magnetic measurements. *Proc. R. Soc. IA*, **263**: 1–30

15　BLUMENSTOCK, D. I. (1949) The upper atmosphere. *Scient. Am.* **180**, No. 1: 30–9

16　BRAMLETTE, M. N. & BRADLEY, W. H. (1940) *Geology and biology of North Atlantic deep-sea cores between Newfoundland and Ireland*. Part I: *Lithology and geologic interpretation*. U.S. Geol. Surv. Prof. Paper 196: 1–34

17 BROECKER, W. S. & KULP, J. L. (1957) Lamont natural radio-carbon measurements. *Science* **126**: 1324–34

18 ——, TUREKIAN, K. K. & HEEZEN, B. L. (1958) The relation of deep sea sedimentation rates to variations in climate. *Am. J. Sci.* **256**: 503–17

19 BROWN, HARRISON (1949) A table of relative abundances of nuclear species. *Rev. mod. Phys.* **4**: 625

20 BULLARD, E. C. (1954) The earth's magnetic field. In *The earth as a planet.* G. P. Kniper, Editor. Univ. of Chicago Press, pp. 123–9

21 CAREY, S. W. (1958) The tectonic approach to continental drift. In *Continental drift, A symposium.* Department of Geology, Univ. of Tasmania: Hobart

22 CAVENDISH, H. (1798) Experiments to determine the density of the earth. *Phil. Trans.* **A, 88**, pt. 1: 469–526

23 CHAMBERLIN, T. C. & SALISBURY, R. D. (1906) *Textbook of geology*, Vol. 3

24 —— (1909) Diastrophism as the ultimate basis for correlation. *J. Geol.* **17**: 685–93

25 —— (1928) *The two solar families.* Univ. of Chicago Press (Chamberlin and Moulton published numerous papers as their ideas evolved; they finally took the form presented in this volume)

26 CHANEY, R. W. (1940) Tertiary Forests and Continental History. *Bull. geol. Soc. Am.* **51**: 469–88

27 COLBERT, E. H. (1964) Dinosaurs of the Arctic. *Nat. Hist.* **73**, No. 4: 20–3

28 *Continental Drift, A Symposium* (1958). Department of Geology, Univ. of Tasmania: Hobart

29 COX, A. & DOELL, R. R. (1960) Review of Paleomagnetism. *Bull. geol. Soc. Am.* **71**: 645–768

30 CROWELL, J. C. (1963) *Displacement along the San Andreas fault, California.* Geol. Soc. Amer., Special Paper **71**

31 DALL, W. H. & HARRIS, G. D. (1892) Correlation papers: Miocene. *Bull. U.S. geol. Surv.* **84**: 26–7

32 DALY, R. A. (1936) Origin of submarine canyons. *Am. J. Sci.* **31**: 401–20

33 DARROW, K. K. (1952) The quantum theory. *Scient. Am.* **186**, No. 3: 47–55

34 DEUTSCH, E. R. (1963) *Polar wandering and continental drift: An evaluation of recent evidence.* Soc. Econ. Paleontologists and Mineralogists Special Publ. 10: 4–46

35 DIETZ, R. S. (1962) *Continent and ocean basin evolution by sea floor spreading.* Preprint of Distinguished Lecture for the Assoc. of Petroleum Geologists

36 DRYER, J. L. E. (1890) *Tycho Brahe.* Adam and Charles Black. Republished (1936) by Dover Publishing Co.: New York

37 DUNBAR, C. O. (1952) Discussion [of Caster's paper in the symposium on the south Atlantic basin]. *Bull. Am. Mus. nat. Hist.* **99**: 105–58

38 —— (1960) *Historical geology*, 2nd Ed., Ch. 2, The Scale of time. John Wiley and Sons: New York

39 —— & RODGERS, J. (1949) *Principles of Stratigraphy*, Ch. 17, The stratigraphic system. John Wiley and Sons: New York

40 DU TOIT, A. L. (1953) *Geology of South Africa*, 3rd Ed. Edited by S. H. Houghton. Hafner Publishing Co.: New York

41 ELASSER, W. M. (1958) The earth as a dynamo. *Scient. Am.* **198**, No. 5: 44–63

42 EMERY, K. O., *et al.* (1954) *Geology of Bikini and nearby Atolls.* Pt. 1: *Geology.* U.S. Geol. Surv. Prof. Paper 260-A

43 —— (1960) *The sea off southern California.* John Wiley and Sons: New York

44 ENGEL, A. E. J. (1963) Geologic Evolution of North America. *Science* **140**: 143–52

45 ERICSON, D. B., *et al.* (1951) Deep-sea sands and submarine canyons. *Bull. geol. Soc. Am.* **62**: 961–5

46 ——, *et al.* (1961) Atlantic Deep-sea Cores. *Bull. geol. Soc. Am.* **72**: 193–286

47 EWING, J. & EWING, M. (1959) Seismic refraction measurements in the Atlantic Ocean basins, Mediterranean sea, on the mid-Atlantic ridge and in the Norwegian sea. *Bull. geol. Soc. Am.* **70**: 291–318

48 EWING, M., *et al.* (1964) Sediment distribution in the oceans: The Argentine Basin. *J. geophys. Res.* **69**: 2003–32

49 FARRAND, W. R. (1962) Postglacial uplift in Northwest Territories. *Am. J. Sci.* **260**: 181–99

50 FAUL, H. (1960) Geologic time scale. *Bull. geol. Soc. Am.* **71**: 637–44

51 FIREMAN, E. L. (1960) Program for collecting meteorites. *Science* **131**: 1824–1831

52 FISK, H. N., *et al.* (1954) Sedimentary framework of the modern Mississippi delta. *J. sedim. Petrol.* **24**: 76–99

53 FLINT, R. F. (1957) *Glacial and Pleistocene geology.* John Wiley and Sons: New York

54 GEIKIE, Sir A. (1905) *The founders of geology.* Macmillan and Company: New York and London

55 GILLULY, J. *et al.* (1948) Origin of Granite. *Mem. geol. Soc. Am.* **28**

56 —— (1949) Distribution of mountain building in geologic time. *Bull. geol. Soc. Am.* **60**: 561–90

57 GOULD, H. R. (1951) *Some quantitative aspects of Lake Meade turbidity currents.* Soc. Econ. Paleontologists and Mineralogists, Special Publ. 2: 34–52

58 GREENE, J. (1959) *The death of Adam.* Iowa State University Press: Ames, Iowa

59 GUTENBERG, B. (1941) Changes in sea level, postglacial uplift, and mobility of the earth's interior. *Bull. geol. Soc. Am.* **52**: 721–72

60 —— (1959) *Physics of the earth's interior.* Academic Press: New York and London

61 HAMILTON, E. L. (1956) Sunken islands of the mid-Pacific mountains. *Mem. geol. Soc. Am.* **64**

62 —— (1957) The last geographic frontier. *Scient. Mon.* **85**: 294–314

63 —— (1959) Thickness and consolidation of deep-sea sediments. *Bull. geol. Soc. Am.* **70**, 1399–422

64 —— (1961) Stratigraphy of the deep-sea floor. In *Oceanography.* Mary Sears, Ed. Amer. Assoc. Petroleum Geologists Publ. 67: 51–84

65 HARSANYI, Z. de (1939) *The star-gazer.* G. P. Putnam's Sons: New York

66 HARTNAGEL, C. A. & BISHOP, S. C. (1921) The mastodons, mammoths, and other mammals of New York State. *Bull. N.Y. St. Mus.* **241–2**: 26–7

239

67 HEDBERG, H. D. (1961) *Stratigraphic classification and Terminology*. Rept. of 21st Session, Intern. Geol. Congress, Pt. XXV: 7–38

68 HEEZEN, B. C. and EWING, M. (1952) Turbidity currents and submarine slumps, and the 1929 Grand Banks earthquake. *Am. J. Sci.*, **250**: 849–73

69 —— *et al.* (1954) Further evidence for a turbidity current following the 1929 Grand Banks earthquake. *Deep Sea Res.* **1**: 193–202

70 —— (1955) Turbidity currents from Magdalena River, Columbia. *Bull. geol. Soc. Am.* **66**: 1572

71 —— (1960) The rift in the ocean floor. *Scient. Am.* **203**, No. 4: 98–114

72 —— *et al.* (1959) *The floor of the oceans*. Geol. Soc. Amer., Special Paper 65

73 —— and DRAKE, C. L. (1962) *The 1929 Grand Banks slump*. Geol. Soc. Amer. Abstract of Program, p. 69A

74 HENDERSON, L. J. (1913) *The fitness of the environment*. The Macmillan Co.: New York

75 HERZ, O. (1903) *Frozen mammoth in Siberia*. Ann. Report of the Smithsonian Institution for 1903, pp. 611–25. Washington, DC

76 HESS, H. H. (1946) Drowned ancient islands of the Pacific basin. *Am. J. Sci.* **244**: 772–91

77 HILGENBERG, O. C. (1933) In *Vom Wachsenden Erdball*. Giessmann and Bartsch

78 HOLMES, A. (1960) A revised geologic time scale. *Trans. Edinb. geol. Soc.* **17**, pt. 3: 183–216

79 HOUGH, J. L. (1953) Pleistocene climatic records in a Pacific Ocean core sample. *J. Geol.* **61**: 252–62

80 HOUTZ, R. E. & WELLMAN, H. W. (1962) Turbidity current at Kadavu Pass, Fiji. *Geol. Mag.* **XCIX**: 57–62

81 HUTTON, J. (1788) Theory of the earth: or an investigation of the laws observable in the composition, dissolution and restoration of the globe. *Trans. R. Soc. Edinb.* **1**, pt. 11: 209–304

82 IRVING, E. (1964) *Paleomagnetism and its application to geological and geophysical problems*. John Wiley and Sons, Inc.: New York, 399 pages

83 JAMES, J. N. (1963) The voyage of *Mariner II*. *Scient. Am.* **209**, No. 1: 70–84

84 JASTROW, R. (1959) Artificial satellites and the earth's atmosphere. *Scient. Am.* **201**, No. 2: 37–43

85 —— (1960) The exploration of the moon. *Scient. Am.* **202**, No. 5: 61–9

86 JEANS, J. H. (1919) *Problems of cosmogony and stellar dynamics*. Cambridge University Press: London

87 JEFFREYS, H. (1918) Monthly Notices, Royal Astron. Soc., **78**, 424–441

88 JOHNSON, D. W. (1939) *The origin of submarine canyons*. Columbia University Press: New York

89 JONES, Sir H. S. (1958) The origin of the solar system. *Endeavour* **17**, No. 67: 140–4

90 KEPLER, J. (1609) *De Motibus Stella Mertis:* Prague

91 —— (1616) *De Harmonica Mundi:* Augsburg

92 KING, L. (1958) Basic Paleogeography of Gondwanaland during the Late Paleozoic and Mesozoic eras. *Q. Jl geol. Soc. Lons.* **114**: 47–70

93 KREUGER, H. W. (1964) K–Ar age of basalt cored in Mohole Project (Guadalupe Site) *J. geophys. Res.* **69**: 1155–6

94 KUENEN, P. H. (1937) Experiments in connection with Daly's hypothesis on the formation of submarine canyons. *Leid. geol. Meded.* Dec **8**: 327–51

95 —— (1950) *Marine geology.* John Wiley and Sons: New York

96 —— (1952) Estimated size of the Grand Banks turbidity current. *Am. J. Sci.* **250**: 874–84

97 KUIPER, G. P. (1951) On the origin of the Solar System. In *Asterophysics.* J. A. Hynek Ed., Ch. 8: 357–427. McGraw-Hill: New York

98 —— (1952) *The Atmosphere of the planets.* 2nd Ed. Univ. of Chicago Press

99 KULP, J. L. (1961) Geologic time scale. *Science* **133**: 1105–14

100 LADD, H. S., *et al.* (1948) Drilling on Bikini Atoll, Marshall Islands. *Science* **107**: 51–5

101 —— *et al.* (1953) Drilling on Eniwetok Atoll, Marshall Islands. *Bull. Am. Ass. Petrol. Geol.* **37**: 2257–80

102 LAPLACE, S. P. (1796) *Exposition du système du monde.* Paris

103 LARSEN, E. S., Jr., *et al.* (1952) Method for determining the age of igneous rocks using the accessory minerals. *Bull. geol. Soc. Am.* **63**: 1045–52

104 LAWSON, A. C. (1885) *Report on the geology of the Lake of the Woods region, with special reference to the Keewatin (Huronian ?) belt of the Archaean rocks.* Canadian Geol. Surv., Ann. Rept I: CC

105 LIBBY, W. F. (1952) *Radiocarbon dating.* University of Chicago Press Also *Endeavour XII,* No. **49**: 5–16

106 LIGHTFOOT, J. (1642–1644) *A few and new observations on the Book of Genesis, most of them certain, the rest probable, all harmless, strange, and rarely heard of before.* T. Badger: London

107 MAYR, Ernest, *et al.* (1949) The problem of land convections across the South Atlantic with special reference to the Mesozoic. *Bull. Am. Mus. nat. Hist.* **99**: New York

108 MCDONALD, J. E. (1952) The coreolis effect. *Scient. Am.* **185**, No. 5: 72–8

109 MEEN, V. B. (1951) The Canadian meteor craters. *Scient. Am.* **184**, No. 5: 64–8

110 MENARD, H. W. (1961) The East Pacific Rise. *Scient. Am.* **205**, No. 6: 52–61

111 —— (1962) Geologic history of Pacific basin (abstract). *Bull. Am. Ass. Petrol. Geol.* **46**: 272

112 MENZEL, D. H. (1958) Exploring our neighbor world, the moon. *Nat. geogr. Mag.* **113**: 277–96

113 NAMAIS, J. (1952) The jet stream. *Scient. Am.* **187**, No. 4: 27–31

114 NEWTON, Sir I. (1687) *Philosophiae Naturalis Principia Mathematica.* London

115 NICOLET, M. (1960) The properties and constitution of the upper atmosphere. In *Physics of the upper atmosphere.* J. A. Ratcliffe, Ed. Ch. 2: 17–71. Academic Press: New York and London

116 NISKANEN, E. (1939) On the upheaval of land in Fennoscandia. *Annales Academiae Scientiarum Fennicae,* Ser. A: **53**, No. 10

117 NORTHROP, J. (1951) Ocean-bottom photographs of the neritic and bathyal environment south of Cape Cod, Massachusetts. *Bull. geol. Soc. Am.* **62**: 1381–3

118 NYDAL, R. (1962) Natural radiocarbon measurements III. *Radiocarbon* **4**:
     160–82
119 O'BRIEN, Brian J. (1963) Radiation belts. *Scient. Am.* **208**, No. 5: 84–96
120 OORT, J. H. (1956) The evolution of galaxies. *Scient. Am.* **195**, No. 3: 101–8
121 *Oxford cyclopedic concordance* (1701). Oxford University Press, p. 54
122 PETTERSSON, H. (1954) *The ocean floor.* Yale University Press: New Haven
123 PICCARD, J. & ABERCROMBIE, T. J. (1960) Man's deepest dive. *Nat. geogr.
     Mag.* **118**: 224–39
124 PIGGOT, C. S. (1937) *Core samples of the ocean bottom.* Smithsonian Institu-
     tion, Ann. Rept.: 207–16
125 *Polar Wandering and Continental Drift* (1963). Arthur G. Munyan Editor.
     Soc. Econ. Geologists and Mineralogists Special Paper **10**: Tulsa, Oklahoma
126 PRATJE, O. (1924) *Korallenbänke im tiefem und kuhlem Wasser.* Centralbl. fur
     Min: 410–15
127 PRESS, F. (1961) The earth's crust and upper mantle. *Science* **133**: 1455–63
128 PURI, G. S. (1947) The occurrence of a tropical fig (*Ficus cunia Buch-Ham*) in
     the Karewa beds at Liddarmarg, Pir Panjal range, Kashmir, with remarks on
     the sub-tropical forests of the Kashmir Valley during the Pleistocene. *J.
     Indian bot. Soc.* **26**, No. 3: 131–5
129 RAFF, A. D. (1961) Magnetism of the ocean floor. *Scient. Am.* **205**, No. 4:
     146–56
130 RAITT, R. W. (1953) *Reflection and refraction of explosive waves by the sea
     bottom.* Scripps Inst. Oceanography Quarterly Progress Report. 53–22
131 REIDEL, W. R., *et al.* (1961) Preliminary drilling phase of the Mohole project,
     2, Summary of coring operations. *Bull. Am. Ass. Petrol. Geol.* **45**: 1793–8
132 ROBERTSON, H. P. (1956) *The universe. Scient. Am.* **195**, No. 3: 73–81
133 RUBEY, W. W. (1951) Geologic history of sea water. *Bull. geol. Soc. Am.* **62**:
     1111–48
134 RUNCORN, S. K. (1963) *Paleomagnetic methods of investigating polar wandering
     and continental drift.* Soc. Econ. Paleontologists and Mineralogists, Special
     Publ. **10**: 47–54
135 RUSSELL, H. N. (1935) *The solar system and its origin.* Macmillan Co.: New
     York
136 SANDAGE, A. B. (1956) The Red-shift. *Scient. Am.* **195**, No. 3: 170–82
137 SCHENCK, H. G. & MULLER, S. W. (1941) Stratigraphic Terminology. *Bull.
     geol. Soc. Am.* **52**: 1419–26
138 SCHMALZ, R. F. (1961) *A case for convection.* Mineral Industries, Penn State
     University, **30**, No. 6: 1–8. University Park, Pennsylvania
139 SCHOTT, W. (1935) *Die Foraminiferen in dem Äquitorialen Teil des Atlantis-
     chen Ozeans.* Deutsche Atlantische Exped: 'Meteor' Wissensch. Ergeb. **3**,
     pt 3: 43–134
140 SCHUCHERT, C. (1955) *Atlas of paleogeographic maps of North America.* John
     Wiley and Sons: New York
141 SHEPARD, F. P. (1923) To question the theory of periodicity. *J. Geol.* **31**:
     599–613
142 —— (1948) *Submarine geology.* Harpers and Brothers: New York

143   SHEPARD, F. P. (1954) High-velocity turbidity currents: A discussion. *Proc. R. Soc.* Sec A, **222**: 323–6. The University Press: Cambridge, England

144   —— (1956) Marginal sediments of the Mississippi delta. *Bull Am. Ass. Petrol. Geol.* **40**: 2537–623

145   —— (1959) *The earth beneath the sea.* The Johns Hopkins Press: Baltimore, Maryland

146   —— & MOORE, D. G. (1954) Sedimentary environments differentiated by coarse-fraction studies. *Bull. Am. Ass. Petrol. Geol.* **38**: 1792–802

147   SPITZER, L. (1939) *Astrophys. J.* **90**: 675

148   STEHLI, F. G. (1957) Possible Permian climatic zonation and its implications. *Am. J. Sci.* **255**, 607–18

149   —— & HELSLEY, C. E. (1963) Paleontologic technique for defining ancient pole positions. *Science.* **142**: 1057–9

150   STILLE, Hans (1924) *Grundfragen der vergleichenden Tektonik.* Gebrüder Borntraeger, Berlin

151   —— (1936) The present tectonic state of the earth. *Bull. Am. Ass. Petrol. Geol.* **20**, pp. 849–80

152   *The Universe* (1956) A scientific American book with many authors. Simon and Schuster: New York

153   TEICHERT, C. (1941) Upper Paleozoic of Western Australia: Correlation and paleogeography. *Bull. Am. Ass. Petrol. Geol.* **25**: 371–415

154   TILTON, G. R. & DAVIS, G. L. (1959) Geochronology. In *Researches in geochemistry*, Philip Abelson, Ed.: 190–216. John Wiley and Sons: New York

155   TRAUTMAN, M. A. & WALTON, Alan (1962) Isotopes Inc. Radiocarbon measurements II. *Radiocarbon* **4**: 35–42

156   UDDEN, J. A. (1924) Laminated anhydrite in Texas. *Bull. geol. Soc. Am.* **35**: 347–54

157   UREY, H. C. (1952) *The planets: Their origin and development.* Yale University Press: New Haven, Connecticut

158   USSHER, J. (1650) *Annals of the world.* London, at the sign of the Ship in St Paul's Church-yard, Fleet Street. [a second edition was published in 1658]

159   VAN ALLEN, J. A. (1959) Radiation belts around the earth. *Scient. Am.* **200**, No. 3: 39–47

160   VAN HILTEN, D. (1962) Presentation of paleomagmatic data, polar wandering, and continental drift. *Am. J. Sci.* **260**: 401–26

161   VEATCH, A. C. & SMITH, P. A. (1939) *Atlantic submarine valleys and the Congo submarine valley.* Geol. Soc. Amer., Special Paper 7

162   VEEVERS, G. & WELLS, A. T. (1961) *The geology of Canning basin, Western Australia.* Bureau Min. Resources, Geology and Geophysics, Bull. **60**

163   VENEG-MEINEZ, F. A. (1948) Major tectonic phenomena and the hypothesis of convection currents in the earth. *J. geol. Soc. Lond.* **103**: 191–207

164   VERHOOGEN, J. (1960) Temperatures within the earth. *Am. Scient.* **48**: 134–59. New Haven, Connecticut

165   WADIA, D. N. (1953) *Geology of India*, 3rd Ed. Macmillan and Co.: London

166   WEGENER, A. (1912) Die Entstehung der Continente. *Geol. Rdsch. Leipzig* **3**, 276–92

167   WEIZSÄCKER, C. F. von (1944) *Z. Astrophys.* **22**: 319

168   WHIPPLE, F. L. (1964) The history of the solar system. *Proc. natn. Acad. Sci. U.S.A.* **52**, 565–93

169   WILDT, R. (1958) Inside the planets. *Publs astr. Soc. Pacif.* **20**: 237–50

170   WILSON, J. T. (1950) An analysis of the pattern and possible cause of young mountain ranges and island arcs. *Proc. geol. Ass. Can.* **3**: 141–66

171   —— (1959) Geophysics and continental growth. *Am. Scient.* **47**: 1–24. New Haven, Connecticut

172   —— (1963) Continental drift. *Scient. Am.* **208**, No. 4: 86–100

173   WEGENER, A. F. (1924) *The Origin of the Continents and Oceans.* Methuen: London (Wegener is the father of the concept of continental drift)

Author Index

[Numbers in square brackets refer to the bibliography, pages 235–242]

Agassiz, L. 170
Aristotle 2, 218
Armitage, A. [1] 5
Axelrod, D. I. [3] 164, 209
Axelrod, D. I. and Ting, W. S. [2] 141, 142, 164

Babcock, H. W. [4] 33
Bacon, Roger 1
Bain, G. W. [5] 202, 209
Baldwin, R. B. [6] 35, 36, 37
Banks, M. R. [7] 174
Bascom, W. [8] 53
Beals, C. S. [9] 35, 36
Beck, A. E. [10] 187
Becquerel, H. 21
Beiser, A. [11] 110
Berkner, L. V. and Marshall, L. C. [12] 131
Berry, E. W. 141
Biermann, L. F. and Lust, R. [13] 44
Blackett, P. M. S. [14]
Blumenstock, D. I. [15] 110
Bohr, Niels 114
Boltwood, B. B. 23
Bowen, N. L. 52
Brahe, Tycho 7, 8
Bramlette, M. N. and Bradley, W. H. [16] 80, 100, 192
Broecker, W. S. and Kulp, J. L. [17]
Broecker, W. S., Turekian, K. K., and Heezen, B. C. [18] 192
Brown, Harrison [19] 128, 129
Buffon, Comte de 13, 14
Bullard, E. C. [20]

Carey, S. W. [21] 187
Cavendish, H. [22] 11
Chamberlin, T. C. and Salisbury, R. D. [23] 170
Chamberlin, T. C. [24] 115, 117, 118, 119, 177, 178, 197
Chaney, R. W. [26] 164

Charpentier, J. de 170
Colbert, E. H. [27] 163
Compton, A. 47
Conrad, T. A. 218
Copernicus, N. 5, 6, 7, 8
Cox, A. and Doell, R. R. [29] 202
Crowell, J. C. [30] 213
Cuvier, G. 220

Dall, W. H. and Harris, G. D. [31] 161, 207
Daly, R. A. [32] 84, 85, 92
Darrow, K. K. [33] 47
Darwin, C. 18
da Vinci, Leonardo 219
Deutsch, E. R. [34] 187, 197, 201, 203
Dietz, R. S. [35] 192, 195
Dryer, J. L. E. [36]
Dudley, Governor 219, 220
Dunbar, C. O. [37], [38]
Dunbar, C. O. and Rodgers, J. [39]
Du Toit, A. L. [40] 175, 210

Elasser, W. M. [41] 66, 67
Emery, K. O., Tracey, J. I. Jr., and Ladd, H. S. [42] 95, 96
Emery, K. O. [43]
Engel, A. E. J. [44] 63, 64, 187
Eratosthenes 2, 3
Ericson, D. B., Ewing, M., and Heezen, B. C. [45] 89, 193
Ericson, D. B., Ewing, M., Wollin, G., and Heezen, B. C. [46] 171
Ewing, M. 82, 190
Ewing, J. and Ewing, M. [47]

Farrand, W. R. [49] 168
Faul, H. [50] 17, 29
Finlay, Dr. C. 113
Fireman, E. L. [51] 42
Fisk, H. N., McFarland, Edw., Jr., Kolb, C. R., and Wilbert, L. J., Jr. [52] 141
Flint, R. F. [53] 168, 169, 170, 171, 173

Galileo, G. 6, 7, 10
Geikie, Sir A. [54]
Gilbert, Wm. 65
Gilluly, J. *et al.* [55] 65, 179
Gilluly, J. [56] 182, 198
Gould, H. R. [57] 85
Greene, J. [58] 218
Gutenberg, B. [59] 169
Gutenberg, B. [60] 188, 189

Hamilton, E. L. [61] 93, 199; [62]; [63, 64]
193, 194, 195
Harsanyi, Z. de [65]
Hartnagel, C. A. and Bishop, S. C. [66] 225
Hedberg, H. D. [67] 21
Heezen, B. C., Ericson, D. C., and Ewing,
M. [69] 88
Heezen, B. C. [70] 86, 89, 91, 190, 191, 192
Heezen, B. C. and Drake, C. L. [73] 89
Heezen, B. C. and Ewing, M. [68] 85, 86, 87
Heezen, B. C., Tharp, M., and Ewing, M.
[72] 83, 90, 91
Henderson, L. J. [74] 68, 69, 70, 71, 72
Herodotus, 218
Herz, O. [75] 223
Hess, H. H. [76] 93, 195
Hilgenberg, O. C. [77] 187
Holmes, A. [78] 17, 29
Hough, J. L. [79] 193
Houtz, R. E. and Wellman, H. W. [80] 89,
90
Hutton, J. [81] 14

Irving, E. [82] 201, 203

James, J. N. [83] 40, 104
Jastrow, R. [84] 111
Jeans, J. H. [86] 120
Jefferson, Thomas 220
Jeffreys, H. [87] 120
Jenner, Dr. E. 113
Johnson, D. W. [88] 84
Jones, Sir H. S. [89] 125

Kant, I. 114
Kepler, J. [90, 91] 8, 9, 10, 11, 116
King, L. [92]
Kreuger, H. W. [93] 53, 194
Kuenen, P. H. [95] 98; [96] 85, 88
Kuiper, G. P. [97] 39, 122, 123, 125,
129; [98]
Kullenberg, B. 80
Kulp, J. L. [99] 17, 29

Ladd, H. S., Tracey, J. I., Jr., Lill, G. G.
[100] 94

Ladd, H. S., Ingerson, Earl, Townsend,
R. C., Russell, Martin, Stephenson, H. K.
[101] 96
Laplace, S. P. [102] 114, 115, 116, 117, 121,
123
Larsen, E. S., Jr., Keevil, N. B., and
Harrison, H. C. [103] 25
Lawson, A. C. [104] 61
Libby, W. F. [105] 26
Lightfoot, J. [106] 13
Lloyd, W. 13
Lucretius, Titus, 113

Mason, R. 183
Mayr, E. [107]
McAlester, L. 233
McDonald, J. E. [108] 107
Meen, V. B. [109] 36
Menard, H. W. [110] 96, 183, 184, 199;
[111] 96
Menzel, D. H. [112] 35
Mohorovicic, A. 55
Moulton, F. A. 115, 117, 118, 119

Namais, J. [113]
Newton, Sir I. [114] 8, 10, 11, 12
Nicolet, M. [115] 105, 106
Niskanen, E. [116] 169
Northrop, J. [117] 82
Nydal, R. [118]

O'Brien, B. J. [119]
Oort, J. H. [120] 45

Pettersson, H. [122] 80
Piccard, J. and Abercrombie, T. J. [123] 82
Piggot, C. S. [124] 79
Pratje, O. [126] 100
Press, F. [127]
Ptolemy 5
Puri, G. S. [128] 141
Pythagoras 2

Raff, A. D. [129] 183, 185, 186
Raitt, R. W. [130]
Reed, Dr. Walter, 113
Reidel, W. R. [131] 53, 194
Robertson, H. P. [132] 45, 46
Romer, A. S. 226
Rubey, W. W. [133] 132, 133, 134
Runcorn, S. K. [134]
Russell, H. N. [135] 116, 121

Salisbury, R. D. 170
Sandage, A. B. [136] 46
Schenck, H. G. and Muller, S. W. [137] 20

Scheuchzer, J. A. 220
Schmalz, R. F. [138]
Schott, W. [139] 192
Schuchert, C. [140] 143, 149, 150, 151, 154, 155, 156
Shakespeare, Wm. 13
Shepard, F. P. [141] 179, 198; [142]; [143] 87; [144]; [145] 84
Shepard, F. P. and Moore, D. G. [146] 78
Smith, Wm. 18
Spitzer, L. [147] 120
Stehli, F. G. [148] 208
Stehli, F. G. and Helsley, C. E. [149] 209
Stiles, Ezra 220
Stille, H. [150, 151] 197

Tennyson, A. 138
Teichert, C. [153] 175
Tentzel, W. 219
Theophrastus 218
Tilton, G. R. and Davis, G. L. [154] 23
Trautman, M. A. and Walton, A. [155] 169

Udden, J. A. [156] 165
Unsold, 128
Urey, H. C. [157] 38, 120, 128, 129, 130, 131
Urry, W. D. 193
Ussher, J. 13

Van Allen, J. A. [159] 111
Van Hilten, D. [160] 202, 203, 204, 205
Van Slyke, D. D. 102
Veatch, A. C. and Smith, P. A. [161]
Veevers, G. and Wells, A. T. [162] 173
Veneg-Meinez, F. A. [163] 180, 181
Venetz-Sitten, Ignaz 170
Verhoogen, J. [164]

Wadia, D. N. [165] 59
Walcott, C. D. 224, 227
Wegener, A. [166] 214
Weizsacker, C. F. von [167] 121, 122, 123
Whipple, F. L. [168] 123
Wildt, R. [169] 40
Wilson, J. T. [170] 179; [171] 187; [172] 188

Subject Index

Italic page numbers refer to pages on which diagrams appear

abyssal plains *86, 91*
abyssal region 101
Age of Enlightenment 4
Age of Invertebrates 16, 17
Age of Mammals 16
Age of Reptiles 16
ages from radioactive isotopes 24, 25, 26
Alexandria 2, 3
Almagest 5
alpha particles 23
Alps 145
Andean uplift 165
Andes Highlands *188*
Andes Mountains 145
Andromeda 45, 46, Pl. 14
Ängstroms 127
angular momentum 116, 124
anhydrite 165
Antarctic ice cap 166, 173
Archbishop Ussher 13
Aristotle 2
asteroids 41, 43, 124
Aswan Dam 2
atmosphere of earth
  layers of 104, *105*
  origin and evolution 130, 131, 133
  ozone layer *105*, 110
  planetary circulation *106, 107, 108,* 160
  temperature 105
atmospheres of planets 39, 40, 41
atolls 92, 94
  Bikini 96
  Eniwetok 96
atomic structure 21, 22, Pl. 2
aurora *105*
Australia, glaciation 173, *174*
axis of rotation 66

Bahama Bank *91*
Baja California *213*
Baltic Sea 169, 198, 210
basalt layer of crust *49*, 54

baselevel of erosion 139
batholiths *58*
bathyscape 82
beach 75
Beresovka mammoth 222, 223
beta particles 23
Bikini atoll 96, 199
Bikini Island 94
Bishop Lloyd 13
Brazil, glaciation *174*
Brook's comet 44, Pl. 13
Bruno, Giordano 6
Buffon, Comte de 13, 14
Burgess shale fossils 224, 225, 227

Caesar, Julius 6
calendar revision 6
  Julian 13
Canadian Rockies 177, Pl. 41
Cape Johnson guyot *95*
carbon dioxide and life 102
Cavendish, Henry 11
Cenozoic Era 16
Challenger Deep 82
Challenger Expeditions 92
Champlain Sea 167
Christian IV 8
chromosphere of the sun 33, Pl. 5
Chubb Crater 36
Chuos tillite 175
Clavius 35
climate, past 161–76
climatic factors 158, 159, 160
climatic zones in the sea 161, 207
Coast Range batholith 60, *61*
coccoliths 101
collation of geologic and absolute dates 27, 28
Columbia Basalt Plateau 58, *59*, 60, Pl. 17
Columbus 4
Coma Berenices galaxy Pl. 16
comets 43, Pl. 13

compression waves 49, 50, 51
Compton effect 47
Congo Basin 159
continental drift 135, 200–9, 215, 216
continental emergences 199
continental fragmentation *211, 212, 213*
continental growth *64*, 187
continental platform 74, 134
continental rise *86, 91*
continental shelf 74, *86*, *91*
continental submergences 149–57
convection cells *135, 136*, 137, *181*
convection currents 55, 57, 134, 180–6,
    195–200
Copernican system 5, 6, 8
Copernican theory 6, 7
Copernicus 5, 6
core of earth *48*, 51, 54, 55
core of ocean floor 53
Coreolis effect 107, 109
corona of the sun 33, Pl. 6
correlation 18, *19*
cosmic abundance of elements 126, 128
Crater Copernicus 37, 38
Creation, date 4
crust of earth 49, 52, 55, 56
crustal depression by ice 167, *168, 169*, 170
crustal rocks 56, 57
Cryptozoic Eon 20, 21
Cryptozoic Era 17
cycles of submergence 199

Darwin, Charles 18, 94
Deccan Plateau *59*, 60
deep sea sediments 88
Deluge 4, 13
depth zones of the sea 74, *75*, 76, 77, 78, 86
desert deposits 165, 210, 211
    distribution 160
deserts, ancient 211
diastrophism 134, 177, 178, 179, 180, 187
diatoms 101
dikes *58*
diluvium 170
dinosaurs and climate 162, Pl. 31
Disco Island *163*
drift of the ocean floor 187, *188, 189*, 190
dunite 51
dust cloud hypothesis 121–5
dust clouds 121, 124
Dwyka tillite 173, 210
dynamo, earth 66

Earth
    changing face 138
    crust 177
    deep interior 49
    magnetism 65, 66

mass 10, 12
model *48*
shape 4
size 3
specific gravity 12
East Pacific Rise 183–188, 191
Eniwetok atoll *95, 96*, 199
epeiric seas 77
erathem 20, 21
Eratosthenes 2, 3
Eros 41, 124
erosion cycle 139
erosion processes 63, 138
expanding universe 46, 47
explosion craters 35

Fiji Islands 89, 90
filament 120
formation 20
formative stages of earth 126–37
fossil controversy 218, 219
fossil insects 223, 224, Pl. 53
fossil plants and climate 163, 164
    and uplift 164, 165
fossil record 226–36
fossilization 221, 222, 225
fossils 15, 218–36, Pls 43–53
Frederick II 7, 8
frozen dunes 165
frozen mammoths 222, 223
Fundy, Bay of 75

galactic systems 44, 46, Pls 14–16
galaxy 45
Galileo 6, 7, 10
Galapagos Islands 100
gamma rays 23
Gaseous-tidal hypothesis 120
gases in solid compounds 128–31
Genesis 2, 4, 220
geochron 20
geologic calendar 14, *16*, 17
geologic column 16, 17, 18, 19
geologic dates
    relative to absolute *27*, 28
geologic record of life *228, 229*, 230
geosynclines
    evolution 182, 195, *196*
glacial deposits 140
glacial drift 140, 141
glacial erosion 140, Pl. 35
glacial and interglacial ages 170, *171, 172*,
    173
glacial outwash 140
glaciated floor 140, Pl. 35
glaciation Pls 36, 37
    Permian 173–5, Pl. 39

glaciation—*contd.*
  Pleistocene 166–72
  Precambrian 175, 176, Pl. 40
glaciomarine deposits 172, 173
globigerina ooze 101, Pl. 19
Glossopteris 215
gneiss 65, Pl. 18
Gonwanaland 210, 215
Gotha mammoth 219
Governor Dudley 219, 220
Gowganda tillite 176, Pl. 40
graded bedding 88, Pl. 38
graded plains 90
Grand Banks
  earthquake 85
  turbidity flow *86, 87,* 88
Grand Canyon of the Colorado Pl. 1
granite 65
granitic layer of crust 56
granitization 65
gravitation 10, 12
greenhouse effect 104
Greenland
  Cretaceous climate 163
  ice cap 166, 173, Pls 36, 37
Griquatown tillite 175
group 20
Guadalupe Islands 53
Gulf current 72, 77, 98, 207
Gulf of Bothnia 169
gumbotil 171
guyots 92, *93, 94, 95,* 199

hail 109
Halimeda 89
Hawaiian Islands 60, 92
heat capacity 69
Hess guyot *95*
Himalaya Mountains 145, 146, 165, 177
history of life 224–34
Hòmo diluvii testis 220
Horizon guyot *95*
horse latitudes 107, *108,* 160
Hudson Bay 168, 169, 198
Hudson River canyon 82, *83,* 91
Hutton, James 14
Hveen Observatory 7
hydrosphere 68
hypothesis as a tool 113, 114

Iceland volcanics 148
identification of elements 127
igneous activity 57, *58, 59,* 60, *61,* 146–9
igneous rocks 57, 65
Iguanodon 162
impact pits 37, Pls 11, 12
India, glaciation *174*
Inquisition, Roman 7

intrusives 60
ionosphere *105,* 110
iron core 66
island arcs 96, 97, *179, 187, 188*
isotopes 22
Isthmus of Panama 77

Japanese Island arc *189*
jet stream 109
Jupiter 39, 40, 41, 44, 121, 123, 124, 125

Kadavu Pass 89
Kepler 8
Kepler's Laws 8, 9, 10, 11, 16
Kilauea 92, 147
Kilimanjaro 159
Kuiper's hypothesis 122, 123
Kullenberg piston corer 80, *81*
Kurile trench 189

Labrador current 73, 99
laccoliths *58*
Lake Mead 85
Lamont Laboratory 86
land bridges 77
land plants
  first appearance 223
  first forests 223
Laplace's hypothesis 114, 115, Pl. 20
latent heat
  of evaporation 70, 71
  of fusion 70
Law of faunal succession 18
light spectrum 127
light-year 45
light waves 127
Lightfoot, John 13
lines of force 66, 67
lithochron 20
lithosphere 48
loess 171
lunar craters 35, 37, Pls 7, 8
lunar pits 37, Pls 11, 12

Madagascar *212*
  glaciation *174*
Magdalena River 89
Magellan 4, 5
magma 57
  acidic *58,* 146
  basic *58,* 146
magnetic compass 65
  field 66, 67
  isoclines 202, *203, 204, 205*
  lines of force *67*
  poles 66, 201
mammoth at Gotha 219
mantle *48,* 49, 51, 52, 177

manuscript in stone Pl. 1
Mare Imbrium 37
maria 35, 37, 38
Mariner II satellite 39, 40, 123
Mars 39, 40, 41, 68, 104, 123, 124
mastodon at Albany 219, Pl. 44
Mauna Kea 60, 92
Mauna Loa 60, 92, 148
Medici 4
Mendocino fault 185, 186
Mercury 39, 40, 68, 123, 124
Mesocordilleran geanticline 182, 183
Mesosaurus 215
mesosphere 105, 110
Mesozoic Era 17
metallic core 54
metamorphic rocks 64, 65, Pl. 18
metamorphism 65, 149
Meteor Crater 36, 42, Pl. 9
meteorites 54, 55, Pl. 10
meteors 35, 42, 105, 124
Mid Atlantic Ridge 91, 92, 190, 191, 214
mid ocean ridges 91, 92, 191
Milky Way 44, 45
Mississippi River sediment 141
Moho 49, 56
Mohole Project 53, 54
Monsoon winds 108, 160
Monterey Canyon 84
moon 9, 32, 34, 73, 125, Pls 7, 8, 11, 12
moraines 167, Pl. 37
Mt Everest 60, 93
Mt Palomar 46
mountain history 142–5
mountains, growth and decay 141–6
Murray fault 184, 185, 186

nebular hypothesis 114–17, Pl. 20
Neptune 39, 41
neritic zone 74–8
Newton 8, 9, 10, 11, 12
nitrogen 104
North Atlantic basin 91
north magnetic pole 66
Numees tillite 175

ocean basins 78, 91
ocean currents 98, 99, 100
    and climate 72, 73
ocean floor
    coring devices 79, 80, 81
    photography 82
    sediment layer 192–5
ocean water
    source 131
    evolution 132, 133, 134
oceans, size 68

Operation Crossroads 94
organic oozes 78, 101, Pl. 19
outer core 48, 54, 55

Pacific Basin, subsidence 199
paleomagnetic isoclines 202, 203, 204, 205, 206
paleomagnetism 66, 200–206, 211
Paleozoic Era 17
Pangea 215
Paracutin 147
pelagic zone 74, 78
Pelly Bay terraces 169
Peloponnesian wars 3
peripheral growth of continents 64
permanence of continents and oceans 134
Permian ice sheets 173, 174, 175
Permian salt basins 165
Phanerozoic
    eon 21
    time 19
phase change 70
photosphere of sun 32, Pl. 3
Piggot cores 100
    corer 79, 80
planetary rotation 123
    wind belts 98, 108
Planetesimal Hypothesis 117–19, Pl. 21
Planets 31, 39, 40
plateau basalts 59, 148, Pl. 17
Pleistocene chronology 172
    ice sheets 166–72, Pl. 34
Pluto 39, 41
plutonic rocks 57, 58
polar wandering, theory of 201, 202
Pope Paul III 6
post-glacial uplift 167, 168, 169
Precambrian glaciation 175, 176
President Stiles 220
primeval atmosphere 128, 129
    loss of 129, 130, 131
protoplanet 126–9
Proxima Centauri 44
Ptolemaic system 5
    theory 7
Ptolemy 5
Puerto Rico trench 91
Pythagoras 2

radioactive disintegration 23
radioactivity 21, 22, 23, 55, 57
radiocarbon dates 26, 27
radiolaria 101, Pl. 19
rain shadow 159
Ranger VII satellite 37
red shift 47
resisting medium 119
retrograde rotation 116, 125

Rift Valley of Africa 148, 191
rifts in Pacific floor 183, *184, 185, 186*
rock units 20
Rocky Mountain geosyncline 142–5, *182*, 183, 198, Pl. 28
    uplift 190
rotation periods 123
Rudolph II 8

salt deposits and climate 165
salt marsh 75
San Andreas rift *213*
satellite 41
satellite systems 115, 119, 120, 124
Saturn 39, 40, 41, 123
Scandinavian ice sheet 167, 210
schist 65
sealevel, eustatic changes 153, 157, 197, 200
    fluctuations 197, 198, 200
seamounts *95*, 96
seas, ebb and flow 198
sediment layer on ocean floor 100, 101
    rate of deposition 192, 193, 194
    thickness 194, 195, 196
sedimentary rocks 63
seismic vibrations 49, 50, 51
shadow zone *48*, 51
shear waves 50, 51
shields 60, *62*, 63, 149
shooting stars 35, 38
Siberian ice sheet 167, Pl. 34
Sierra Nevada batholith 60, *61*
    uplift 164, 165
sills *58*
Sinus Iridium 37
slate 65
solar system 30, *31*
    origin 113–24
Solenhofen fossils 223
solid flow in the mantle 181–6
Solikamsk salt deposits 165
sonic depth recorder *79*
sound waves 126
South Africa, glaciation *174*
specific heat 69
spectroscope 127
spectrum 127
Stassfurt salt deposits 165
Strait of Dover 77
stratigraphic record 15
stratigraphic units 20
    naming 21
stratosphere 103, *105*, 109, 110
stratum 20
Stringocephalus 161, Pl. 29
Sturtian tillite 175
sublittoral zone 75
submarine canyons 82, *83*, 84

submergences of North America
    Cretaceous *150, 151*
    Devonian 152, *154, 155*
    Pennsylvanian *156*
sun 30–33, Pls 3–6
sun spots 32, 33, Pl. 3
superposition 15
Syene 2
Sylacauga Meteorite 42

Talchir tillite 175
tectogene 195, *196*
Tethyan geosyncline 145
Thomas Jefferson 220
tidal disruption theory 117, *118*, 119, 120
tidal zone 75
till 140, 171, Pl. 37
time scale
    absolute *16, 17*, 21
    relative 15, *16, 17*
time units 20
tornadoes 109
torsion balance *11*
trade winds 98, *108*, 160
Trajan 4
transportation of sediment 139
trenches, oceanic 96, *97*, 98, *188*
Trieste bathyscope 82
troposphere 103, *105*, 106
turbidites 90
turbidity currents 84, 85, 90, 101
    Bermuda 89
    Fiji Islands 89, *90*
    Grand Bank *86, 87*
    Lake Mead 85
    Magdalena River 89
Tycho Brahe 7, 8

Uniformitarianism 14
universal gravitation 114
Uranus 39, 41
Ursa Major galaxy Pl. 15

Van Allen radiation belts 40, 66, 67, *111*, 112
varved clay 167, Pl. 38
Venus 39, 40, 68, 104, 123, 124
Vesuvius 147
volcanoes 146, 147, 148, 149

water 69–74
Wegener 214
Weizacker's hypothesis 121, *122*
westerlies 98, *108*
Weston Meteorite 42, Pl. 10
William Smith 18
wind belts *108*
Wolfe Creek crater 36

Yucatan Peninsula 100